The NHS handbook
2010/11

Peter

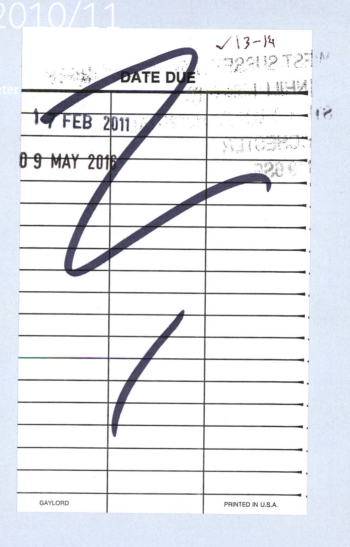

The twelfth edition of The NHS handbook.

First, second, third, fourth, fifth, sixth, seventh, eighth, ninth (then called The Pocket Guide), tenth and eleventh editions published by:

The NHS Confederation
29 Bressenden Place
London SW1E 5DD
Tel: 020 7074 3200
Fax: 0844 774 4319

To order further copies of this handbook or other Confederation publications, contact our publications sales team on 0870 444 5841 or visit www.nhsconfed.org/publications

978-1-85947-179-1

Printed in the UK in June 2010. The information included is correct at time of print.

Design by Grade Design Consultants, London
www.gradedesign.com

POC00601

This publication has been manufactured using paper produced under the FSC Chain of Custody. It is printed using vegetable-based inks and low VOC processes by a printer employing the ISO14001 environmental accreditation.

Contents

Please contact us on 0870 444 5841 for more information about the versions of the *NHS handbook 2010/11* suitable for those with a visual impairment.

Sponsor's foreword

 We are proud to sponsor *The NHS handbook* for 2010/11 and to be working alongside the NHS Confederation to make such a useful resource available to the NHS. Like our own solutions the handbook provides valuable information on how the NHS runs and helps managers and clinicians to make more informed decisions.

The NHS is entering a period of significant challenges. Most pressing is the need to cut costs whilst maintaining or enhancing the quality of healthcare services. We are expected to maintain our NHS services in the face of unprecedented reductions in public spending. A tall order for anyone!

More than ever, senior NHS managers are dependent on good information to ensure they make the right decision. Good leaders also have a responsibility to keep their colleagues informed. Business intelligence is no longer just for the boardroom. With the advent of service line reporting every clinician and manager can see how his or her organisation is performing and use this information to make local decisions relating to quality, efficiency and effectiveness.

A big issue with business intelligence is trust. Can you believe the information? Is it accurate? Is it up to date?

Our job at PSCAL is to provide the NHS with timely, accurate, auditable information on their activities and finances - information on which you can rely to make far-reaching decisions.

We work with over 200 NHS trusts and we understand the pressures you are under and aim to support you by providing management information you can trust.

Mike Singer
Director
PSCAL
www.pscal.com

Foreword

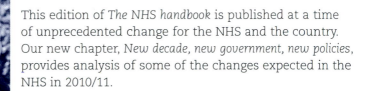

This edition of *The NHS handbook* is published at a time of unprecedented change for the NHS and the country. Our new chapter, *New decade, new government, new policies*, provides analysis of some of the changes expected in the NHS in 2010/11.

Your guide to how the NHS works, the handbook sets out how the NHS is structured in England. It includes a step-by-step guide to the different sectors including: primary care, acute (or hospital) services, foundation trusts, and mental health and ambulance services.

The change in the Government will not alter the requirement of the NHS to focus on quality and a key consideration for 2010/11 is how the NHS can delivery efficiency savings while continuing to provide high-quality services for patients. The handbook sets out the current structure of how the NHS is funded and which organisation is responsible for deciding which services to run and provide for patients. And you will also see how the independent sector is involved.

In recent years there has been increasing divergence between the health systems in England, Scotland, Wales and Northern Ireland so the handbook provides an overview of the key structures, bodies and operating principles in the four countries of the UK.

The handbook is again supported by advertising from selected organisations already working alongside the NHS Confederation. In particular I am very grateful to PSCAL, who have kindly agreed to support this year's edition.

Whether you're new to the health sector or have a wealth of experience, I hope you find it an invaluable source of the information you need to navigate your way around the system.

If you have any comments or suggestions for future editions please contact our publications team on 020 7074 3200 or email **publications@nhsconfed.org**

Keith Pearson
Chair

Who we are

The NHS Confederation is the independent membership body for the full range of organisations that make up the modern NHS. We represent over 95 per cent of NHS organisations including ambulance trusts, acute and foundation trusts, mental health trusts, primary care trusts and a growing number of independent sector organisations that deliver services within the NHS.

Our family of networks meet the specific needs of the different sections of our membership and include: Ambulance Service Network; Foundation Trust Network; Mental Health Network; NHS Partners Network; Primary Care Trust Network.

NHS Employers is part of the NHS Confederation and represents and supports NHS organisations on workforce issues.

The Welsh NHS Confederation and the Northern Ireland Confederation for Health and Social Services support members in their countries and we provide a subscription information service for NHS organisations in Scotland.

What we do

We work to inform and influence the development of healthcare policy to help ensure that new and existing initiatives lead to real improvements in the system and genuine advancements in patient care.

We help to make sense of the complex policy environment and support our members to deliver strong and innovative leadership to the NHS – providing unique insight, analysis and guidance on national healthcare policy and its implementation and offering a valuable forum for NHS leaders to come together to discuss, reflect, and learn.

We also provide a source of fresh thinking and help to shape the healthcare debate – using our expertise and harnessing the knowledge and experience of our members to define the future agenda and assess the long-term challenges and solutions.

Further information

To find out more about the NHS Confederation, please visit our website: **www.nhsconfed.org**

Introduction
One system – four structures

The National Health Service is based on common principles throughout the four constituent parts of the United Kingdom, although its structure in each is quite distinctive – and increasingly so. Ever since the NHS's foundation more than 60 years ago, it has adapted its shape to the particular administrative and geographical conditions of England, Scotland, Wales and Northern Ireland. But since devolution in 1999, and the transfer of responsibility for healthcare in Scotland, Wales and Northern Ireland to the Scottish Parliament, Welsh Assembly and the Northern Ireland Assembly, the divergence in structure has become more marked. The NHS has also pursued different priorities in each of the four countries.

UK population (2008)

	(million)	% of total
England	51.44	83.8
Scotland	5.16	8.4
Wales	2.99	4.9
Northern Ireland	1.77	2.9
Total	**61.36**	**100**

Source: Office for National Statistics

Vital statistics: NHS spending per head in the UK 2007/08 (£)

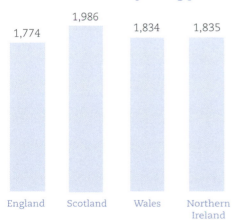

England	Scotland	Wales	Northern Ireland
1,774	1,986	1,834	1,835

Sources: UK health departments

However, the service's underlying values remain the same. These originate from the 1944 white paper, *A national health service*, which stated that:

The government ... want to ensure that in future every man, woman and child can rely on getting all the advice and treatment and care they may need in matters of personal health; that what they shall get shall be the best medical and other facilities available; that their getting these shall not depend on whether they can pay for them or any other factor irrelevant to the real need.

Both society and the health service have altered almost beyond recognition since then, but the NHS still strives to provide a broadly comprehensive service, mostly free to all at the point of need. As the NHS Constitution, devised in 2008 for the health service in England, expresses it: 'Everyone counts. We use our resources for the benefit of the whole community, and make sure nobody is excluded or left behind.'

Of course, the NHS has had to move with the times to take advantage of scientific and technological advances, as well as political, social and economic change. Major reform programmes have been under way in all four parts of the UK for most of the past decade, although certain principles remain common to all four systems. On the NHS's 60th anniversary in July 2008, the four UK health ministers declared that 'the NHS belongs to all the people of England, Scotland, Wales and Northern Ireland', and affirmed their commitment to a statement of common principles:

- the NHS provides a comprehensive service, available to all
- access to its services is based on clinical need, not an individual's ability to pay
- the NHS aspires to high standards of excellence and professionalism
- NHS services must reflect the needs and preferences of patients, their families and their carers
- the NHS works across organisational boundaries with other organisations in the interests of patients, communities and the wider population
- the NHS is committed to providing the best value for taxpayers' money, making the most effective and fair use of finite resources
- the NHS is accountable to the public, communities and patients that it serves.

They also agreed a 'joint statement on NHS values' that stressed the service was 'based on strong partnerships between the Government, the public, patients, staff and their trade unions'. In England, the NHS

Constitution (see page 122) formally sets out the service's overarching principles as well as specifying rights and pledges to patients and the public.

What the NHS does

Across the UK, the NHS employs 1.75 million staff, 1.4 million of them in the English NHS. In a typical year, people in England visit GP practices 300 million times, make 19 million visits to accident and emergency departments and over 6.5 million calls to NHS Direct. There are more than 4 million ordinary and day case admissions to hospital, and more than 45 million outpatient appointments. People also attend 1.2 million appointments with independent inpatient, day case and surgical outpatient services, and make over 3 million visits to independent outpatient services.

Estimates show that on average people use the NHS 2,153 times during their lifetime – the equivalent of once a fortnight. They take out 1,330 prescriptions, make 31 visits to accident and emergency and make 12 ambulance journeys, according to research for the Department of Health.

What the NHS does: contacts per day (thousands)

1   Total community contacts 389 (24%)
2   A&E attendances 49 (3%)
3   Outpatient attendances 124 (7%)
4   In bed as emergency admission to hospital 94 (6%)
5   In bed as elective admission to hospital 36 (2%)
6   NHS Direct calls 18 (1%)
7   Courses of NHS dental treatments for adults 73 (4%)
8   Walk-in centres 6
9   GP or practice nurse consultations 836 (51%)
10 NHS sight tests 28 (2%)

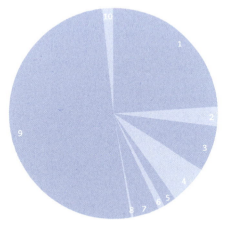

Figures are for England only.
Source: Department of Health

New decade, new government, new policies

The Liberal Democrat-Conservative coalition formed after the May 2010 general election says in its programme for government that amalgamating the two parties' ideas and attitudes has resulted in plans 'more radical and comprehensive than our individual manifestos'. In the NHS, 'Conservative thinking on markets, choice and competition' combined with 'Liberal Democrat belief in advancing democracy at a much more local level' have produced 'a united vision for the NHS that is truly radical'. It promises that 'our ideas will bring an emphatic end to the bureaucracy, top-down control and centralisation that has so diminished our NHS'.

Reiterating its commitment to an NHS 'free at the point of use and available to everyone based on need', the coalition Government says it believes 'the NHS is an important expression of our national values'. It summarises its aims for the service as a desire 'to free NHS staff from political micromanagement, increase democratic participation in the NHS and make the NHS more accountable to the patients that it serves'. In that way it will 'drive up standards, support professional responsibility, deliver better value for money and create a healthier nation'.

Structure
An independent NHS Board will be set up to allocate resources and provide commissioning guidelines. The coalition says it intends to 'stop the top-down reorganisations of the NHS', although it will 'significantly cut' the number of arm's-length bodies.

Commissioning
GPs will take on the main responsibility for commissioning. Primary care trusts will commission 'those residual services that are best undertaken at a wider level' while acting 'as a champion for patients'. PCTs will also be responsible for improving public health.

Public health
The coalition promises to give local communities greater control over public health budgets 'with payment by the outcomes they achieve in improving the health of local residents'. GPs will have greater incentives to tackle public health problems. Access to preventive care for those in disadvantaged areas will be improved to help tackle health inequalities.

Providing services

The coalition Government promises to stop the 'centrally dictated closure' of A&E and maternity wards. Local authorities concerned about a proposed closure can refer the case to the Independent Reconfiguration Panel (see page 93).

Patients will be given the right to register with any GP they want, regardless of where they live. A 24/7 urgent care service, including GP out-of-hours services, will be developed in every area and made accessible through a single phone number.

The coalition says it is 'committed to the continuous improvement of the quality of services to patients, and to achieving this through much greater involvement of independent and voluntary providers'. Patients will be able to choose any healthcare provider that meets NHS standards, within NHS prices, including independent, voluntary and community sector providers.

Accountability and regulation

Primary care trusts are to have directly elected individuals on their boards, with other members 'appointed by the relevant local authority or authorities'; the chief executive and senior directors will be appointed by the Secretary of State on the advice of the new NHS board.

The Care Quality Commission (see page 171) will be strengthened 'so that it becomes an effective quality inspectorate', while Monitor (see page 172) will develop into an economic regulator' overseeing aspects of access, competition and price-setting. NICE (see page 172) will be reformed and moved to 'a system of value-based pricing'.

Performance management

The coalition says it will judge the success of its health policies 'on the health results that really matter – such as improving cancer and stroke survival rates or reducing hospital infections', and 'detailed data' about providers' performance will be published online. Patients 'will enable patients to rate hospitals and doctors according to the quality of care they received'.

Finance

The coalition Government has pledged to guarantee annual real-terms increases in health spending, 'while recognising the impact this decision will have on other departments'. The Secretary of State has said the NHS may have to identify more than the £15-20 billion efficiency savings to be made by 2013/14 demanded by the previous Labour Government (see page 200). The coalition intends to cut NHS 'administration' by a third, transferring resources to frontline services.

Staffing and human resources

The GP contract (see page 215) will be renegotiated, with incentives to improve access to primary care in disadvantaged areas. A new dentistry contract 'will focus on achieving good dental health and increasing access to NHS dentistry, with an additional focus on the oral health of schoolchildren'.

Frontline staff will be given 'more control of their working environment'.

Professional staff from overseas will have to pass 'robust language and competence tests'.

Public sector workers will have a right to form employee-owned cooperatives and bid to take over the services they deliver.

Social care

A commission on long-term care will be set up and report within a year. The ideas it will consider include 'a voluntary insurance scheme to protect the assets of those who go into residential care, and a partnership scheme'.

Personal budgets (see page 90) will be rolled out further, and barriers between health and social care funding broken down 'to incentivise preventative action'.

Other plans include:
• dementia research will be prioritised within the health research and development budget
• a cancer drugs fund to enable patients to access cancer drugs their doctors think will help them
• £10 million a year beyond 2011 from within the Department of Health budget to support children's hospices
• an extra 4,200 Sure Start health visitors.

Further information
The Coalition: our programme for government, HM Government, May 2010.

01 The structure of the NHS in England

Ultimate responsibility for the NHS lies with Parliament. At a strategic level, the Department of Health is one of the largest central government departments; it is assisted nationally by a range of 'arm's-length bodies' and regionally by the strategic health authorities. At an operational level, primary care trusts occupy a pivotal position as local commissioning organisations, while NHS trusts, foundation trusts and independent healthcare organisations provide the services. A chain of accountability therefore runs from local bodies up through the regions to Government and Parliament.

Parliament

As the NHS is financed mainly through taxation it relies on Parliament for its funds, and has to account to Parliament for their use through the Secretary of State for Health, the cabinet member responsible for the service. Parliament scrutinises the service through debates, MPs' questions to ministers and select committees. These procedures mean that the Government has to publicly explain and defend its policies for the NHS. The Scottish Parliament (page 248), the Welsh Assembly (page 274) and the Northern Ireland Assembly (page 290) are responsible for oversight of the NHS in their parts of the UK. Health services in the Isle of Man and the Channel Islands are not part of the NHS.

Select committees

Three select committees, each comprising backbench MPs representing the major parties, are particularly relevant to the NHS. They are all able to summon ministers, civil servants and NHS employees to give oral or written evidence to their inquiries, usually in public. Their reports are published throughout the parliamentary session.

Health committee

The health committee's role is 'to examine the expenditure, administration and policy of the Department of Health and its associated bodies'. It has a maximum of 11 members. Recent inquiries have covered the NHS's use of management consultants, commissioning and patient safety. www.parliament.uk

Public accounts committee

The public accounts committee scrutinises all public spending and is concerned with ensuring the NHS is operating with economy, efficiency and effectiveness. Its inquiries are based on reports about the service's 'value for money', produced by the Comptroller and Auditor General,

who heads the National Audit Office. It aims to draw lessons from past successes and failures that can be applied to future activity. The committee has 16 members, and is traditionally chaired by an Opposition MP. Recent inquiries examined healthcare-associated infections, alcohol misuse services and NHS pay modernisation.
www.parliament.uk
www.nao.gov.uk

Public administration committee
The public administration committee examines reports from the Health Service Commissioner (better known as the Ombudsman, page 173). Its remit now includes responsibility for scrutinising third sector policy. It has 11 members.
www.parliament.uk
www.ombudsman.org.uk

Health ministers
Usually six ministers, all appointed by the Prime Minister to the Department of Health, are responsible in Parliament for health and social care. They provide the DH with political leadership and are responsible for making the main executive decisions on:
• strategy
• overall policy framework
• framework of laws
• performance objectives for the DH and for the public services for which they are responsible
• agreeing overall resource levels with the Chancellor and the Prime Minister
• priorities for distributing resources, based on the strategy and policy framework.

Ministers do not generally become involved in local decisions or individual cases (although exceptions do occur), and should not be involved in DH-related decisions about their own constituencies.

The DH's ministers typically comprise the Secretary of State, three ministers of state – responsible for health services, public health and care services respectively – and two parliamentary under-secretaries of state, usually one of whom sits in the House of Lords. The Secretary of State is a member of the cabinet and has overall responsibility for NHS and social care delivery, system reforms, finance, resources and strategic communications. The other ministers each have specific areas of NHS activity assigned to them, and lead on particular regions. The Department for Children, Schools and Families has the lead for children's issues, and the Department for Work and Pensions has the lead for issues affecting older people. Both work closely with the Department of Health.

The Department of Health

The Department of Health provides strategic leadership to the NHS and social care organisations in England, setting their overall direction while deciding and monitoring standards. Its key objectives are:
- better health and well-being: helping people stay healthy, empowering them to live independently and tackling health inequalities
- better care: ensuring the best possible, safe and effective health and social care, provided when and where people need it
- better value: delivering affordable, efficient and sustainable services, contributing to the wider economy and the nation.

Until now the DH has been the national headquarters of the NHS, negotiating funding with the Treasury and allocating resources to the health service at large, but the new NHS Board (see page 12) will alter this. It is accountable for about £104 billion of public money. The DH's running costs in 2009/10 were estimated at £214 million. Its 2,200 core staff are based mainly in London and Leeds but also in the nine Government Offices for the Regions. The DH receives on average more parliamentary questions than any other Whitehall department, as well as 8 per cent of all Freedom of Information requests.

The Scottish Government Health Directorates (page 250), the Welsh Department for Health and Social Services (page 275) and Northern Ireland's Department of Health, Social Services and Public Safety (page 291) provide strategic leadership for the NHS in their parts of the UK. However, the DH has UK-wide responsibility for international and European Union business and for:
- coordinating plans to cope with a flu pandemic
- licensing and safety of medicines and medical devices
- ethical issues such as abortion and embryology.

Further information
Department of Health Business Plan 2009–11, DH, June 2009.
Departmental report 2009: the health and personal social services programmes, DH, June 2009.
The DH guide: a guide to what we do and how we do it, DH, December 2007.
www.dh.gov.uk

Managing the DH
Three senior leaders
Its three most senior staff, all of equal rank, are the permanent secretary, NHS chief executive and chief medical officer. These posts are not political appointments and do not change with a change of government. The permanent secretary and NHS chief executive roles were combined in 2000 but then separated again in 2006. The permanent secretary is responsible for running the department day-to-day. The NHS chief executive is responsible for the health service's management and performance. Both are responsible to the Secretary of State. The DH's chief medical officer is the UK Government's principal medical adviser and the professional head of all medical staff in England (there are also CMOs for Scotland, Wales and Northern Ireland).

The chief executive's report to the NHS is published each year and outlines the service's progress towards meeting key objectives. The CMO publishes an annual independent report to Parliament on the state of the nation's health.

Further information
On the state of the public health: annual report of the chief medical officer 2009, DH, March 2010.
The year 2009/10: NHS chief executive's annual report, DH, May 2009.
Department of Health development plan, DH, September 2007.

Department of Health organisation chart

Chief medical officer	Permanent secretary	NHS chief executive
Research and development	Finance and operations	Chief nursing officer
Health improvement and protection	Policy and strategy	NHS medical director
9 regional public health groups/directors of public health	Social care, local government and care partnerships	Commissioning and system management
	Communications	Workforce
	Deputy chief medical officer/chief government adviser on inequalities	Commercial
	Equality and human rights	NHS finance, performance and operations
		Chief information officer

Departmental board members

Source: Department of Health

Departmental board: meets about six times a year and focuses on major strategic cross-cutting issues facing the DH.

Corporate management board: provides corporate leadership. Its six or seven meetings each year are scheduled around the annual business planning and quarterly performance management cycle.

NHS management board and executive groups: bring together monthly all strategic health authority chief executives and the NHS chief executive's leadership team of DH directors-general. The board provides leadership for the NHS and is responsible for ensuring the service's performance and financial delivery are on track.

NHS operations board: a subgroup of the NHS management board including the ten strategic health authority chief executives, it oversees day-to-day running of the NHS and achievement of the operating framework.

National Leadership Council
Created in 2009 to champion leadership in the NHS, the NLC is a subcommittee of the NHS management board chaired by the NHS chief executive. It focuses on standards, has its own budget and can commission development programmes. It has 26 core members, supported by five patrons who are renowned leadership experts, and a faculty of 12 fellows. Its priorities are clinical leadership, board development, top leaders, emerging leaders and inclusion. Current activities include:
• setting priorities for culture change and leadership across the NHS
• producing an annual report for NHS staff featuring examples of inspiring leadership and best practice, progress and future challenges
• ensuring standards of leadership and leadership development, including accreditation
• overseeing national funding and commissioning programmes
• making policy recommendations
• exchanging knowledge with other sectors.

Further information
Future of leadership paper 1: Reforming leadership development ... again, NHS Confederation, March 2009.
www.nhsleadership.org.uk

Department of Health and its partners

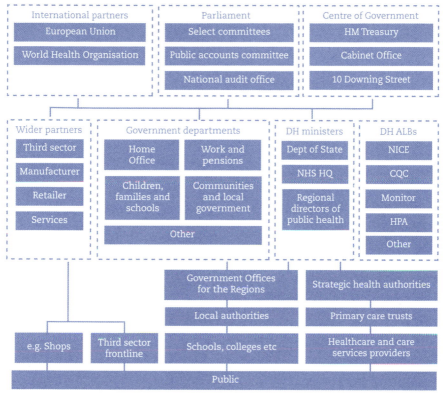

Source: Department of Health

Chief professional officers

The DH's chief professional officers provide expert knowledge in specialist health and social care disciplines to ministers, other government departments and the Prime Minister. They comprise:

- chief medical officer
- chief nursing officer
- chief dental officer
- chief health professions officer
- chief pharmaceutical officer
- chief scientific officer.

National clinical directors

National clinical directors are clinical specialists and figureheads for specific national service frameworks or clinical strategies (see page 136), representing the interests of the NHS and social care within the DH. Focused on delivering care rather than DH policy, their most important role is spearheading change by engaging with professionals and providing leadership. The clinical directors are led by the NHS medical director, a post created in 2007. They number about 20, meet monthly and also:

- visit health and social care practitioners
- chair taskforces with health and social care professionals and health service managers
- work with the Royal Colleges to ensure changes in health and social care are reflected in training and education
- chair taskforces to develop national clinical strategies, bringing together health professionals, service users and carers, health service managers, partner agencies and other advocates.

Arm's-length bodies

The DH is responsible for 21 arm's length bodies employing 17,500 staff. Each is a stand-alone national organisation with executive functions. They vary in size but tend to have boards, employ staff and publish accounts. They include special health authorities (see below), executive agencies and non-departmental public bodies, which are set up when ministers want independent advice without direct influence from Whitehall departments.

ALBs are accountable to the DH and sometimes directly to Parliament. They have existed since the NHS was set up in 1948. ALBs have been cut in number from 38 to 21 since 2004, reducing posts by 25 per cent and saving £250 million a year. Their roles are:

- regulating the health and social care system and workforce
- establishing national standards and protecting patients and public
- providing central services to the NHS.

The coalition Government has said it will 'significantly cut the number of health quangos'.

Further information

Department of Health's public bodies 2009, DH, January 2010.

Releasing resources to the frontline: the Department of Health's review of its arm's length bodies, NAO, January 2008.

Special health authorities

Special health authorities provide a service to the whole of England rather than to a local community. They are independent, but can be subject to ministerial direction like other NHS bodies. They currently comprise:

- National Institute for Health and Clinical Excellence
- National Patient Safety Agency
- National Treatment Agency for Substance Misuse
- NHS Blood and Transplant
- NHS Business Services Authority
- NHS Litigation Authority
- NHS Professionals
- Health and Social Care Information Centre
- NHS Institute for Innovation and Improvement.

Strategic health authorities

In England, strategic health authorities (SHAs) have acted as the local headquarters of the NHS since their creation in 2002. Originally 28 in number, they were reduced to ten in 2006. With the advent of the NHS Board (see page 12), SHAs' role as the NHS's intermediary tier is under review. They do not deliver services, but provide leadership, coordination and support across a defined geographical area, managing the performance of PCTs and NHS trusts. (For management arrangements in Scotland, see page 251; Wales, page 278; and Northern Ireland, page 292.) SHAs are almost coterminous with the Government Offices for the English Regions (see page 63). SHAs draw up plans to recruit, retain and develop NHS staff, and they devise financial solutions for service needs. They also work with partner organisations in local government, education and the charitable and voluntary sector.

Their three main tasks are:
- developing a strategic framework that clarifies short, medium and long-term priorities
- managing and improving performance, establishing performance agreements with all local NHS organisations and redesigning care processes to focus on patient pathways
- building capacity and capability in terms of people, facilities and buildings within and across organisations.

Primary care trusts

In England, primary care trusts (PCTs) are the cornerstone of the NHS locally. Their equivalents in Scotland, community health partnerships, manage primary and community health services. Wales's seven health boards are responsible for managing primary and secondary services. Since 2009 Northern Ireland has had five local commissioning groups driven by GPs.

Strategic health authorities

North
East

Yorkshire and
the Humber

North
West

East
Midlands

West
Midlands

East of
England

South
Central   London

South East
Coast

South West

PCTs number 151 (reconfigured in 2006 from 303), although some share a chief executive. They oversee England's 29,000 GPs and 18,000 dentists, and have an average population of 330,000. PCTs are responsible for over 80 per cent of the NHS budget; ten have budgets of over £1 billion each. About 70 per cent of them are coterminous with the 150 social care departments.

PCTs' main functions are:
• improving the health of their population – reducing health inequalities in partnership with the local authority; protecting health; emergency planning

- commissioning services (see page 44), including hospital care, mental health, GP practices, screening programmes, patient transport, NHS dentists, pharmacies and opticians – assessing need, reviewing provision and deciding priorities; designing services; shaping supply through placing contracts; managing demand and performance-managing providers
- developing staff skills, investing capital in buildings, equipment and IT.

PCTs are now able to change their names by adopting the NHS prefix before their place name: for example, Blackpool PCT is now known as NHS Blackpool. PCTs felt that as they are responsible for most local NHS expenditure, their title should convey that they are a major NHS presence in a locality.

Traditionally PCTs have provided a wide range of out-of-hospital services directly, such as district nursing, health visiting, various therapy services and disease prevention such as smoking-cessation support. They have now been asked to separate commissioning and provider functions by April 2011. The most likely options are:
- integration with an NHS acute or mental health provider
- integration with another community-based provider
- social enterprise – the Next Stage Review (see page 127) gave staff the 'right to request' to set up social enterprises (see page 33) to provide services.

Other possibilities that are not expected to be the norm are:
- community foundation trust
- continued PCT direct provision, where partnered by strong commissioning
- care trust which includes provision where partnered by strong commissioning.

Further information
Transforming community services: the assurance and approvals process for PCT-provided community services, DH, February 2010.
Transforming community services: governance arrangements to support PCT provider committees, Appointments Commission/DH, July 2009.
Guidance on internal separation for SHAs to support business readiness in PCT provision, DH, February 2009.

Teaching PCTs

Teaching PCTs (tPCTs), set up mainly in areas of deprivation or where it has been difficult to recruit, are able to offer GPs and other health professionals clinical posts that involve teaching, research or development. They are not confined to traditional teaching activities such as postgraduate clinical training, continuing professional development and lifelong learning, but aim to provide activities that encompass the ethos of learning, development, research, dissemination and good practice. By offering this type of career development, tPCTs hope to attract additional high-quality staff, particularly to deprived areas.

After the 2006 reconfiguration, tPCTs did not automatically keep their teaching status but had to seek approval from their SHA. There are currently 31 tPCTs out of the total of 151 PCTs.

Key organisation: PCT Network
The PCT Network was established as part of the NHS Confederation to provide a distinct voice for PCTs. Launched in 2007, over 90 per cent of PCTs are members. Current work focuses on strengthening commissioning, partnership with local government, regulation and system management, PCT provider services and communication, engagement and reputation management.
www.nhsconfed.org/pctn

NHS trusts

There are about 200 NHS trusts, overseeing 1,600 hospitals and specialist care centres. There are also 11 ambulance trusts. The number of NHS trusts is shrinking as more are granted foundation trust status (see opposite).

NHS trusts were abolished in Scotland in 2004. Wales abolished trusts in 2009, except for specialist service trusts, while Northern Ireland reduced its 18 trusts to five.

NHS trusts earn their income through providing healthcare commissioned by PCTs and practice-based commissioners, and paid for on a 'payment-by-results' basis (see page 192). They have a legal duty to break even financially, earn a 6 per cent return on their capital and achieve minimum quality standards. They must work in partnership with other NHS organisations, local authorities, independent providers and the voluntary sector. Trusts are also obliged to deliver national priorities.

Although strategic health authorities manage their performance, trusts are largely self-governing organisations. Their boards comprise a chair, five non-executive directors and five executives – including the chief executive and usually the medical, nursing and finance directors.

Foundation trusts

Foundation trusts have freedom from central government control. Their establishment formed part of the wider programme of reforms to move from a service controlled nationally to one where standards and inspection are national but delivery and accountability are local. They are unique to the NHS in England, and the first were established in 2004.

They are independent public benefit corporations, but remain part of the NHS and subject to its standards, performance ratings and inspection systems. Foundation trusts are accountable to Parliament, to the regulator Monitor, and to their governors, who are elected by local foundation trust members (see page 159).

Monitor, the independent regulator of foundation trusts (see page 172), authorises NHS trusts applying for foundation status and ensures they comply with the terms of their authorisation. Monitor is accountable to Parliament but independent of the Secretary of State, and has powers to intervene in the running of a foundation trust if it fails to meet standards or breaches the terms of its authorisation. The Care Quality Commission (see page 171) is responsible for inspecting the quality of foundation trust services, as it is for all other NHS organisations.

Foundation trusts' main advantages include:
- freedom from central government, giving them greater freedom to decide their own strategy, and how they run their services
- increased freedom to retain any operating surpluses and then reinvest the surpluses in projects such as service innovation or estate refurbishment
- the ability to make decisions more speedily, responding to needs identified by their local communities and local stakeholders
- access to capital from both the public and private sectors; the amount a foundation trust can borrow is determined by a formula based on its ability to repay the loan, and governed by the prudential borrowing code set by Monitor

- an obligation to achieve national targets and standards like the rest of the NHS, but not subject to performance management by strategic health authorities and the DH or to directions from the Secretary of State
- the ability to vary staff pay from nationally agreed terms and conditions, although Agenda for Change (see page 213) can apply to foundation trusts
- a unique line of accountability to their local communities through their members and governors, enabling them to be more responsive to local needs and wishes.

By March 2010 there were 129 foundation trusts, of which 40 were mental health trusts. Ambulance trusts are currently preparing themselves for foundation trust status, and the Labour Government piloted a number of community foundation trusts, formed from the provider services of PCTs.

Foundation trusts represent more than half of all acute trusts, and over 70 per cent of all mental health trusts. They employ over 420,000 staff. Some have revenues as high as £600 million and in size and complexity are equivalent to FTSE 250 private sector companies. As part of the FT/FTSE link project launched in 2006, 14 foundation trusts have partnerships with such companies. This project is being expanded to incorporate large mutuals.

All remaining NHS trusts are expected to have submitted plans by March 2010 detailing how they intend to reach foundation status by 2013/14 at the latest, according to the NHS operating framework for 2010/11.

Further information
NHS foundation trusts: consolidated accounts 2008–09, Monitor, July 2009.
Form following function: getting the structure right for foundation trust business models, Foundation Trust Network, July 2009.
Foundation trusts and Monitor: sixth report of session 2007–08, House of Commons health committee, October 2008.
Applying for NHS foundation trust status: guide for applicants, Monitor/DH, December 2008.
A powerful partnership, Foundation Trust Network/FTSE link project, July 2008.
Towards autonomy: lessons from aspirant community foundation trusts, PCT Network/NHS Confederation, April 2008.
Monitor **www.regulator-nhsft.gov.uk**

Care trusts

Care trusts are designed to allow close integration of health and social
care (a measure unnecessary in Northern Ireland, where the two services
are fully integrated). They commission and provide both within a single
NHS organisation.

The NHS and local authority may establish a care trust together where
both agree it offers the best way to improve health and social care. NHS
and local authority health-related functions are delegated to the trust, not
transferred, and the arrangement is voluntary – partners can withdraw.
Local authority councillors are members of the care trust's board. Care
trusts may be based on either a primary care trust or an NHS trust.

The concept is intended to be flexible enough to allow for a range of models
and service configurations, but care trusts are likely to focus on specialist
mental health and older people's services. Among the total of 151 PCTs,
ten are care trusts. However, there are increasing examples of PCT and
adult social care coming together in shared management arrangements,
although not generally using the care trust organisational mode.

Children's trusts

The Labour Government's aim, as stated in the 2004 green paper, *Every
child matters*, was to integrate key children's services within a single
organisational focus, the preferred model for which was children's trusts.
Children's trusts are not legal entities but partnerships between
organisations that provide, commission or are involved in services for
children and young people. They are normally led by local authorities.

The essential features of a children's trust are:
- a child-centred, outcome-led vision, informed by children's views and those of their families
- inter-agency governance and cooperation
- integrated strategy, including joint planning and commissioning and pooled budgets
- integrated processes, including joint working
- integrated frontline delivery organised around the child, young person or family rather than professional boundaries or existing agencies.

The children's plan called for children's trusts to be able by 2010 to identify all children and young people needing additional help and intervene early on their behalf. Children's trusts are in the process of being strengthened by extending the number of their partners and making their boards statutory bodies. Health visitors and GPs are key players in children's trusts.

Further information
The children's plan two years on: a progress report, DCSF, December 2009.
What is a children's trust? DCSF, November 2008.
Are we there yet? Improving governance and resource management in children's trusts, Audit Commission, October 2008.
The children's plan: building brighter futures, DCSF, December 2007.

Independent providers

By using independent providers – private sector companies, voluntary organisations and social enterprises – to offer care to NHS patients, the health service has been able to expand capacity and improve choice. The Labour Government introduced this policy in 2002, believing that competition from a plurality of providers would act as an incentive to the NHS to improve its response to patients' needs. It declared: 'The NHS cannot remain a monolithic, centrally run monopoly provider', and predicted that 'Working with providers from the independent sector and from overseas is not a temporary measure. They will become a permanent feature of the new NHS landscape and will provide NHS services.'

Since 2008, health service patients have had free choice of any hospital or treatment centre in England that meets NHS standards and costs, including those in the independent sector. For routine elective care, 'any willing provider' may now offer to supply services, and since 2007 independent sector hospitals on the Extended Choice Network have provided almost 150,000 procedures.

'Patients expect that wherever they receive their NHS-funded treatment, the same values and principles should apply,' according to the Next Stage Review (see page 127). 'All organisations are part of an integrated system for the benefit of patients.'

Further information
New providers: new solutions – the independent sector partnering with the NHS, NHS Confederation, February 2009.
Growing capacity: a new role for external healthcare providers in England, DH, June 2002.

The private sector
Traditionally, private healthcare providers in the UK tended to concentrate on secondary care, but new entrants to the market have looked for opportunities in primary and community care too. They have also become major suppliers of diagnostic services to the NHS.

The Labour Government initially encouraged private sector companies to set up treatment centres (see page 95) to carry out elective surgery and diagnostic tests for NHS patients under five-year contracts, to help alleviate waiting times. This paved the way for them gradually to play a bigger role, and volumes of services they provide to the NHS rose rapidly. Independent sector treatment centres (ISTCs) have provided more than 1.7 million operations, diagnostic assessments and primary care consultations for NHS patients, and a recent patient satisfaction survey found 96 per cent rated their care as excellent or very good.

The first ISTC contracts are due to end in 2010. In 2009, several 'wave one' ISTCs (those announced in 2002) performed below their contracted utilisation rates, and attracted criticism as under the contracts they were paid for procedures that did not take place. During 'phase two' (beginning in 2004), ISTCs were not guaranteed payment and initial plans were scaled down. A planned third phase was cancelled. As wave one contracts expire, each will be reviewed case-by-case by the commissioning PCT, and any new services will be supplied under national contracts at national tariff prices. There are 25 fixed-site wave one ISTCs. Phase two contracts do not expire until 2011–17.

NHS Partners Network is an alliance of commercial and not-for-profit independent healthcare providers spanning elective, diagnostic, dental, primary and community care. Set up in 2005, it became part of the NHS Confederation in 2007. Its aims are to influence policy and debate, share information, foster networking and develop solutions to benefit NHS patients and the public.
www.nhsconfed.org/nhspn

The third sector

'Third sector' describes the range of institutions that fall between the public and private sectors. These include small local community and voluntary groups, large and small registered charities, foundations, trusts, cooperatives and social enterprises. They often provide inpatient and outpatient mental health services, sexual health services, drug rehabilitation and palliative care. Many smaller voluntary organisations play a crucial part in community services, particularly for vulnerable and excluded groups, and are often able to bridge divides between statutory services. PCTs are encouraged to ensure third sector organisations are included in the planning process. The aim is that third sector organisations can become 'equal players' in providing services.

DH research into the third sector's potential contribution in 2007 found 35,000 third sector organisations provided health or social care, and another 1,600 planned to do so. Total funding for these services amounted to £12 billion a year, with just over half from the public sector – 36 per cent of which was for healthcare and 62 per cent for social care.

The DH has launched a £5.5 million 'third sector strategic partner programme' with 11 third sector organisations, aimed at:
• improving the sector's understanding of commissioning
• nurturing its role in moves to 'personalise' care
• increasing understanding of health inequalities
• raising awareness of how emergencies may affect the sector
• examining equality issues
• improving the way the sector works at a regional level.

Vital statistics: NHS spending on non-NHS providers (£m)

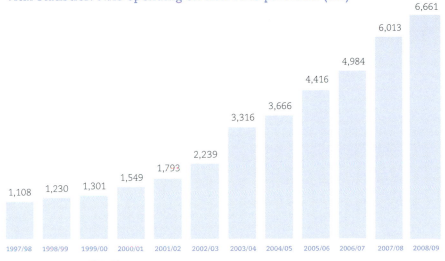

1,108	1,230	1,301	1,549	1,793	2,239	3,316	3,666	4,416	4,984	6,013	6,661
1997/98	1998/99	1999/00	2000/01	2001/02	2002/03	2003/04	2004/05	2005/06	2006/07	2007/08	2008/09

Source: Department of Health

In 2010/11 the programme is seeking third sector partners among organisations serving mental health; the women's sector; carers; lesbian, gay, bisexual and transgender people; offender health and social care; and armed forces and veterans charities.

Further information

NHS Next Stage Review: what it means for the third sector, DH, December 2008.

Partnership in public services: the public services action plan one year on, Cabinet Office, August 2008.

Eleventh report of session 2007–08: public services and the third sector: rhetoric and reality, House of Commons public administration committee, July 2008.

Third sector mapping report, DH, February 2007.

No excuses. Embrace partnership now. Step towards change! Report of the third sector commissioning task force, DH, July 2006.

Office of the Third Sector **www.cabinetoffice.gov.uk/thirdsector**

Third sector investment programme **www.dh.gov.uk/thirdsectorinvestment**

Social enterprises

Social enterprises are organisations run on business lines, but which reinvest profits in the community or in service developments. The Labour Government saw encouragement for social enterprise in health and social care as key to reforms. Social enterprises take different forms, and may include cooperatives, trusts or community interest companies. They number 62,000, contribute £24 billion to the economy and employ 800,000 people. Social enterprises involve patients and staff in designing and delivering services, improving quality and tailoring services to meet patients' needs. Many feature partnerships with third sector organisations (see page 32).

Under the 'right to request' commitment in the Next Stage Review (see page 127), PCT boards are obliged to consider requests from staff to set up a social enterprise and, if approved, support its development. The first wave of 20 projects, announced in 2009, includes schemes for homeless people, children and young people and mental health services. Each will receive £30,000 of DH funding, a dedicated mentor and access to professional development opportunities.

The DH's £100 million social enterprise investment fund helps social enterprises develop initiatives such as women's refuges, migraine clinics and exercise programmes for elderly people. The DH's Innovation for Life Challenge Fund, developed with the Social Enterprise Coalition, invites health and social care commissioners to propose innovative ways of using social enterprises. Strategic health authorities can bid for up to £100,000 revenue funding to help commission cross-sector social enterprise solutions.

Further information
Innovative partnerships: foundation trusts embracing social enterprises, Foundation Trust Network/NHS Confederation, October 2009.
Social enterprise – making a difference: a guide to the right to request, DH, November 2008.
Social Enterprise Investment Fund **www.dh.gov.uk/seif**
Social Enterprise Coalition **www.socialenterprise.org.uk**

Working in partnership
The concept of partnership has become a cornerstone of policy for modernising institutions across the whole field of civil and public life. It is one of the NHS's 'common principles' (see page 10), and partnership arrangements – with local government, the private and third sectors, and indeed with patients and the public – are a central feature of health and social care policy.

Local strategic partnerships (LSPs)
LSPs are intended to:
• bring together the different parts of the public sector and the private, business, community and voluntary sectors

- enable strategic decisions to be taken while still being close enough to individual neighbourhoods to allow decisions to be made at community level
- create strengthened, empowered, healthier and safer communities.

(Scotland's equivalents are community planning partnerships, while Wales has local service boards.)

The NHS has a key role to play in LSPs and neighbourhood renewal by improving health and reducing health inequalities.

The core tasks of LSPs are to:
- develop and deliver a local neighbourhood renewal strategy to secure more jobs, better education, improved health, reduced crime and better housing, narrowing the gap between deprived neighbourhoods and the rest and contributing to the national targets to tackle deprivation
- prepare and implement a community strategy for the area, identify and deliver the most important things that need to be done, keep track of progress and keep it up to date
- bring together local plans, partnerships and initiatives to provide a forum through which mainstream service providers (local authorities, police, health services, central government agencies and bodies outside the public sector) work effectively together to meet local needs and priorities
- work with local authorities that are developing a local area agreement (see page 53) to help devise and meet suitable targets.

The Audit Commission has found LSPs are still 'evolving and maturing', with too few taking an area-wide approach to performance and resource management. Comprehensive area assessment (see page 54) will provide a means of judging how effective LSPs are.

Further information
Working better together? Managing local strategic partnerships, Audit Commission, April 2009.
Planning together: updated practical guide for local strategic partnerships and planners, Communities and Local Government, April 2009.

Total Place is designed to examine how a 'whole area' approach can improve public services at less cost. Thirteen pilots, each with a different economic, geographical and demographic profile, are examining the totality of public spending in a range of services with a view to cutting duplication, saving money and improving quality. Each pilot has selected at least one theme to explore in more detail: they include children's services, aged care, drugs and alcohol, housing, crime and mental health services. The initiative involves chief executives and leaders from each local authority, PCTs, Jobcentre Plus, the police and others in the local strategic partnership. Councils can use the efficiency savings they make to reinvest in local services or to hold down council tax.
www.localleadership.gov.uk/totalplace

Government departments

A range of Government departments – apart from the DH – has responsibilities that impinge on health, and work in partnership with the NHS. They include:

- **Communities and Local Government**: responsible for housing, regional and local government.
  www.communities.gov.uk
- **Home Office**: lead responsibility for progress on the drug strategy; the Home Secretary chairs the cross-government Cabinet ministerial subcommittee on drugs policy; local crime and disorder reduction partnerships.
  www.homeoffice.gov.uk/drugs
  www.drugs.gov.uk
- **Department for Education**: responsible for children's social care policy, the Change for Children programme, Every Child Matters strategy and Sure Start, which aims to improve health, education and emotional development for young children in disadvantaged areas. The Healthy Schools programme is run jointly with the DH.
  www.education.gov.uk
- **Department for Environment, Food and Rural Affairs**: responsibilities include water, farming, fisheries, horticulture and some aspects of rural health and well-being. Protection from the effects of pollution or toxic chemicals are particular concerns.
  www.defra.gov.uk

02 Commissioning

Commissioning is the process by which the NHS decides what services are needed, acquires them and then ensures they are being provided appropriately. It involves assessing the population's needs and deciding which are priorities, procuring the services to meet them and managing the providers. If done effectively, it ultimately ensures people live healthier and longer lives.

The origins of commissioning can be traced to the advent of the internal market in 1991 and the division of the NHS into purchasers and providers. Then it was referred to as 'purchasing'. The past decade's reforms have altered the nature of commissioning. 'World-class commissioning' attempted to create a new form of commissioning and lead the way internationally. The coalition Government now wants GPs to play a bigger role.

Responsibility for commissioning rests mainly with primary care trusts and general practice (see practice-based commissioning, page 48) and local government. Joint commissioning with local government brings together PCTs and social services for strategic planning and development.

The basics

Essential elements

The essential elements of sound commissioning are:
- assessing needs – based on rigorous analysis
- reviewing service provision – identifying gaps and potential for improving existing services
- deciding priorities – the PCT should produce a strategic plan for the health community
- designing services – practices work individually or in groups to develop strategies and models to improve services
- strategic plans – signalling the strategic direction for local services and highlighting commissioning priorities over the next five years
- shaping the structure of supply – PCTs must be clear about the services and specifications needed, and agree contracts with local providers within the new national contracting framework
- managing demand and ensuring appropriate access to care – practices and PCTs should establish strategies for the use of care and resources
- clinical decision-making – individual practices and clinicians undertake individual needs assessments, make referrals and advise patients on choices and treatments

- managing performance – practices must manage their indicative budget to maximise the benefits from available resources
- patient and public feedback – PCTs are responsible for measuring and reporting on patients' experience.

In particular, commissioning is attempting to:
- shift towards services that are personal, sensitive to individual need and that maintain independence and dignity
- reorient towards promoting health and well-being, investing to reduce the future costs of ill health
- focus more on services and interventions that will achieve better health, across health services and local government, promote inclusion and tackle health inequalities.

Further information
Commissioning framework for health and wellbeing, DH, March 2007.
Health reform in England: update and commissioning framework, DH, July 2006.
DH Care Networks: Commissioning **www.dhcarenetworks.org.uk/bettercommissioning**

Setting priorities

The ability to identify priorities is a key skill for commissioners. Many NHS resources still reflect historic patterns of provision or the particular approach of local providers, or even of individual clinicians. To break free of this requires systematic, evidence-based decisions about what treatments and services to commission. The number of high-cost treatments and increasingly vocal interest groups make allocating resources a politically sensitive and complex issue. Need and demand for healthcare always have and always will exceed the NHS's available funds – which means that PCTs must prioritise needs into those that will be met and those that will not.

PCTs stand a better chance of arriving at fair decisions that properly balance competing needs if their priority setting shows:
- a sound grasp of the concept – to reduce uncertainty and risk, and be more robust to challenge
- organisational cohesion – so that everyone in the PCT understands how priorities are set and acts accordingly, leading to consistent decision-making
- consistency – especially in relation to individual funding requests
- protocol-driven decision-making – which is consistent, efficient and timely, as PCTs repeatedly face the same scenarios.

NHS CONFEDERATION

Further information

Priority setting: strategic planning, PCTN/NHS Confederation, April 2008.
Priority setting: managing individual funding requests, PCTN/NHS Confederation, March 2008.
Priority setting: legal considerations, PCTN/NHS Confederation, March 2008.
Priority setting: managing new treatments, PCTN/NHS Confederation, February 2008.
Priority setting: an overview, PCTN/NHS Confederation, October 2007.

World-class commissioning

Although the NHS introduced commissioning in 1991, unlike hospital management it has never had a chance to mature as a discipline because of frequent reorganisation and general underinvestment in skills development. As a result, and despite pockets of excellence, there is an imbalance in the influence that providers and commissioners exert over the system. Launched at the end of 2007, 'world-class commissioning' is a response to that: it seeks to transform how the NHS goes about commissioning, redressing the balance. It represents the most serious attempt to reposition commissioning as central to the way the NHS operates since the early 1990s. In particular it aims to make full use of the advantages that the NHS – as a publicly funded system free to all – offers commissioners: it can provide rich clinical data that, if used to its potential, could have a direct impact on individuals and the population as a whole, reducing inequalities in health. As the Next Stage Review (see page 127) expressed it: 'The world-class commissioning programme is designed to raise ambitions for a new form of commissioning that delivers better health and well-being for the population, improving health outcomes and reducing health inequalities – adding life to years and years to life.'

World-class commissioning focuses on assessing and prioritising population needs, strategic outcomes, procuring services and managing providers to deliver the required outcomes. It requires a longer-term and more strategic approach than hitherto. PCTs need to:
• lead the NHS locally
• work with community partners
• engage with public and patients
• collaborate with clinicians
• manage knowledge and assess needs
• prioritise investment
• stimulate the market
• promote innovation and improvement
• secure procurement skills

- manage the local health system
- spend efficiently and effectively.

World-class commissioning has had a significant impact since its launch. The profile of PCTs as local leaders of the NHS has risen, and commissioners have formulated ambitious strategic plans.

An assurance system, managed by SHAs, recognises and rewards performance and ensures milestones are reached while allowing PCTs to set local priorities. It specifies a level all PCTs have to reach in the short term and one they will need to achieve over time. In 2009, 27 PCTs achieved the second highest rating for their strategy, board governance and finance; none has yet reached the highest rating. Results from the second year of the assurance system are expected in July 2010.

The change of government and requirement to make management cost savings may mean that the world-class commissioning approach is significantly revised over the next year.

Further information
World class commissioning: an introduction, DH, December 2009.
World class commissioning assurance handbook year 2: 2009/10–2010/11, DH September 2009.
The role of the PCT board in world class commissioning, DH, November 2008.
www.dh.gov.uk/worldclasscommissioning

Support for commissioning: FESC
The Framework for procuring External Support for Commissioners (FESC) comprises 13 private sector companies that PCTs can call on for support with their world-class commissioning endeavours. They offer specialist expertise in services such as data analysis and contract management, which is not always widely available in PCTs.

Each company has been appointed to FESC by the DH on the basis of its technical and commercial ability. PCTs remain responsible for managing the services provided. A FESC-appointed commissioning supplier cannot be a provider of clinical services in the same PCT area. Several FESC schemes are being piloted across the country to demonstrate various ways in which the framework might be used. The interim Next Stage Review report (see page 127) commented that 'given the variation in NHS commissioning skills currently on offer', there should be 'extensive use within every SHA' of FESC. www.dh.gov.uk/fesc

Commissioning and competition

There is no general requirement for NHS services to be subject to formal procurement: provision of healthcare in the UK has usually not involved contracts enforceable in the courts but 'NHS contracts' agreed between organisations belonging to the health service. But as the use of independent and third sector providers for NHS-funded services has become more common, and foundation trusts have become established – with which contracts are legally binding – a formal procurement process must now be followed in some circumstances.

In addition, the 2006 commissioning framework required commissioners to review services systematically, focusing initially on any where quality caused concern; this could lead to a decision to tender a service that failed to meet standards or failed to improve. The introduction of free choice of provider for patients and the opportunity for any willing provider to supply services further increased competition to supply services.

With this growing diversity of providers, the DH formulated principles and rules to ensure competition is fair and transparent, and safeguard the NHS's reputation. It also set up a panel to enforce the rules and a website for commissioners and providers to publicise opportunities to tender for services.

The DH is setting up regional commercial support units (see page 204) at a cost of £20 million in 2009/10. These will offer commissioners commercial support to 'stimulate the market' and give providers a single point of contact with the NHS. They will take over some of the functions of the NHS Purchasing and Supply Agency, now abolished. In addition, a strategic market development unit will help commissioners with market analysis and market-making.

Further information
Commercial skills for the NHS, DH, March 2010.

Principles and rules of competition

The principles and rules of cooperation and competition were revised in 2010. There are now ten principles and 36 rules. The principles are:
- Commissioners must commission services from the providers best placed to deliver the needs of their patients and populations.
- Commissioning and procurement must be transparent and non-discriminatory and follow the *PCT procurement guide*.

- Payment regimes and financial intervention in the system must be transparent and fair.
- Commissioners and providers must cooperate to improve services and deliver seamless and sustainable care to patients.
- Commissioners and providers should encourage patient choice and ensure that patients have accurate and reliable information to exercise more choice and control over their healthcare.
- Commissioners and providers should not reach agreements which restrict commissioner or patient choice against patients' and taxpayers' interests.
- Providers must not refuse to accept services or to supply essential services to commissioners where this restricts commissioner or patient choice against patients' and taxpayers' interests.
- Commissioners and providers must not discriminate unduly between patients and must promote equality.
- Appropriate promotional activity is encouraged as long as it remains consistent with patients' best interests and the brand and reputation of the NHS.
- Mergers, including vertical integration, between providers are permissible when sufficient choice and competition remain or where they are otherwise in patients' and taxpayers' interests – for example, because they will deliver significant improvements in quality of care.

Further information
Principles and rules for cooperation and competition, DH, March 2010.
PCT procurement guide for health services, DH, May 2010.

Code of practice for promoting services
The code sets out rules for promotional material issued by providers of NHS services, whether they are from within the NHS, third sector or private sector. Its 46 clauses aim to ensure that information patients receive is not misleading, inaccurate, unfair or offensive. It is also designed to protect the NHS brand and reputation, and ensure spending on promotion is not excessive. PCTs are responsible for enforcing the code through their contracts, overseen by SHAs. Where they cannot resolve a dispute, the matter can be referred to the NHS Co-operation and Competition Panel or, if appropriate, to the Advertising Standards Authority.

Further information
Code of practice for the promotion of NHS-funded services, DH, March 2008.

NHS Co-operation and Competition Panel

The panel, set up in 2009, is designed to ensure the principles and rules of competition are followed. It advises SHAs, the DH and Monitor on resolving disputes, and is responsible for considering complaints about procurement of clinical services, advertising and promotion, and the merger or acquisition of healthcare providers where an NHS body is involved. It only considers disputes not resolved locally. The panel is likely to become part of the new economic regulator into which Monitor will be developed.

Further information

Co-operation and Competition Panel progress report, Co-operation and Competition Panel, February 2010.
Guide to the Co-operation and Competition Panel: who we are, what we do, and how we do it, Co-operation and Competition Panel, February 2010.

NHS Supply2Health

This website helps PCTs advertise clinical services they wish to commission and enables suppliers to identify business opportunities in the NHS. All NHS commissioners must post information about tendering opportunities and contract awards here, making it easier for suppliers to locate single opportunities and understand what PCTs want. Supply2Health helps commissioners meet their European Union and other legal requirements to advertise, and potentially increases responses to adverts by reaching a wider audience. It also offers email alerts when new opportunities are posted.
www.supply2health.nhs.uk

PCTs and commissioning

PCTs commission most health services from other organisations, including GPs, dentists, community pharmacists, optometrists, NHS trusts, foundation trusts, voluntary sector organisations and private healthcare providers. However, they may lose some responsibility for commissioning to GPs under the coalition Government's plans. They are responsible for managing contracts with providers: this includes monitoring service quality, ensuring standards are being met and intervening if things go wrong. PCTs must also commission comprehensive well-being and prevention services, personalised to meet the local population's needs.

PCTs commission care in partnership with practice-based commissioners – local GPs well placed to assess their community's health needs and design services for them. They also work closely with local authorities to ensure health, social care and other public services are 'joined-up', especially services for children, older people and those with mental health problems, learning and physical disabilities. Local area agreements (see page 53) set out how PCTs, local authorities and other public bodies will work together to improve the quality of life for people in their area.

Further information

Discussion paper 6: Commissioning for quality, PCT Network/NHS Confederation, December 2009.

Discussion paper 5: Commissioning in a cold climate, PCT Network/NHS Confederation, June 2009.

The role of the primary care trust board in world class commissioning, DH, November 2008.

Commissioning primary care

The current primary medical care contracting arrangements were introduced in 2004 to enable the NHS to provide a wider range of services closer to where patients live and improve the quality of care. PCTs have four options for commissioning primary care services.

• They can use the nationally agreed general medical services (GMS) contract (see page 215) to determine the services a GP practice will provide. Amended annually, the GMS contract has since evolved in partnership between NHS Employers and the British Medical Association's GP Committee. It allows GPs flexibility over the services they offer. It has enabled some to reduce their workload – important in helping the NHS recruit and retain GPs – while others have taken on new services; remuneration is adjusted accordingly. Practices have to provide essential services – which means treating sick and terminally ill patients – but can opt out of providing 'additional' services such as child immunisation, maternity and contraceptive services and cervical tests. Most have maintained or expanded the range of services they provide.

• PCTs can use a locally agreed arrangement with practices, the personal medical services (PMS) contract. This enables them to offer salaried appointments to GPs, particularly useful where it has been difficult to recruit and retain them using the GMS contract. PMS contract terms are decided between the PCT and GP to tailor services to local needs. In 2008, 42 per cent of practices – just over 47 per cent of GPs – worked to PMS contracts.

- Under the alternative provider medical services (APMS) arrangements, PCTs can contract with non-NHS bodies such as voluntary or commercial sector providers to supply primary medical services. They may also contract with NHS secondary care organisations – foundation trusts, NHS trusts or other PCTs – for them to provide primary care services. The Government sees APMS as offering substantial opportunities for restructuring services for greater patient choice, improved access and greater responsiveness to specific community needs. It believes APMS can be a valuable tool in areas that have always been underprovided with primary care, where practices have opted out of providing some services or in areas finding it difficult to recruit GPs.

- Finally, PCTs can provide services themselves (PCTMS), employing GPs and their practice staff and taking on practice lists and services.

PCTs also hold dental and pharmacy contracts in order to ensure provision of these services locally.

PCTs may in addition, commission 'enhanced services' to plug a gap in essential services or deliver higher than specified standards, usually to help reduce demand on secondary care. The three types are:
- **directed enhanced services (DES)** – services which the PCT must provide for its population: for example, the pandemic flu vaccination scheme for priority groups
- **local enhanced services (LES)** – locally developed services designed to meet local health needs
- **national enhanced services (NES)** – services to meet local needs, commissioned to national specifications and benchmark pricing: for example, enhanced care for homeless people, specialised services for multiple sclerosis and depression.

Further information
World class commissioning: primary and community services: improving GP services, NHS East of England, Primary Care Contracting and DH, January 2009.
NHS Primary Care Commissioning (employers' web area): **www.pcc.nhs.uk**

Commissioning acute and other services
Since 2009, standard NHS contracts have governed agreements between PCTs and providers of acute, mental health, learning disability and ambulance services. They replaced a wide variety of individual contracts and service level agreements.

Standard NHS contracts have three parts:

- mandatory elements – centrally set, standard NHS terms and conditions that cannot be altered or removed
- required elements – compulsory contractual or legal requirements defined centrally that must be completed by the contracting parties
- locally defined elements – for which there is no national or legal requirement but which can be added by local agreement, provided they do not undermine mandatory or required elements.

The contracts are intended to assure and clarify accountability, as well as improve performance. For the first time, all providers now have the same contractual standard terms. The price for most acute services is fixed under the payment-by-results system (see page 192). The standard contract for acute services will not be in use for the independent sector before April 2011.

Further information
The standard NHS contracts for acute hospital, mental health, community and ambulance services and supporting guidance, DH, December 2008.
Briefing 173: The new standard NHS contracts, PCT Network/NHS Confederation, January 2009.

Commissioning specialised services
Specialised services are those with low patient numbers but which need a critical mass of patients to make treatment centres cost-effective. Nationally the NHS commissions over 50 specialised services, benefiting about 10,000 patients, at an annual cost of £480 million. They are provided in relatively few specialist centres to catchment populations of more than 1 million people, and are subject to different commissioning arrangements from other NHS services. As they are high-cost, low-volume treatments, the risk to an individual PCT of having to fund expensive, unpredictable activity is reduced by PCTs grouping together to commission them collectively and share financial risk.

Commissioning arrangements for specialised services were strengthened after the independent Carter Review in 2006/07. Specialised services are either commissioned regionally, by ten specialised commissioning groups (SCGs), or nationally by the National Commissioning Group (NCG), depending on the rarity of the condition or treatment.

Each SCG is aligned with a strategic health authority and acts on behalf of a population of between 3 and 7 million people. They commission – for example – haemophilia services and blood and marrow transplantation.

The NCG advises ministers on which NHS services are best commissioned nationally rather than locally. Most services it commissions relate to conditions suffered by fewer than 400 people nationally. Examples include heart and lung transplantation and secure forensic mental health services for adolescents. The NCG is supported by the 30-strong National Specialised Commissioning Team.

In addition, the National Specialised Commissioning Group (NSCG) oversees national commissioning and encourages SCGs to collaborate. SCG chairs – usually PCT chief executives – form NSCG's core membership.

The DH has recently consulted on dissolving the NCG and replacing it with a National Commissioning Advisory Group that would make recommendations directly to ministers and take on responsibility for considering new drugs and technologies that would be appropriate for national commissioning.

Further information
Strengthening national commissioning: a consultation document, DH, December 2009.
www.specialisedcommissioning.nhs.uk

Practice-based commissioning
Practice-based commissioning is designed to give GPs and practice nurses more say in how the NHS provides services for patients, putting clinicians at the heart of world-class commissioning. Practice-based commissioners work closely with PCTs and secondary care clinicians, leading work on deciding clinical outcomes. They also play a key role in providing PCTs with valuable feedback on provider performance.

Since 2005, GP practices have been able to hold an 'indicative' budget – money their PCT would otherwise control – to spend on secondary services. The intention is they will reflect their patients' preferences, leading to greater variety of services from a greater number of providers and more convenience for patients, as well as more efficient use of resources. Practices may combine together to commission services. PCTs continue to be legally responsible for contracting, but practices can keep up to 70 per cent of any savings to reinvest in premises, diagnostic or other equipment, patient services or staff. Although practice-based commissioning remains voluntary, virtually all practices are now involved.

However, practice-based commissioning seems overall to have failed to capture the imaginations of clinicians, NHS managers and the public. The Next Stage Review (see page 127) acknowledged 'a widespread view' that with some exceptions, practice-based commissioning 'has not yet lived up to its potential', while the King's Fund concluded it had proved expensive and delivered little in terms of better services for patients or financial savings.

Nevertheless, under the coalition Government's plans, GPs are set to take on the main responsibility for commissioning.

A DH survey of practice-based commissioning leads during autumn 2009 found:
- 84 per cent had agreed a budget with their PCT
- 82 per cent had submitted proposals to their PCT for redesigning some services
- 54 per cent said practice-based commissioning had influenced clinical practice
- 80 per cent believed access to services had improved, while 77 per cent thought they had become more cost-effective and provided a better patient experience
- 82 per cent reported a good relationship with their PCT.

The DH has created a practice-based commissioning development framework through which PCTs, SHAs and practice-based commissioners can call on help from five approved external organisations.

It is expected that the coalition Government will make GP commissioning a contractual obligation. This will necessitate the formation of GP groups.

Further information
Clinical commissioning: our vision for practice-based commissioning, DH, March 2009.
Practice-based commissioning in action: a guide for GPs, DH, June 2009.
Discussion paper 3: practice-based commissioning – delivering the vision, PCT Network/ NHS Confederation, January 2009.
PBC development framework: an introduction, DH, December 2008.
Practice-based commissioning: reinvigorate, replace or abandon?, King's Fund, November 2008.

Joint commissioning

The NHS and local government commission some services jointly. Indeed, the Government's planning framework (see page 121) treats health and social care as one system, with shared-lead priorities where both health and social care organisations have a major contribution to make. In Northern Ireland, health and social care have been combined since 1973. In Scotland, community health partnerships have increased coterminosity between NHS and local authority boundaries.

In all areas, joint working and the engagement of local authorities are required – especially in tackling health inequalities, expanding intermediate care, implementing national service frameworks, improving services for vulnerable people and those with long-term conditions, as well as tackling neighbourhood renewal. Sixteen pilot sites are conducting a trial into how health and social care can be provided together (see page 84).

Measures to help make this a reality include:
• continuing development of local area agreements (see page 53)
• integrated health and social care planning cycles
• joint health and social care plans for people with long-term conditions
• a single complaints procedure across health and social care (see page 166)
• a national framework for NHS continuing care assessments
• strengthening the public health director's role to link it more closely with local authority overview and scrutiny committees (see page 175)
• national criteria on means-testing services and a commitment to extend personalised budgets and direct payments.

Encouraging cooperation through legislation

Powers to enable health and local authority partners to work together more effectively were contained in Section 31 of the 1999 Health Act and came into force in 2000. These were reinforced by the Local Government and Public Involvement in Health Act 2007.

The Health Act 1999 created a duty of cooperation between NHS bodies and local authorities in England and Wales. It provides for them to develop together local strategies for improving health and healthcare, and allows them to make joint arrangements for commissioning or providing health and health-related services. Strategic health authorities, primary care trusts, social care, housing, transport, leisure and library services, community and many acute services can all be involved.

Specifically, the Act introduced flexibilities to enable NHS organisations and local authorities to set up:
- pooled funds – to be spent on agreed projects for designated services
- lead commissioning – they can agree to delegate commissioning of a service to one lead organisation
- integrated provision – combining staff, resources and management structures to integrate a service from managerial level to the front line.

The NHS Act 2006 enabled the health service and local authorities to pool functions and resources. The Audit Commission found that pooled funds are mainly used for learning disability, community equipment and mental health services, but rarely for older people's services. Joint expenditure accounted for a relatively small amount (3.4 per cent in 2007/08) of total health and social care spend.

PCTs have the key role in representing the NHS in developing partnerships. For this they are required to work flexibly.

The NHS and local government have clear common aims, objectives and activity, much of which contribute to delivering NHS priorities. Involvement in planning and prioritising provides ways of engaging with local communities and the voluntary sector, and ensures stakeholders' involvement in NHS planning objectives.

The Children Act 2004 enhances the NHS's role in working with local partners to safeguard children. For example, NHS trusts and local authorities can pool their children's budgets. The Act set up the role of children's commissioner for England and established a statutory duty for all agencies working with children to cooperate.

One of the health service's seven guiding principles enshrined in the NHS Constitution states: 'The NHS works across organisational boundaries and in partnership with other organisations in the interest of patients, local communities and the wider population.' It adds: 'The NHS is committed to working jointly with local authorities and a wide range of other private, public and third sector organisations at national and local level to provide and deliver improvements in health and well-being.'

Further information

Means to an end – joint financing across health and social care: health national report, Audit Commission, October 2009.
Delivering health and wellbeing in partnership: the crucial role of the new local performance framework, CLG/DH, December 2007.
Partnership working: the facts, PCT Network/NHS Confederation, April 2007.

Joint strategic needs assessment

Under the Local Government and Public Involvement in Health Act 2007, PCTs and local authorities must carry out a joint strategic needs assessment (JSNA) to provide a firm foundation for commissioning. The aim of JSNA is to identify areas for priority action through local area agreements and to help commissioners – including practice-based commissioners – specify outcomes that encourage local innovation. It focuses on population – not individual – need, and is a tool to identify groups whose needs are not being met and whose healthcare is producing poor results.

The JSNA should:
• describe the local population's future health, care and well-being needs, and how services will meet them
• look ahead three to five years
• analyse data
• define where inequalities exist
• use local views and evidence of how effective or ineffective services are to shape investment and disinvestment
• define achievable improvements in health and well-being.

In practice, JSNA is led by the directors of public health, adult social care and children's services, working closely with the directors of commissioning and finance. It examines all the factors that impact on health, including employment, education, housing and the environment.

Further information

Implementing joint strategic needs assessment: pitfalls, possibilities and progress, Health Services Management Centre, University of Birmingham for Department of Health and Integrated Care Network, July 2008.
Guidance on joint strategic needs assessment, DH, December 2007.

Local area agreements

Local area agreements (LAAs) aim to improve local public services by setting out the 'deal' between central and local government and its partners. They are based on the principle that developing services collectively is more effective than in isolation. Every area in England has had an LAA since March 2007. They cover one or more local authorities, and focus on a collection of goals across a range of services that relate to either national or local priorities. To set these priorities the local authority liaises with other organisations, which pool or align their budgets in order to achieve them. The Government Office for the Region handles the negotiations with the local authority and its partners, with regional public health directors representing health interests.

The LAA is then sent to ministers for approval. Proposed LAAs are sent to the Secretary of State for Health accompanied by the regional public health director's assessment of the health content and a view as to whether the LAA should be agreed. Once signed off, LAA targets have statutory status. LAAs have a three-year focus and include up to 35 targets drawn from central government priorities, with scope to add local targets. Out of 5,813 chosen by localities, 2,684 – about 47 per cent – contribute to health and well-being. Targets are structured around four key themes:
• children and young people
• safer and stronger communities
• healthier communities for older people
• economic development and the environment.

LAAs are a means of tackling major health and well-being issues, such as increasing levels of obesity, an ageing population, inability to work because of ill health and the increasing number of people reporting mental health problems. They are judged to have had a significant impact on how central and local government work together since they were piloted in 2004. Current LAAs run until March 2011. New arrangements need to be introduced by autumn 2010 to allow preparation for any very different model following the general election.

Further information
Negotiating new local area agreements, Communities and Local Government, September 2007.
Evidence of savings, improved outcomes, and good practice attributed to local area agreements, Communities and Local Government, February 2007.

Comprehensive area assessment

Since 2009, 'comprehensive area assessment' has examined how well local services are working together to improve quality of life and provide value for money. However, the coalition Government is committed to abolishing CAA. CAA looks across councils, health bodies, police forces, fire and rescue services and other bodies responsible for local public services that are increasingly expected to work in partnership. It takes LAA priorities as its starting point.

Other service or organisation-specific assessments feed into the collective over-arching report, but try to avoid duplication. CAA brings together six inspectorates:
• Audit Commission
• Care Quality Commission
• Ofsted
• Her Majesty's Inspector of Constabulary
• Her Majesty's Inspector of Probation
• Her Majesty's Inspector of Prisons.

Green and red flags are used to highlight problem areas or exceptional performance. Four themes underpin assessment:
• sustainable development – creating just and healthy societies
• inequality – the effectiveness of strategies to alleviate it
• value for money – taking a cross-organisational view
• vulnerable people – such as those in need of or just having left care services, children, offenders and people on probation.

CAA results are published on the Oneplace website.

Further information
Oneplace national overview report, Oneplace, February 2010.
Briefing 182: Comprehensive area assessment, NHS Confederation, May 2009.
Oneplace http://oneplace.direct.gov.uk

Public health
Public health is concerned with improving the population's health, rather than treating the diseases of individual patients. Safeguarding and enhancing public health is therefore an important objective of commissioning. The official definition of public health, devised by former Chief Medical Officer Sir Donald Acheson, is: 'the science and art of preventing disease, prolonging life, and promoting health through the

organised efforts of society'. Many of the aims of public health can only be achieved through partnerships across Government departments and between the Government, NHS, local authorities, the private and voluntary sectors. This is especially true for tackling inequalities in health. Other major challenges include obesity, smoking, sexually transmitted diseases, alcohol and drug misuse and mental health.

Public health professionals monitor the health status of the community, identify health needs, develop programmes to reduce risk and screen for early disease, control communicable disease, promote health, plan and evaluate healthcare provision and manage and implement change.

Framing public health policy
Choosing health, the public health white paper published in 2004, is based on the principle that the NHS should improve health and prevent disease, not just provide treatment for those who are ill. It encompasses the view that people should make their own choices about their lifestyle, and consequently their health, but that these should be guided by good information and advice about the choices available. The NHS will help, support and encourage people to choose healthy lifestyles.

Principles behind this approach to public health are:
• informed choices – people want to be able to make their own decisions about choices that affect their health and to have good-quality information to help them do so
• personalisation – support to be tailored to the realities of individual lives
• working together – progress depends on effective partnerships across communities.

The white paper pushed public health towards the top of priorities across government. It recognised the significant health benefits that could be gained by tackling public health issues, and it acknowledged – importantly – that the NHS could not solve all health-related problems on its own.

The DH has devised a plan to use social marketing to improve public health, basing targeted action on evidence of what motivates people to lead healthier lives. *Ambitions for health* focuses on:
• health capacity – increasing public health professionals' skills and knowledge through conferences, seminars and research materials
• health insight – a 'one-stop research shop' to collect useful data in one place

- health innovations – learning from the successes of programmes such as health trainers and life checks
- health partnerships – a £1 million a year fund to support partnerships.

Current public health initiatives include NHS Health Checks and the Communities for Health programme.

The 15 million people in England aged 40 to 74 are gradually being invited for a free health check to identify their risk of conditions such as coronary heart disease, stroke, diabetes and kidney disease, which currently affect 4 million people in England and are responsible for a fifth of all hospital admissions. It is estimated that health checks could prevent 1,600 heart attacks and strokes each year and help save 650 lives.

Under the Communities for Health programme, more than 80 local authorities have undertaken 360 local activities to encourage behaviour change and enable people to take control of their own health and well-being, tackling obesity, smoking, drugs and alcohol. The programme received £11 million funding in 2008/09 and a further £9 million in 2009/10.

The coalition Government has put significant emphasis on controlling the effects of alcohol, violence and obesity, and an early-years development.

Further information

Communities for Health: unlocking the energy within communities to improve health, DH, October 2009.

Putting prevention first – vascular checks: risk assessment and management – next steps guidance for primary care trusts, DH, November 2008.

Ambitions for health: a strategic framework for maximising the potential of social marketing and health-related behaviour, DH, July 2008.

Choosing health progress report, DH, May 2007.

Health Challenge England – next steps for choosing health, DH, October 2006.

Delivering choosing health: making healthier choices easier, DH, March 2005.

Choosing health: making healthier choices easier, DH, November 2004.

Spotlight on policy: Health Work Wellbeing

Health Work Wellbeing is a Government-led initiative to improve the health and well-being of working-age people. Founded on evidence that working is good for health, it brings together employers, unions and healthcare professionals to help more people with health conditions find and stay in employment. A cross-government programme, it was launched in 2005 by the DH, Department for Work and Pensions and the Health and Safety Executive. It now also includes the Scottish and Welsh Assembly governments. Its aim is 'to break the link between ill health and inactivity, to advance the prevention of ill health and injury, to encourage good management of occupational health, and to transform opportunities for people to recover from illness while at work'.

The strategy is led by a national director for health and work, Dame Carol Black, who found that ill health cost £100 billion a year and that access to good work-related health support was inadequate in the early stages of sickness, with provision disproportionately concentrated among a few large employers, leaving most without support. She proposed:

* piloting a Fit for Work service for patients in the early stages of illness
* if successful, the service to be extended to those on incapacity and other out-of-work benefits
* the traditional 'sick note' to be replaced by an electronic 'fit note' stating what people can do rather than what they cannot
* occupational health to be brought into the mainstream of healthcare provision.

The Labour Government accepted most of the recommendations and those in a report into NHS staff health and well-being, led by Dr Steve Boorman (see page 220).

Further information

Briefing 56: The healthy workplace agenda, NHS Employers, December 2008.
Improving health and work: changing lives – the Government's response to Dame Carol Black's review of the health of Britain's working-age population, TSO, November 2008.
Working for a healthier tomorrow, TSO, March 2008.
Health, work and wellbeing – caring for our future: a strategy for the health and wellbeing of working age people, DWP, DH & HSE, October 2005.
www.workingforhealth.gov.uk

Reducing health inequalities

Health inequalities start early in life, persist into old age and are repeated in subsequent generations. They exist in many forms. Different regions have different health outcomes. Children born into lower socio-economic backgrounds are more likely to die at birth, suffer more illness throughout their life and die younger. Unemployment and poor housing, in particular, are significant causes of ill health. Ethnicity also plays a major role, with a higher prevalence of disease among different racial groups. Health inequality is found by gender, disability, sexual orientation and lifestyle. It is both avoidable and fundamentally unfair.

Action to break the cycle of deprivation and its impact on health was central to much Labour Government policy. Tackling health inequalities and improving health require active commitment by Government departments and groups at all levels – national, regional and local. Joint working, partnerships, networking, shared funding and resources are crucial.

Vital statistics: Health inequalities

- Children from manual social backgrounds are 1.5 times as likely to die during infancy than those from non-manual backgrounds.
- The rate of infant deaths is 70 per cent higher in the West Midlands than in the South East.
- UK infant mortality rates are higher than in France, Spain, Germany and Italy.
- Manchester men have the lowest life expectancy in England – 73 years. Men in Kensington and Chelsea can expect to live until they are 83.1 years old. The national average is 77.4 years.
- People from black and minority ethnic groups are up to six times more likely to develop diabetes.
- People in lower socio-economic groups are 50 per cent more likely to smoke.
- Obesity levels are nearly 50 per cent higher among women from lower socio-economic groups.

Source: Department of Health

Government action

Since 2004 the DH's public service agreement with the Treasury (see page 123) has contained a target to reduce inequalities in health outcomes by 10 per cent by 2010, as measured by infant mortality and life expectancy at birth. The life-expectancy element focuses on reducing the health gap between the fifth of local authority areas with the lowest life expectancy at birth and the rest of the population. The infant mortality aspect of the target seeks to reduce the gap between manual groups and the rest of the population.

In addition, other initiatives designed to reduce inequalities include:
- national minimum wage
- working families tax credit
- child tax credits
- minimum income guarantee for pensioners
- winter fuel payments
- the New Deal
- Sure Start.

A group of 'spearhead' PCTs covering 70 local authorities identified as the most health-deprived areas are piloting initiatives, such as health trainers and enhanced smoking-cessation services, to reduce health inequalities. Over a quarter of the population of England are included in the initiative.

The NHS at national level has also appointed a director for equality and human rights 'to tackle inequalities in all aspects of health and social care delivery'.

Although a DH progress report in 2008 found some improvements, it acknowledged that the health of the most disadvantaged people had not improved as quickly as that of the better-off, and in some cases health inequalities had widened. In particular, smoking, drinking and obesity are major contributors to health inequalities, with people from lower socio-economic groups more susceptible to them.

The DH commissioned a post-2010 strategic review of health inequalities by Professor Sir Michael Marmot, focusing on how the social determinants of health influence health inequalities. It identified six policy objectives that require action if health inequalities are to be reduced:
- give every child the best start in life
- enable all children, young people and adults to maximise their capabilities and have control over their lives

- create fair employment and good work for all
- ensure a healthy standard of living for all
- create and develop healthy and sustainable places and communities
- strengthen the role and impact of ill health prevention.

Marmot said that achieving these objectives would need action by central and local government, the NHS, the third and private sectors and community groups. National policies would not work without effective local delivery systems focused on health equity in all policies. Effective local delivery required 'effective participatory decision-making at local level', which could only happen by empowering individuals and local communities.

How the NHS can help reduce health inequalities

The NHS cannot tackle health inequalities alone. Housing, local authorities, employment agencies, the police and employers all have a major role to play. Such a complex problem has no simple national solution: every local area has within it many kinds of inequality with different underlying causes. But some aspects of health and healthcare either exacerbate inequalities or could be better used to narrow the inequality gap.

The NHS can help by:
- finding the millions of people who do not access services, through better disease mapping
- assisting people from poorer backgrounds to access services in the early stages of disease when cure or condition management is possible
- using its power as the UK's largest employer to offer equal opportunities in employment and encouraging local organisations to work together.

PCTs are responsible locally for leading partnerships and influencing partners so that their services help improve health and narrow health inequalities.

Further information

Fair society, healthy lives: the Marmot Review, Marmot Review, February 2010.
Tackling health inequalities: 2006–08 policy and data update for the 2010 national target, DH, December 2009.
Transforming community services: ambition, action, achievement – transforming services for health, wellbeing and reducing inequalities, DH, July 2009.

Government response to the health select committee report on health inequalities, DH, May 2009.
Third report of session 2008–09: Health inequalities, House of Commons health committee, February 2009.
In sickness and in health: how the NHS can help tackle health inequalities, NHS Confederation, December 2007.
The Marmot review **www.ucl.ac.uk/gheg/marmotreview**

Landmarks in tackling health inequalities

1998 The Labour Government-commissioned independent inquiry led by Sir Donald Acheson makes 40 recommendations on areas including poverty, income and ethnicity.

1999 The white paper *Saving lives: our healthier nation* sets objectives to improve the whole nation's health and the health of the worst off. *Reducing health inequalities: an action report* is also published.

2000 The NHS Plan commits the Government to setting national health inequality targets.

2002 The comprehensive spending review contains a cross-cutting review on health inequalities.

2003 The DH, with the support of 11 other government departments, publishes *Tackling health inequalities – a programme for action*, a three-year plan covering a range of local, regional and national organisations including the NHS, local authorities, social services, education, planning and employment.

2004 The Wanless Report recommends radical changes in primary care, investments in workforce and a much more rigorous approach to tackling public health. The DH's public service agreement further raises the profile of tackling inequalities.

2009 The Marmot Review sets out measures to tackle health inequalities since the Acheson report.

2010 The target date by which inequalities in health outcomes should be reduced by 10 per cent.

Public health workforce

The public health workforce comprises people in a range of disciplines who work in one of three categories:
• health improvement and reducing inequalities: teachers, local business leaders, managers, social workers, transport engineers, housing officers, other local government staff and the voluntary sector, as well as doctors, nurses and other healthcare professionals

NHS CONFEDERATION

- public health practice: health visitors, environmental health officers and community development workers, and those who use research, information, public health science or health promotion skills in specific public health fields
- public health consultants and specialists, who work at a strategic or senior management level or at a senior level of scientific expertise.

The public health system in England has ten core functions:
- health surveillance, monitoring and analysis
- investigation of disease outbreaks, epidemics and health risks
- establishing, designing and managing health promotion and disease prevention programmes
- enabling communities and citizens to promote health and reduce inequalities
- creating and sustaining cross-governmental and inter-sectoral partnerships to improve health and reduce inequalities
- ensuring compliance with regulations and laws to protect and promote health
- developing and maintaining a well-educated and trained, multi-disciplinary public health workforce
- ensuring the effective performance of NHS services to meet goals in improving health, preventing disease and reducing inequalities
- research, development, evaluation and innovation
- quality-assuring the public health function.

Key organisation: **Health Protection Agency**
The Health Protection Agency advises the Government on public health protection policies and programmes. It also supports the NHS and other agencies in protecting people from infectious diseases, poisons, chemical and radiological hazards. It provides a rapid response to health protection emergencies. The HPA merged with the National Radiological Protection Board in 2005 and with the National Institute of Biological Standards and Control in 2009 to form a UK-wide comprehensive health protection service. It has 3,000 staff based in three major centres and locally throughout England.
www.hpa.org.uk

Getting ahead of the curve: a strategy for combating infectious diseases

This sets out an infectious diseases strategy for England and was published by the DH in 2002. The strategy describes the scope and nature of the threat posed by infectious diseases, and establishes priorities for action to combat present as well as possible future threats. Among these measures are a local health protection service, a strengthened and expanded system of surveillance, rationalisation of microbiology laboratories, a programme of new vaccine development and plans to combat the deliberate release of biological, chemical or radiological agents.

Regional public health groups

When strategic health authorities were reorganised in 2006, their public health teams were combined with the DH's regional public health teams, which have been located in the nine Government Offices for the English Regions (GOs) since 2002.

The regional public health groups are charged with:
- developing a cross-government and cross-sector approach to tackling the wider determinants of ill health
- informing regional work on economic regeneration, education, employment and transport
- ensuring a proper health contribution to local strategic partnerships
- accountability for the protection of health (including against communicable diseases and environmental hazards) across the region
- making sure the public health function is properly managed locally
- emergency and disaster planning and management
- being the main point of contact for serious concerns about clinical standards and associated inquiries.

The nine GOs are: North East, North West, Yorkshire and the Humber, East Midlands, West Midlands, East of England, London, South East and South West.
www.gos.gov.uk/national

Spotlight on policy: Coping with the flu pandemic

The first case of the new swine flu strain H1N1 was detected in Mexico in April 2009, and the first UK case was reported in Scotland later the same month. The World Health Organisation declared a level-6 global pandemic alert in June 2009.

The health service has been well prepared to deal with the flu pandemic. A five-year cross-government international pandemic preparedness strategy was devised in 2006, and before the pandemic started WHO had found the UK's plans to be among the world's most advanced. The DH appointed a national director for NHS flu resilience to take charge of the health service's response to the pandemic, as well as a national director of pandemic influenza preparedness who took up post in 2006. The Scientific Pandemic Influenza Advisory Committee (SPI) also advises the Government on scientific matters relating to the pandemic.

A National Pandemic Flu Service operated between July 2009 and February 2010 to help manage the outbreak in England. By phone and internet it provided a checklist to diagnose swine flu and gave people access to anti-flu drugs if necessary, easing pressure on GPs. The service can be restored within seven days if necessary.

A vaccination programme began in October 2009. In phase 1, priority groups were:
• individuals aged six months to 65 years who were eligible for seasonal flu vaccine
• pregnant women
• people who live with those whose immune systems are compromised, such as cancer patients or people with HIV/AIDS
• people aged 65 and over eligible for seasonal flu vaccine.

Phase 2 covered children between six months and five years. Frontline health and social care staff were also offered the vaccine. By early 2010, a total of 4.25 million people in priority groups and 393,000 health workers had been vaccinated.

It is now anticipated that the attack rate for adults will be at worst 12 per cent rather than the 30 per cent initially feared. But the virus remains lethal in some cases, and the revised assumptions anticipate a possible additional 35,000 hospital admissions with 5,300 requiring critical care. By early 2010 there had been 423 deaths from swine flu: 309 in England, 68 in Scotland, 28 in Wales, and 18 in Northern Ireland.

Further information
Briefing 187: Pandemic flu: ensuring the NHS is ready, NHS Confederation, July 2009.
Pandemic flu: UK international preparedness strategy, Cabinet Office/DH, October 2008.
Pandemic flu: a national framework for responding to an influenza pandemic, Cabinet Office/DH, November 2007.
National Pandemic Flu Service **www.direct.gov.uk/pandemicflu**

Public health observatories
Public health observatories (PHOs) are closely linked to the regional public health groups. Their job is to support local bodies by:
• monitoring health and disease trends, highlighting areas for action
• identifying gaps in health information
• advising on methods for assessing the impact of health inequalities
• drawing together information on new ways to improve health
• carrying out projects to highlight particular health issues
• evaluating local agencies' progress in improving health and reducing inequality
• giving early warning of public health problems.

The 12 observatories are coordinated by the Association for Public Health Observatories and work across England, Scotland, Wales, Northern Ireland and the Republic of Ireland.
www.apho.org.uk

Tobacco control
Smoking in enclosed public places was banned in England in July 2007, and in Wales and Northern Ireland in April 2007; it was banned in Scotland in March 2006. The ban follows similar decisions in other parts of Europe – the Irish Republic introduced a ban in 2004 – and the USA.

Anyone smoking in an enclosed public place may be fined £50, while those in charge of the premises may be fined £2,500. Failure to display no-smoking signs could lead to a £200 on-the-spot fine. One year after the ban, compliance stood at 98 per cent; 76 per cent of people said they supported the ban – including 55 per cent of smokers.

Under the Health Act 2009 shops will no longer be allowed to display tobacco products, and tobacco sales from vending machines will be banned. Displays will cease from 2011 for larger stores and 2013 for smaller ones.

In 2007, a reported 21 per cent of adults smoked, compared with 39 per cent in 1980. But smoking still caused 83,900 deaths among people over 35 in 2008 and cost the NHS £5.2 billion to treat the illness and disease associated with it in 2005/06. The latest strategy aims to halve the number of smokers to 10 per cent of the population by 2020, with more people being encouraged to get free smoking-cessation support from the NHS.

Further information
A smokefree future: a comprehensive tobacco control strategy for England, HM Government, February 2010.
Smokefree England – one year on, DH, July 2008.

Public health national support teams
Ten public health national support teams have been set up to work directly alongside senior colleagues in PCTs and local authorities to support them to deliver their public health priorities. They focus on:
• alcohol harm reduction
• childhood obesity
• health inequalities
• infant mortality
• response to sexual violence (England and Wales)
• sexual health

- teenage pregnancy
- tobacco control
- vaccination and immunisation
- children and young people's psychological well-being and mental health.

Each draws expertise in clinical areas, service management, change management, commissioning and public health from the NHS, local government and the voluntary sector.

Spotlight on policy: **Tackling climate change**
The potential impacts of climate change on health are many and varied. In the UK, hotter drier summers, milder wetter winters, more flooding and heat waves could mean:
- fewer cold-related winter deaths and more heat-related summer deaths
- more cases of food poisoning and insect-borne diseases
- more cases of sunburn and skin cancer.

The DH's priorities for coping with climate change are:
- adapting the health and social care infrastructure to cope with new demands
- ensuring national and local adaptation plans are implemented and evaluated
- raising awareness among public and professions of the health impacts.

The NHS is responsible for over 18 million tonnes of carbon dioxide a year – 3.2 per cent of England's emissions – and for 25 per cent of public sector emissions. Its carbon reduction strategy commits the NHS to a 10 per cent reduction in its 2007 carbon footprint by 2015. The carbon reduction commitment scheme began in April 2010, affecting 180 NHS organisations: participating trusts must report their carbon emissions to the Environment Agency and buy carbon allowances.

The NHS Sustainable Development Unit was set up in 2008. Its seven-strong team based in Cambridge aims to:
- provide leadership, expertise and guidance on sustainable development
- promote a culture of measurement and management that underpins carbon governance
- help shape NHS policy locally, nationally and internationally

• evaluate and cost best practice and innovations on sustainability, helping the NHS with implementation.

The 'NHS Forest' project intends to plant 1.3 million trees in the next five years – one for every NHS employee in England – as part of a plan to create wooded areas equivalent to 2,500 football pitches on NHS sites. The Campaign for Greener Healthcare, which is working on the project with the Forestry Commission, Woodland Trust, Natural England and others, says that when the forest reaches maturity in 20 years' time it will reduce the NHS's carbon footprint by 10 per cent. By the end of 2009, it had planted 366 trees.

Further information

Briefing 190: The CRC energy efficiency scheme and the NHS, NHS Confederation, October 2009.

Sustainable development action plan 2009–11, DH, July 2009.

Briefing 185: Climate change and the NHS: new legislation and initiatives, NHS Confederation, June 2009.

Saving carbon, improving health: NHS carbon reduction strategy for England, NHS Sustainable Development Unit, January 2009.

The health impact of climate change: promoting sustainable communities – guidance document, DH, April 2008.

Health effects of climate change in the UK 2008: an update of the Department of Health report 2001/2002, DH, February 2008.

NHS Sustainable Development Unit **www.sdu.nhs.uk**

NHS Forest **http://nhsforest.org**

03 Providing services

NHS organisations provide a wide range of services, outside hospitals and within them. Historically, hospitals have dominated the NHS's resources, but today much more care can be provided in GP surgeries and health centres closer to people's homes – and it is Government policy that it should be. It wants patients to have much more choice than hitherto over where they are treated, and it wants the services provided to feel more personal, taking greater account of people's preferences than was customary in the past.

Primary care

Primary care is normally the patient's first point of consultation with the health service. It is concerned with promoting health as well as treating and managing conditions that do not require specialist care in hospital. For NHS patients, primary care provides the key to navigating the rest of the healthcare system: GPs, community nurses, health visitors, allied health professionals, pharmacists, dentists and opticians have a role as advocates for patients needing services from other parts of the NHS. Providing continuity of care is another important aspect.

About 90 per cent of NHS patients receive their treatment in primary care, and over 300 million consultations take place every year in England alone. The Next Stage Review (see page 127) stated: 'It is a central part of our strategy for primary and community care that we support the NHS and community clinicians in transforming these services and according them an equal status to other NHS services.' Advances, especially in diagnostics and minor surgery, mean many more treatments once carried out in hospital can be performed in primary care – a rapidly growing trend convenient for patients and of benefit to the system as a whole. Over 5 million people in England live more than ten miles from their nearest hospital.

A wide range of staff work in primary care in England. In 2008 there were:
- 37,213 GPs
- 22,048 practice nurses
- 92,436 practice staff, including practice managers, receptionists, IT support and notes summarisers, physiotherapists, podiatrists, counsellors, phlebotomists and healthcare assistants.

The NHS was ranked as having one of the world's best primary care systems in a 2009 survey of 10,000 physicians in 11 developed countries by the Commonwealth Fund, a US think tank. It was rated top in several categories, which included being the only country where the majority of doctors felt healthcare quality was improving.

Further information
The Commonwealth Fund international health policy survey 2009, Commonwealth Fund, November 2009.
www.commonwealthfund.org

General practitioners

Most GP practices are independent contractors and are run as partnerships, although some salaried GPs are employed by primary care trusts, while specialist companies run some practices. The number of practices has fallen from 9,090 in 1998 to 8,230 in 2008 although the number of GPs has increased, suggesting practices have become bigger: the average number of patients per practice has risen from 5,624 to 6,555 in that time. Single-handed GPs have fallen in number by 28 per cent to 1,408 since 2004.

GPs held on average 87 surgery and 17 telephone consultations a week in 2006/07, and made five home visits. Each surgery consultation lasted 12 minutes on average, and each phone consultation seven minutes.

Under the general medical services contract, all GP practices are required to provide 'essential services': they must manage patients who are ill or believe themselves to be ill, giving health promotion advice and making referrals as necessary. They must also manage patients who are terminally ill and those with chronic diseases. All practices are expected to provide 'additional services' such as contraception or childhood immunisations, but they can opt out of them. They may also choose to provide 'enhanced services' in response to need, such as minor surgery, specialised services for patients with multiple sclerosis and specialised sexual health services. The Quality and Outcomes Framework (see page 138) is designed to maintain high standards and broaden the range of services GPs offer.

The DH is keen for GPs to widen their role to include services traditionally found only in hospitals. It believes that those with accredited specialist skills could handle more minor operations, while specially trained GPs and senior consultants should routinely work together in community hospitals and health centres. Operations for conditions such as cataracts, hernia and varicose veins could be done on the same site, reducing waiting times and potentially saving money. Ambitions for primary care over the next decade include:

- greater choice of GP, with patients able to register online and routinely consult their GP by phone or email
- practice funding that rewards GPs who take on new patients to support greater patient choice
- faster and simpler access to community-based services for minor ailments, health checks in high street pharmacies and walk-in centres, and self-referral to physiotherapy or podiatry
- high-performing GPs given greater freedom to develop new services
- increasing access to 'healthy living services' such as exercise classes, stop-smoking support or help in managing stress
- identifying those most at risk of ill health and offering early interventions
- new programmes of clinical leadership, innovation and high-quality training.

Improving access to GP services has been a priority, and under the Equitable Access to Primary Medical Care programme £250 million was made available to provide 112 new practices in the quarter of PCTs with the worst provision, as well as one new GP-led health centre in each PCT. By mid-2009, more than three-quarters of GP practices in England were offering extended opening hours following changes to the GP contract to encourage them to do so.

Patients are also to be given a wider choice over which practice they register with, and will no longer be limited by the system of practice boundaries.

The 2009/10 GP patient survey found:
- 91 per cent of patients were very or fairly satisfied with care at their surgery
- 81 per cent wanting a quick appointment got one within 48 hours
- 81 per cent were very or fairly satisfied with surgery opening hours
- 65 per cent knew how to contact an out-of-hours GP service
- 66 per cent rated care from the out-of-hours service as good and 13 per cent as poor.

Further information

World class commissioning – primary care and community services: improving GP access and responsiveness, DH, June 2009.
NHS Next Stage Review: our vision for primary and community care, DH, July 2008.
Keeping it personal – clinical case for change: report by David Colin-Thomé, national director for primary care, DH, February 2007.
www.gp-patient.co.uk/surveyresults

GP out-of-hours services

'Out-of-hours' usually refers to the period from 6.30pm Monday to Thursday until 8am the following day, and from 6.30pm on Friday until 8am on the following Monday, as well as public holidays. About 75 per cent of out-of-hours provision is carried out by PCTs or GP cooperatives and 25 per cent by commercial providers, ambulance trusts and others, with NHS Direct supplying initial call-handling for many providers.

A recent DH review, following the death of a patient after treatment by a locum GP from Germany, found unacceptable variation in how PCTs commission and monitor out-of-hours services. Its 24 recommendations included:

• guidance to assist PCTs in making decisions about whether a doctor has the necessary knowledge of English
• out-of-hours providers should consider recruitment and selection processes for clinical staff
• providers should cooperate with each other to share concerns over staff working excessive hours for their services.

The coalition Government plans to develop an urgent care service that includes GP out-of-hours services.

Further information

General practice out of hours services: project to consider and assess current arrangements, Dr David Colin-Thomé and Professor Steve Field, DH, January 2010.

Practitioners with a special interest

One way in which primary care services are expanding is by developing the role of practitioners with special interests.

GPs with a special interest (GPSIs) have additional training and expertise enabling them to provide a clinical service beyond the scope of normal general practice, undertake advanced procedures or develop services. They take referrals from colleagues for conditions in specialties such as ophthalmology, orthopaedics, dermatology and ear, nose and throat surgery, or undertake diagnostic procedures such as endoscopy. GPSIs do not offer a full consultant service, replace consultants or interfere with access to consultants by local GPs. Typically they undertake two sessions a week in their specialty.

Spotlight on policy: Patient choice

The NHS is attempting to offer more convenient, 'personalised care' that takes account of patients' preferences concerning where and when they are treated. Since 2008, all patients referred for an elective procedure have had a 'free choice' of any hospital, clinic or treatment centre in England which meets NHS standards and price, including those in the independent sector. This became a legal right under the NHS Constitution in April 2009 (see page 122). GPs may refer to any clinically appropriate provider, and PCT commissioning arrangements do not restrict where patients are offered a choice. Patients can also choose the date and time of their appointment.

Providers are listed in a national directory of services that is part of the Choose and Book facility on the NHS Choices website (see page 242), from which they can be booked directly. Services are displayed in distance order from the patient's postcode, although they can also be sorted by waiting time. NHS Choices claims to be 'the single most comprehensive, validated and easily searchable source of comparative data on the quality and availability of services'. It includes information on hospitals' MRSA rates, survival rates and car parking.

By late 2009, there were 510,000 bookings a month made through Choose and Book. A DH survey in March 2009 found 50 per cent of patients were aware before they visited their GP that they had a choice of hospitals for their first appointment, and 47 per cent recalled being offered a choice. Of these, 89 per cent were able to go to the hospital they wanted. Hospital cleanliness and low infection rates were selected most often (by 74 per cent) as important when choosing a hospital. However, the DH warned SHAs at the end of 2009 that delivery of patients' legal right to choice 'varies considerably across the country' and that 'this is unacceptable'.

The 2003 strategy paper, *Building on the best*, first outlined aspects of patient choice the Labour Government wanted to see, and the introduction of free choice is the culmination of a six-year process. This has coincided with improvements in waiting times – although it remains controversial, with concerns about equity, the stability of NHS providers and a perceived threat to professional judgement. However, all political parties now endorse patient choice in principle, and to varying degrees in practice.

Further information
Responsibilities and operational requirements for the correct use of Choose and Book, DH/
British Medical Association, December 2009.
Report on the national patient choice survey – March 2009 England, DH, August 2009.
Framework for managing choice, cooperation and competition, DH, May 2008.
Choice matters 2007–8: putting patients in control, DH, June 2007.
Building on the best; choice, equity and responsiveness in the NHS, DH, December 2003.
NHS Choices **www.nhs.uk**
Choose and Book **www.chooseandbook.nhs.uk**

GPSIs can increase the capacity of primary care to undertake outpatient appointments, reduce patient waiting times, provide a more convenient service and help to free consultant time in secondary care. Over 1,750 GPSIs are currently practising.

Initially, emphasis was on developing GPs with special interests, but dentists and pharmacists have now been included. Nurses and allied health professionals have developed their own approaches without adopting the terminology. A national accreditation framework for GPs and pharmacists with a special interest was launched in 2007 to ensure standards of care in the community are equivalent to those in acute care. PCTs have accreditation panels to verify GPs' and pharmacists' skills. Re-accreditation is carried out within three years.

Research has shown that while GPSI services improve access, they can be more costly than hospital clinics.

Further information
Implementing care closer to home – convenient quality care for patients, DH, April 2007.
Briefing paper: an assessment of the clinical effectiveness, cost and viability of NHS general practitioners with special interest (GPSI) services, NHS SDO R&D Programme, September 2006.

Redesigning the fabric of primary care
The GP surgery is the focus of most primary care and the source of ever wider-ranging services. In 2000 the NHS Plan described a vision of the GP surgery of the future:

Many GPs will be working in teams from modern multi-purpose premises alongside nurses, pharmacists, dentists, therapists, opticians, midwives and social care staff. Nurses will have new opportunities, and some GPs will tend to specialise in treating different conditions. The consulting room will become the place where appointments for outpatients and operations are booked, test results received and more diagnosis carried out using video and tele-links to hospital specialists. An increasing number of consultants will take outpatient sessions in local primary care centres.

Since then, PCTs have been encouraged to set up one-stop health centres – sometimes referred to as 'supersurgeries' or polyclinics – which bring services such as GPs, health visitors, dentists, a pharmacy, a cardiology clinic, x-ray facilities, optometry, Sure Start and a healthy living café under one roof. About 750 such centres have been built since 2001, and 3,000 other GP premises – about a third of the total – substantially refurbished or replaced. The Next Stage Review (see page 127) called for a further 150 'GP-led health centres' that would open from 8am to 8pm seven days a week, almost 100 of which were open by the end of 2009.

In addition, walk-in centres provide fast access to advice and treatment for minor ailments and injuries without an appointment. Walk-in centres – also known as minor injury units or urgent care centres – are open seven days a week, from 7am to 10pm, and offer assessment by an experienced NHS nurse as well as information on out-of-hours GP, dental and local pharmacy services. The centres are helping improve access for groups with particular needs, including young or homeless people. An established walk-in centre sees around 2,500 patients per month.

There are about 90 walk-in centres throughout England, which see 3 million patients a year. They include a five-year pilot programme of six instant-access GP-led centres for commuters commissioned from the independent sector. The first opened at Manchester Piccadilly Station in 2005. However, research suggests some see only 30 patients a day despite capacity for up to 180, with attendances costing £33 each compared to £13 at NHS walk-in centres.

Further information
Ideas from Darzi: polyclinics, NHS Confederation, April 2008.
Community Hospitals Association **www.communityhospitals.org.uk**

Dental services

Most dentists in primary care are self-employed and contract their services to PCTs, like most GPs. They numbered 21,343 in 2008/09. The number of dental graduates beginning NHS training has expanded by 25 per cent in recent years. A fourfold increase to 200 training places for dental therapists is also underway.

Policy on dental services lagged behind other health sectors until 2006, when over 400 charges for treatment were replaced by three standard charges for all treatments and the £1.9 billion budget for primary care dental services was devolved to PCTs. This covers surgery salaries and expenses instead of the piecework pay system set up when the NHS was founded. Access to dentistry has been a high-profile issue for more than 15 years, with increasing concerns about gaps in access to NHS-funded services and many practices opting out or closing to new NHS patients. Surgeries have therefore been encouraged to broaden their range of services. The intention is that dentists can focus on prevention and health promotion, as well as treatment within their NHS contracts, and spend more time with patients.

An independent review of NHS dentistry, which examined access and other issues raised by the Commons health committee, recommended:
- linking a significant part of dentists' income to the number of NHS patients registered with them, not just the number of treatments they provide
- making dentists more explicitly accountable for providing high-quality and long-lasting treatments, and supporting dentists to take time to advise patients on preventive care
- defining more clearly patients' rights when they register with an NHS dentist, both for urgent treatment and continuing care.

Selected dental practices are piloting the review's recommendations, with results expected in 2010/11. The coalition Government plans to change the existing contract to improve access to services.

Further information
NHS dental services in England: an independent review led by Professor Jimmy Steele, DH, June 2009.
World class commissioning – primary care and community services: improving dental access, quality and oral health, DH, January 2009.
Dental services: fifth report of session 2007–08, House of Commons health committee, June 2008.

Community pharmacies

Britain's 10,475 high street pharmacies receive 1.6 million visits a day and employ 73 per cent of pharmacists. They increasingly offer services traditionally available only at GPs' surgeries. The pharmacy contract introduced in 2005 aims to improve the range and quality of services of the community pharmacy and integrate it more into the NHS. It defines three tiers of service:

- Essential services must be provided by all community pharmacists. They include dispensing, disposal of medication and support for self-care.
- Advanced services require the pharmacist to have accreditation and/or their premises to meet certain standards. So far, medicines use review and prescription intervention fall in this category.
- Enhanced services are commissioned locally by PCTs. Examples include minor ailment schemes and smoking-cessation services.

Many pharmacies now offer new services such as:
- repeat prescribing, so that patients can get up to a year's supply of medicines without having to revisit their GP
- clinics for people with conditions such as diabetes, high blood pressure or high cholesterol
- signposting other health and social care services and supporting self-care
- consultation areas.

The DH white paper, *Pharmacy in England*, included proposals for pharmacies to:
- be able to prescribe common medicines and be the first port of call for minor ailments – saving every GP an hour a day and totalling 57 million GP consultations a year
- support people with long-term conditions, half of whom may not take their medicines as intended
- screen for vascular disease and certain sexually transmitted infections
- play a bigger role in vaccination.

The Health Act 2009 gave PCTs greater powers to commission pharmaceutical services and address poor performance, as well as provide the services themselves in an emergency where there is no alternative.

Further information
World class commissioning – primary care and community services: improving pharmaceutical services, DH, March 2009.
Briefing 160: Pharmacy in England, PCT Network/NHS Confederation, May 2008.
Pharmacy in England: building on strengths, delivering the future, DH, April 2008.
Review of progress on reforms to the 'control of entry' system for NHS pharmaceutical contractors – report, DH, January 2007.
The new contractual framework for community pharmacy, DH, October 2004.

Opticians
There were 11.3 million NHS eye tests carried out in England in 2008/09. There are three kinds of registered optician:

Optometrists – or ophthalmic opticians – carry out eye tests, look for signs of eye disease and prescribe and fit glasses and contact lenses. They are graduates who have undertaken a three- or four-year degree in optometry, then spent at least a year in supervised practice before taking professional exams leading to registration with the General Optical Council. There are about 9,500 registered optometrists in the UK, of whom 96 per cent are optometrists and the remainder ophthalmic medical practitioners.

Dispensing opticians fit and sell glasses, and interpret prescriptions, but do not test eyes. Some dispense low-vision aids, and some are qualified to fit contact lenses under instruction from an optometrist.

Ophthalmic medical practitioners are doctors specialising in eyes and eye care. They work to the same terms of service as optometrists.

In addition, **ophthalmologists** are doctors specialising in eye diseases and most perform eye surgery. They usually work in hospital eye departments. **Orthoptists** treat disorders of binocular vision, and work in eye departments under the supervision of ophthalmologists. They may also undertake visual screening of children in the community. Some GPs have a special interest in ophthalmology, while ophthalmic nurses and ophthalmic technicians – or ophthalmic science practitioners – also provide services.

Optometrists are independent contractors. Some have specialist skills – for example, in contact lenses, low vision or paediatrics – and can treat patients who would otherwise have to be seen in hospital. Most practices have much of the equipment found in ophthalmology clinics.

Under co-management, or shared care, optometrists working to an agreed protocol undertake specified clinical procedures designed to relieve GPs and the hospital eye service, as well as move patient care into the community. This may cover conditions such as glaucoma, diabetes, cataracts and minor acute eye problems. Throughout the UK, optometrists can now prescribe medicines for conditions of the eye and surrounding tissue if they are registered to do so with the General Optical Council and have undertaken special training.

PCTs are responsible for managing optometrists' contracts. Some employ optometric advisers to provide guidance on issues such as service development, new techniques and treatments, interpreting regulations, investigating complaints and audit.

The 2007 general optical service review assessed how eye-care services are currently provided and found potential for eye-care professionals in primary care to work alongside hospitals in developing more responsive services for patients with eye conditions such as glaucoma. It also identified scope for greater collaboration between the NHS, social care and the third sector in providing integrated services for patients with low-vision problems and in taking wider action to improve eye health. The DH has set up an eye care strategy group for guidance on best practice and support for people with vision problems.

Further information

World class commissioning – primary care and community services: improving eye health services, DH, July 2009.

General ophthalmic services review: findings in relation to the framework for primary ophthalmic services, the position of dispensing opticians in relation to the NHS, local optical committees, and the administration of general ophthalmic services payments, DH, January 2007.

Community health services

Community health services are a major part of the NHS, employing 250,000 people and costing over £11 billion a year. Historically they have often been overlooked by policy-makers, but they are well placed to play a central role in achieving many of the aims of NHS reform, such as providing more personalised care closer to patients' homes, helping avoid unnecessary hospital admissions or shortening hospital stays, as well as leading efforts on preventive and wellness services.

A variety of staff and organisations provide a range of health services in the community.

Allied health professionals – AHPs number over 82,500 and form a diverse group of statutory-registered practitioners who include art therapists, drama therapists, music therapists, chiropodists/podiatrists, dietitians, occupational therapists, orthoptists, orthotists and prosthetists, paramedics, physiotherapists, diagnostic radiographers, therapeutic radiographers and speech and language therapists. The DH has given AHPs the power to accept patients who refer themselves to AHP services.

Community nurses – who include district nurses with a postgraduate qualification, registered nurses and nursing assistants. More than half the patients they see will be aged over 75. About half their work comes from GP referrals and a quarter from hospital staff; patients and carers can also refer themselves.

Community matrons – as experienced nurses, community matrons use case management techniques with patients who make intensive use of healthcare to help them remain at home longer.

Health visitors – who are qualified nurses or midwives with additional training and experience in child health, health promotion and education. Much of their work is with mothers and babies using a child-centred, family-focused approach, although they do provide more general health advice to people of all ages. Their support staff include nursery nurses and healthcare assistants, who focus on less complex family support and parenting skills. A review of the health visitor's role in 2007 recommended they concentrate on leading a renewed child health promotion programme and on intensive early intervention and prevention for families who need help most.

Specialist nurses – with expertise in stoma care, continence services, palliative care and support for people with long-term conditions.

School nursing – providing support and advice to schools on health issues, a role which has evolved considerably in recent years.

Community dentistry and dental public health – providing services to schools and people who are difficult to treat.

NHS CONFEDERATION

The DH and Department for Education are jointly responsible for promoting the health and well-being of all children and young people. A Child Health and Well-being Board oversees progress on the public service agreement to improve children's and young people's health, as well as the national service framework for children, young people and maternity. It comprises chief executives of PCTs and SHAs and directors of children's services.

The two departments have developed a joint strategy for children's health, setting out what children and their families can expect from child health services from birth to the age of 19. The strategy promises:

- stronger and better joined-up support during the early years of life, including more health visitors
- a strengthened role for Sure Start children's centres with each having access to a named health visitor
- expansion of the family nurse partnerships programme to support first-time mothers from 30 sites to 70 by 2011, with a view to extending it nationwide over the next decade
- an antenatal programme and preparation-for-parenthood package for mothers and fathers
- free school meal pilots looking at the health and educational benefits of universal access
- £340 million to support children with disabilities and their families.

In addition, the NHS chief executive has commissioned Sir Ian Kennedy to review NHS children's services. He will examine

- care of children outside paediatric settings
- health visiting and community services
- pathways of care
- primary care, including A&E arrangements to safeguard children
- management of the transition to adult care
- how the NHS works with its partners to support children
- how the NHS responds to family and individuals' needs.

Recommendations are expected during 2010.

Further information

Aiming high for disabled children: delivering improved health services, NHS Confederation, September 2009.

Transforming community services: ambition, action, achievement – transforming services for children, young people and their families, DH, June 2009.

Briefing 176: Healthy lives, brighter futures – the strategy for children and young people's health, NHS Confederation, March 2009.

Healthy lives, brighter futures: the strategy for children and young people's health, DH/ DCSF, February 2009.

Podiatry – foot care for elderly people or those with diabetes, gait or lower limb problems. Independent contractors provide much of this care. More than half the service is for people aged over 65.

Physiotherapy – sometimes provided by GPs or hospitals in a community setting, with emphasis on rehabilitation.

Occupational therapy – providing advice, aids and adaptations. Some staff specialise in adults, some in children. The service is often provided by other agencies, such as local government, although in some cases the NHS provides local authority OT services.

Speech and language therapy – services for children and adults who have difficulty with communicating, eating, drinking or swallowing.

Clinical psychology – often provided by specialist mental health trusts, although more than 40 per cent of referrals come from general practice.

Midwives – generally attached to hospitals, but working in community settings.

Family planning services – may cover sexual health problems as well as contraception, vasectomy and termination clinics and specialist clinics for young people.

Community rehabilitation – often for stroke or cardiac conditions. Services may be delivered by specialist teams in the patient's home or by combining intermediate care or community hospital care with home care.

Further information

Getting it right for children and families: maximising the contribution of the health visiting team – 'ambition, action, achievement', DH/Unite/CPHVA, October 2009.
Briefing 181: the future for community services, PCT Network/NHS Confederation, April 2009.
Community health services: making a difference to local communities, PCT Network/NHS Confederation, February 2009.

Integrated care

According to the Next Stage Review (see page 127): 'Integrated care means GPs, community nurses, pharmacists, social care teams, ambulance services, schools and others coming together on a collaborative basis with clear leadership, shared goals and shared information – and designing services around the needs of individuals and local communities.'

Integration is especially important for continuing care, long-term care, intermediate care and end-of-life care, which – to be effective – all depend on a high degree of coordination between different organisations providing health and social care. Integration might involve bringing together different kinds of expertise and interventions – for example, by creating teams of primary and secondary care clinicians, or health and social care professionals. Better integration could potentially support key Government objectives such as more personalised services and greater emphasis on health promotion and prevention.

Integrated care pilot programme

In 2009 the DH launched a £4 million programme involving 16 PCTs to test different models of integrated care. The pilots will run for two years and be evaluated over three years on criteria such as better health outcomes, improved quality of care, patient satisfaction, and effective relationships and systems. The sites involve partnerships of primary care with social care, secondary care, the voluntary and private sectors. Issues they are examining include dementia, care for the elderly, substance misuse, chronic obstructive pulmonary disease and end-of-life care. The methods involved include partnerships, new systems and care pathways that span primary, community, secondary and social care.

Further information

Integrated care pilots: an introductory guide, DH, September 2009.
Delivering care closer to home: meeting the challenge, DH, July 2008.
Integrated Care Network **www.dhcarenetworks.org.uk/icn**
www.dh.gov.uk/integratedcare

Continuing care

Continuing care is care provided over an extended period to someone aged 18 or over to meet physical and mental health needs that have arisen as a result of disability, accident or illness. The person may require services from the NHS and/or local authorities. Where they are assessed as having mainly health needs, the NHS will arrange and fund the complete package, which may be provided in any setting – hospital, hospice, home or care home. If they live in a care home, the NHS will contribute to their registered nursing care. Financial issues are not taken into account when deciding eligibility for NHS continuing care. If a person does not qualify, the NHS may still have responsibility for contributing to a 'joint package' to meet their health needs.

Further information

The national framework for NHS continuing healthcare and NHS-funded nursing care (revised), DH, July 2009.

Care for long-term conditions

More than 17.5 million people in the UK (15.4 million in England) suffer a long-term or chronic condition such as diabetes, asthma or arthritis. They represent 55 per cent of GP appointments, 68 per cent of outpatient appointments and accident and emergency attendances, and 77 per cent of inpatient bed days. In total, they account for around 70 per cent of total health and social care spend, according to the DH's 'best estimate'.

Best practice requires early recognition, prompt diagnosis and treatment, early and specialist rehabilitation, equipment and accommodation and support for family and carers. To ensure best quality care – and maximise service efficiency – it is important that long-term conditions are effectively managed outside hospital wherever possible.

Health and social care organisations should assign 'community matrons' to the most vulnerable patients with complex multiple long-term conditions to monitor their condition, anticipate any problems and coordinate their care. Multi-professional teams should identify all people with a single serious long-term illness, assess their needs as early as possible and provide proactive care before their condition deteriorates. Everyone with a long-term condition should be educated about their health and encouraged to manage their own care more effectively.

Key organisation: Expert Patients Programme CIC
A 2001 DH policy document, *The expert patient*, defined a new relationship between patient and professional, in which 'the era of the patient as the passive recipient of healthcare is changing and being replaced by a new emphasis on the relationship between the NHS and the people whom it serves'. Since then, over 30,000 people have attended an 'expert patients programme' in England. The EPP is a free six-week course for people with chronic or long-term conditions that aims to give them the confidence to self-manage their health, while encouraging them to collaborate with health and social care professionals. Topics include healthy eating, dealing with pain and extreme tiredness, relaxation techniques and coping with feelings of depression.

Since 2007 the Expert Patients Programme has been a community interest company (CIC) with the purpose of expanding course places from 12,000 a year to over 100,000 by 2012.
www.expertpatients.nhs.uk

Spotlight on policy: Older people's health
Older people are the main users of the NHS: although they make up about a fifth of the population, they occupy two-thirds of hospital beds, and are three times more likely to be admitted to hospital. For the first time, older people now outnumber children in the UK, and a cross-departmental 'ageing strategy', *Building a society for all ages*, has therefore been developed.

The DH's main contribution is a prevention package for older people's resources. Its main features include:
• information on existing health 'entitlements', including sight tests, flu vaccination and cancer screening
• best practice on falls prevention and effective fracture management
• measures to improve access to affordable foot care services
• updates to national intermediate care guidance
• a summary of progress on audiology and telecare.

In addition, the DH launched the first national dementia strategy, which aims to increase awareness of the condition, ensure early diagnosis and intervention and radically improve care quality. Backed by £150 million for the first two years, proposals include introducing a dementia specialist into every general hospital and care home. Demonstrator sites have been set up in 22 areas and another 18 sites will test different kinds of support networks for families and carers. However, the National Audit Office found the strategy 'lacks the mechanisms needed to bring about large-scale improvements, and without these mechanisms it is unlikely that the intended and much needed transformation of services will be delivered within the strategy's five-year timeframe.'

Partnerships for Older People Projects (POPP) was launched in 2005 with £60 million to develop and evaluate services and approaches aimed at promoting health, well-being and independence, and preventing or delaying the need for higher-intensity or institutional care. POPP evaluated service models in 29 local authority-led pilots, which aimed to shift resources and culture away from institutional and hospital-based crisis care towards earlier interventions for older people within their own homes and communities.

Over 250,000 people have used one or more POPP services, ranging from rapid-response services, mental health cafés with open-door access for older people, falls prevention services, telephone advice services and befriending schemes. The final evaluation found many projects improved quality of life and achieved considerable savings as well as better local working relationships.

Further information
National evaluation of Partnerships for Older People Projects: final report, DH, January 2010.
Improving dementia services in England – an interim report, NAO, January 2010.
Building a society for all ages, HM Government, July 2009.
Living well with dementia: a national dementia strategy implementation plan, DH, July 2009.
Living well with dementia: a national dementia strategy, February 2009.
www.hmg.gov.uk/buildingasocietyforallages

By mid-2009, according to the progress report on implementing the Next Stage Review's recommendations, 9.3 million patients with long-term conditions had a personal care plan.

Further information

Transforming community services: ambition, action, achievement – transforming services for people with long term conditions, DH, June 2009.

Supporting people with long-term conditions: commissioning personalised care planning, DH, January 2009.

Your health, your way – a guide to long-term conditions and self care (the 'Patients' Prospectus'), DH, November 2008.

National Service Framework for long-term conditions, DH, March 2005.

The Long Term Conditions (LTC) Community **www.ltc-community.org.uk**

Self-care

The DH has devised seven core principles of self-care to help health and social care staff support people with long-term conditions or complex needs to live independently and stay healthy. They are:

- ensure people can make informed choices to manage their self-care needs
- communicate effectively to enable people to assess their needs and gain confidence to care for themselves
- support and enable people to access appropriate information to manage their self-care
- support and enable individuals to develop skills in self-care
- support and enable individuals to use technology for self-care
- advise individuals how to access support networks and participate in planning, developing and evaluating services
- support and enable risk management and risk-taking to maximise independence and choice.

A networking and resource website, Self Care Connect, is run by the Expert Patients Programme for those with a professional interest in self-care.

Further information

Self care: a national view in 2007 compared to 2004–05, DH, June 2007.

www.selfcareconnect.co.uk

End-of-life care

Half a million people die in England each year, three-quarters after a chronic illness. Surveys show most people would prefer to die at home, although only 18 per cent do so; 58 per cent die in hospital, 17 per cent in care homes, 4 per cent in a hospice and 3 per cent elsewhere. End-of-life care is becoming more complex, with people living longer and the incidence of frailty and multiple conditions in older people rising. The DH therefore launched a ten-year end-of-life care strategy to help more people to die in the setting they choose, promote dignity and respect, properly coordinate services and support carers. It is being implemented with £286 million of extra resources between 2009 and 2011.

It focuses on:
- improved community services – ensuring rapid-response community nursing services are available everywhere around the clock
- workforce training and development – in assessing patients' and carers' needs and providing best-quality care
- developing specialist palliative care outreach services – in the community, to support all adults regardless of their condition
- setting up a national end-of-life research initiative – on how best to care for those at the end of their lives
- quality standards – against which PCTs and providers can assess themselves and be assessed by regulators.

The National End of Life Care Programme aims to support implementation of the strategy by sharing good practice.

Further information

End of life care strategy: first annual report, DH, October 2009.

Transforming community services: ambition, action, achievement – transforming end of life care, DH, June 2009.

End of life care strategy – promoting high quality care for all adults at the end of life, DH, July 2008.

End of life care, NAO, November 2008.

National End of Life Care Programme **www.endoflifecare.nhs.uk/eolc**

Spotlight on policy: Personal health budgets

Personal health budgets are designed to enhance independence and choice for people receiving care or support. A personal budget brings together resources from different funding streams into a single sum. The purpose is to give people a clear idea of the finance available and enable them to make their own decisions about their care – for example, by having someone support them at home rather than going into residential care. Those receiving budgets include older people, people with learning disabilities, physical disabilities and/or sensory impairments and mental health service users.

Personal budgets were originally developed for social care and ruled out for adoption by the health service in 2006 amid fears they 'would compromise the founding principle of the NHS that care should be free at the point of need', according to the white paper, *Our health, our care, our say*. They are now being piloted for healthcare at 68 sites in 75 PCTs, with 20 taking part in an in-depth evaluation. The pilot will run until 2012.

Personal budgets can take three forms:
• a notional budget held by a commissioner, such as a doctor or PCT
• a budget managed on behalf of an individual by a third party, such as a charity
• a direct cash payment made to an individual and managed by them.

Research reveals wide support among senior NHS leaders for personal health budgets as a concept that could benefit people managing long-term conditions. But they have concerns about the cost and complexity of implementing and sustaining a large number of patients receiving personal budgets. They also fear that the NHS's organisational culture and staff attitudes could resist devolving choice and control to users. Much more evidence therefore needs to be produced to support proponents' claims for personal health budgets before their potential is likely to be realised.

Further information

Understanding personal health budgets, DH, December 2009.
Shaping personal health budgets: a view from the top, National Mental Health Development Unit/Mental Health Network/NHS Confederation, December 2009.
Personal health budgets: first steps, DH, January 2009.
Personal Health Budget Learning Network **www.dhcarenetworks.org.uk/PHBLN**

Secondary care

The changing role of hospitals

Acute hospitals have always dominated healthcare spending and provision, but their role has begun to change fundamentally. The Next Stage Review (see page 127) noted: 'The potential to use community settings for some services traditionally provided in hospitals – and in a way that really shifts the emphasis to supporting health and well-being rather than simply curing disease – is set to grow faster in the coming years as a result of demographic, economic and technological changes.'

Changes in the last two decades have revolutionised surgery: lasers and 'keyhole' techniques have led to quicker recovery and less risk of infection. Procedures that previously required long stays in hospital, such as hernia operations, can now be done as day cases more locally. New drugs have made some surgery, such as treatment for stomach ulcers, completely unnecessary. The national adviser on surgery recommended that 80 per cent of all surgery should be done locally and the most complex 20 per cent take place at specialist centres with the most highly skilled surgeons using the latest technology.

Meanwhile, patient choice, payment by results and practice-based commissioning are affecting the balance of power between organisations,

Vital statistics: average length of hospital stay – general and acute (days)

1997/98	1998/99	1999/00	2000/01	2001/02	2002/03	2003/04	2004/05	2005/06	2006/07	2007/08
7.0	6.8	6.7	6.9	7.1	7.0	6.8	6.3	5.9	5.5	5.3

Source: Department of Health

stimulating further change – especially as value for money will become ever more important with the slowdown in spending.

The DH's National Clinical Advisory Team provides a pool of clinical experts to guide the local NHS on service change proposals to ensure they are safe and accessible for patients.

The result of these development is that the traditional model of the district general hospital is changing. Local hospitals are likely to remain important, but rather than working in isolation will have to work much more in collaboration with other providers and each other as part of 'multi-hospital networks of care'. Rather than exercising local monopolies, hospitals will need to promote competition and choice.

Change to local health services is often controversial for staff and the public, who need to be involved in developing plans from early on. Proposals should be subject to independent clinical and management assessment before consultation. Since 2008 this has been conducted under the Office of Government Commerce's gateway review process. It comprises a series of short reviews carried out at key stages and designed to highlight risks which could threaten a project's success. The review usually takes three to four days and involves interviewing clinicians, patients, users, boards, staff and managers.

DH guidance on major change to NHS services consists of 15 recommendations intended to ensure the process is open, transparent and fair. They include that:
• each SHA should oversee proposals
• PCTs should normally lead the proposal's preparation and consultation
• proposals should be specific about their impact on the quality of patient services, including number of lives saved and reduction in health inequalities
• a senior clinical lead should be identified at the outset and helped to involve other clinicians
• chairs, chief executives and boards are accountable for and should take a personal lead in the proposals
• stakeholders should be involved throughout.

There are currently about 1,500 NHS hospitals and mental health sites in England, which include 258 acute hospitals, 402 community hospitals and 428 mental health units. They range from state-of-the-art new buildings to those that pre-date the NHS.

Further information

Transforming community services: ambition, action, achievement – transforming services for acute care closer to home, DH, June 2009.

Local hospitals: lessons for the NHS – Central Middlesex Hospital case study, NHS Confederation, January 2009.

Delivering care closer to home: meeting the challenge, DH, July 2008.

Changing for the better: guidance when undertaking major changes to NHS services, DH, May 2008.

Saws and scalpels to lasers and robots: advances in surgery – clinical case for change; report by Sir Ara Darzi, national adviser on surgery, DH, April 2007.

Key organisation: Independent Reconfiguration Panel

Set up in 2003, the IRP advises the Secretary of State on proposals for changes to NHS services that have been contested locally. It also offers advice to the NHS, local authorities and others on NHS reconfiguration issues.

The local authority overview and scrutiny committee (see page 175) may refer a proposal if it is not satisfied:
• with the content of the consultation or the time allowed
• with the reasons given for not carrying out consultation
• that the proposal is in the interests of the health service locally.

Although the IRP is a last resort when other options for local resolution have been explored, it welcomes early informal contact to avoid formal referral if possible. Once a case is accepted, the chair agrees any specific terms of reference and a timetable for reporting. The chair will normally appoint a subgroup of three (one health professional, one health manager, one patient and citizen representative) to consider the case. The IRP encourages locally acceptable solutions. Its advice takes account of public and patient involvement and the rigour of local consultation. As a non-departmental public body, the IRP offers advice only: final decisions rest with the Secretary of State.

Further information

Learning from reviews: an overview, second edition, IRP, December 2009.

www.irpanel.org.uk

NHS CONFEDERATION

NHS rules previously prohibited patients from supplementing their treatment by paying for additional care or medication. DH guidance stated: 'A patient cannot be both a private and an NHS patient for the treatment of one condition during a single visit to an NHS organisation.'

But these rules were challenged by cancer patients wishing to buy drugs unapproved by NICE (see page 172), who would have been denied the rest of their NHS treatment as a result. Some new drugs – particularly for cancer – can be effective for certain people, extending life by a few months, but fail cost-effectiveness tests that NICE and PCTs apply. It was argued that allowing patients to 'top up' their treatment would undermine NHS principles of equity. Patients affected may be few at present but trends indicate they will increase.

Concerns arose that the top-up rule was being applied inconsistently, with trusts threatening or enforcing it in places, while others surrendered to pressure or reversed earlier decisions after individual campaigns. Some felt public and private funding were already blurred where, for example, a patient paid for private tests to reduce waiting time for surgery. It was argued that denying treatment to those topping up undermined the principle that everyone should have equal access to NHS services according to need.

After a review, the DH instructed the NHS not to withdraw treatment from patients who pay privately for additional drugs, although private treatment should take place in a private facility and must not be subsidised by the NHS. In addition, access to drugs on the NHS is to be substantially widened and the need for patients to resort to private treatment reduced. NICE has devised a new system for appraising expensive drugs designed to help those close to the end of life, and is speeding up its appraisal process.

Concerns remain that having two patients with similar needs receiving different levels of treatment could contravene the principle of equity of access. A longer-term concern is that topping up may lead to a two-tier NHS, with a basic core package supplemented with a system of co-payments or means-testing for 'high-quality' care.

Further information
The Government's response to the health select committee's report on top-up fees, TSO, July 2009.
Fourth report of session 2008–09: Top-up fees, House of Commons health committee, May 2009.
Guidance on NHS patients who wish to pay for additional private care, DH, March 2009.
Improving access to medicines for NHS patients: a report for the Secretary of State for Health by Professor Mike Richards CBE, COI, November 2008.

Treatment centres

Treatment centres are units that carry out planned surgery and treatment in areas that have traditionally had the longest waiting times, separating them from unplanned care and so lessening the risk that operations have to be cancelled. The DH looked to them to create innovation, increase productivity and rapidly expand capacity. They have developed new staff roles, including perioperative specialist practitioners, advanced nurse practitioners/advisers and healthcare assistant technicians in radiology, ophthalmology and surgery.

A treatment centre's essential features include:
• delivering a high volume of routine treatments and/or diagnostics
• streamlined services using defined pathways
• planned and booked services, with emphasis on patient choice and convenience.

Treatment centres have developed on two models. Some are run by the NHS, others by the independent sector under contract to the NHS (see page 31). They may be:
• virtual treatment centres – defined services within an existing hospital, using care pathways to ensure efficiency and enhance the patient's experience
• stand-alone new-build treatment centres – purposely designed for maximum efficiency and to ensure the best patient flows
• refurbished sites – possibly using surplus estate to give quick access to suitable buildings.

The type of work they do falls into three categories:
- short-stay inpatient work, often in a single specialty such as orthopaedics or ophthalmology
- day-case or outpatient work
- community-based diagnostic work, such as endoscopy and ultrasound, and minor surgical procedures such as excision of cysts and lesions, and vasectomies.

Centres may care for patients within a single specialty or a range of specialties.

Managed clinical networks
Clinical networks, first developed in Scotland (see page 257), are not statutory bodies but partnerships of all organisations and professionals involved in commissioning, planning and providing a particular service in a geographical area. They form, in effect, virtual organisations, and have the potential to break down barriers between primary, secondary and tertiary care and between health and social care. Good working relationships are crucial to their success, and they need multi-disciplinary leadership and management.

Networks help ensure all staff with whom a patient has contact are working to the same protocols and policies – for example, on admission, discharge and transfer: this can ease bed shortages and reduce the need for transferring patients between facilities. By collecting all information relevant to a clinical condition they enable network-wide audit to inform practice and future service developments. They encourage staff to work as one on common issues, and share learning, although such collaboration has to be balanced with the DH's rules on competition (see page 42).

Networks are now well developed in cancer care, bringing together commissioners and providers, the voluntary sector and local authorities. There are currently 34 cancer care networks in the UK, each serving 1 to 2 million people.

Urgent and emergency care
The system for delivering urgent and emergency care includes:
- NHS Direct
- community pharmacy and self-care
- GP services, including out-of-hours services (see page 73)

- urgent care centres, including walk-in centres and minor injuries units (see page 75)
- ambulance services
- hospital accident and emergency departments
- critical care services.

Urgent care is for patients who have an injury or illness that requires immediate attention but is not usually serious enough to require a visit to an accident and emergency department.

Emergency care has been undergoing major changes since the launch of a ten-year strategy, Reforming Emergency Care, in 2001. The strategy is based on six key principles:
- services should be designed from the patient's point of view
- patients should receive a consistent response wherever, whenever and however they contact the service
- patients' needs should be met by the professional best able to help them
- information from each stage of the patient's journey should be shared with other professionals involved in their care
- assessment or treatment should not be delayed through the absence of diagnostic or specialist advice
- clear and measurable standards should be applied to emergency care.

The strategy aims to transform the patient's experience of emergency care through:
- shorter waits – no patient should spend more than four hours from arrival in A&E to admission, transfer or discharge
- faster ambulance response times and better training and equipment for crews
- more streamlined access, including more primary care-based services for minor complaints
- a more integrated approach to emergency and critical care.

The Healthcare Commission (forerunner of the Care Quality Commission) found 'significant improvements' in emergency and urgent care had been achieved in recent years as a result of new services such as NHS Direct and NHS walk-in centres, faster ambulance response times and shorter waits in A&E. This was despite an increase in numbers using A&E and urgent care centres from 16.5 to 19.1 million in the four years to 2007/08. But it called on PCTs to address gaps in the system due to lack of integration.

Further information

Good practice in delivering emergency care: a guide for local health communities, Emergency Services Review/OSHA, October 2009.

Not just a matter of time: a review of urgent and emergency care services in England, Healthcare Commission, September 2008.

Emergency care ten years on: reforming emergency care, DH, April 2007.

Spotlight on policy: 111 – the national number for non-emergency care
A new, free telephone service, available by dialling 111, will make it easier for people to access non-emergency healthcare in the same way the existing 999 service enables instant access to emergency care.

Available 24 hours a day, the 111 service will assess callers' needs and provide clinical advice or information, or route them to a local service such as a walk-in centre or minor injuries unit. In the event of a caller needing emergency treatment, an ambulance will be sent without the need for further assessment.

The service will be piloted in the North East, East of England and East Midlands strategic health authority areas during 2010 before a national launch if it proves successful, when Scotland, Wales and Northern Ireland may also choose to adopt it.

111 will not replace existing local telephone services or NHS Direct, although in the long-term it could become the single number to access non-emergency care services, including NHS Direct.

NHS Direct

NHS Direct is a 24-hour telephone health advice and information service staffed by nurses. It provides callers to its helpline with information on what to do if they or their family are feeling ill, advice on particular health conditions, details of local healthcare services, such as doctors, dentists or late-night pharmacies, as well as self-help and support organisations. Staff use a computer-based decision-support system to suggest the best course of action, and can pass calls directly to emergency services; about 3 per cent of calls are emergencies.

Launched in 1998, NHS Direct employs almost 3,400 staff, of whom more than 1,300 are nurses. Its 33 contact centres around the country handle 23,500 calls every day. NHS Direct's phone number provides a single point of access for out-of-hours care and handles all low-priority 999 ambulance calls. The top ten symptoms people call about are fever, abdominal pains, vomiting, rash, cough, diarrhoea, headache, cold or flu, toothache and chest pain. Typically, NHS Direct refers 11 per cent of callers to A&E, 28 per cent to their GP (10 per cent for urgent appointments), 5 per cent to walk-in centres, 4 per cent to a dentist and 3 per cent to a pharmacist. Nearly 70 per cent of calls are completed either by NHS Direct or with referral to routine in-hours services.

NHS Direct also offers services to other parts of the health service, including:
• out-of-hours support for GPs and dental services
• telephone support for patients with long-term conditions
• pre- and post-operative support for patients
• 24-hour response to health scares
• remote clinics via telephone.

PCTs acting in consortia are responsible for commissioning most NHS Direct services. Formerly a special health authority, NHS Direct became an NHS trust in April 2007.

NHS Direct in England and Wales operate from the same telephone number – 0845 4647 – while Scotland's information service is called NHS 24 and uses 08454 242424.

NHS Direct Interactive
NHS Direct Online (**www.nhsdirect.nhs.uk**) is an interactive website that provides:
• a self-help guide to treating common problems at home
• a health encyclopaedia with over 400 topics
• personal responses to specific requests for information
• a searchable database of hospitals and community health services, GPs, dentists, opticians and pharmacies.

Visits to NHS Direct Online number more than 1.5 million a month. The service is also available via the NHS Choices website.

Ambulance services

Ambulance services have changed significantly in the past decade, with big improvements in response times for 999 calls, in training and quality of care, vehicle standards, equipment and technology. But as demand for ambulances is rising steadily every year, the Government has set a new strategic direction. The intention is to transform ambulance services to provide more diagnosis, treatment and care in people's homes, helping avoid unnecessary A&E admissions. In 2006, many of the 32 ambulance trusts merged to create 11 new organisations.

Ambulance services respond to 999 calls, doctors' urgent admission requests, high-dependency and inter-hospital transfers, referrals from NHS Direct and major incidents. Key standards for ambulance services include responding to :
- 75 per cent of category A calls within eight minutes
- 95 per cent of category A calls within 19 minutes
- 95 per cent of category B calls within 19 minutes.

In 2008, ambulance services introduced 'call connect', meaning response times are measured from the moment the call is connected to the control room rather than from when details are taken from the caller. Since 2004, local NHS organisations have discretion over whether their ambulance service should automatically respond to category C calls: for these non-urgent conditions, callers may be referred to another NHS provider or treated at home.

NHS ambulances in England received 7.48 million urgent and emergency calls in 2008/09 – 250,000 more than the previous year – of which 6.15 million resulted in an emergency response vehicle arriving on the scene. In many areas ambulance trusts also provide transport to get patients to hospital for non-emergency treatment.

Crews now use satellite navigation systems, and emergency ambulances are equipped with technology such as ECG machines and telemetry, which lets crews send information about a patient's condition directly to the receiving hospital. As well as deploying solo responders such as motorcycles and rapid-response vehicles that can travel through heavy traffic more easily, ambulance trusts have introduced community responder schemes, which equip volunteers with a defibrillator and train them in basic life support. This is especially useful in remote areas.

Ambulance services are improving their ability to assess, diagnose and
treat patients over the telephone and face-to-face. For example, new
critical care paramedics – authorised to use pain-relief drugs and with
enhanced resuscitation skills – are improving care for critically ill and
injured patients. Emergency care practitioners (ECPs) assess, diagnose and
treat minor illnesses and injuries in the community or in people's homes,
helping reduce unnecessary A&E admissions. ECPs also support GPs in and
out of hours by carrying out home visits. Ambulance staff are able to refer
patients to other health and social care providers, including GPs,
intermediate care services and falls teams. In parts of the country,
ambulance services coordinate a single point of access to urgent care,
ensuring patients get the most appropriate services for their clinical need.

Further information
A vision for emergency and urgent care: the role of ambulance services, Ambulance Service
Network/NHS Confederation, June 2008.
Taking healthcare to the patient: transforming NHS ambulance services, DH, June 2005.

Accident and emergency
In 2008/09, there were 19.5 million visits to A&E departments in England.
About one-fifth were admitted to hospital as emergencies. Before a patient
is admitted for further care, transferred or discharged, there can often be a
lengthy chain of decisions, tests and treatment that can be subject to delay.
Since 2004 A&E departments have had a target of seeing, diagnosing and
treating all patients within four hours of their arrival. As a result, A&E
departments have improved pre-admission and assessment procedures,
as well as ensured better access to diagnostic facilities and equipment.
Some have set up clinical decision units or have access to medical
assessment units. Figures since 2005 show the NHS is generally meeting
the four-hour target although the coalition Government is reviewing it.

Ambulance trust areas

North
East

Yorkshire and
the Humber

North
West

East
Midlands

West
Midlands

East of
England

Great
Western

South
Central

London

South East
Coast

South West

Source: Department of Health

The DH's two national clinical directors for emergency care and for heart disease and stroke have argued for changes to how their services are delivered. They point out that despite recent improvements, traditional hospital A&E departments are no longer the only – or even the most – appropriate place to treat such conditions since survival rates are better in specialist centres, for example.

Further information

Emergency access – clinical case for change: report by Sir George Alberti, the national director for emergency access, DH, December 2006.

Mending hearts and brains – clinical case for change: report by Professor Roger Boyle, national director for heart disease and stroke, DH, December 2006.

Trauma services

Major trauma – severe injury including head injury – is the main cause of death in people under 40 and a cause of long-term disability. As it constitutes only a small proportion of acute activity – on average about two per hospital per week – it has historically received relatively little management and planning attention. A series of critical reports from the Royal Colleges, the National Confidential Enquiry into Patient Outcome and Death and most recently from the National Audit Office, have shown that services are inadequate and more lives could be saved.

The Next Stage Review (see page 127) set improving major trauma services as a priority, and most strategic health authorities outlined plans for reorganising services in their regional reviews in 2008. A national clinical director was appointed in 2009 and is pushing for regional networks to be established across England. The first formal trauma network, with emergency departments designated as local trauma centres linked to three central trauma hubs, will begin in London in 2010.

Research highlighted by the NHS Confederation and Ambulance Service Network shows that while trauma networks can improve outcomes, facilities rather than volume of cases are what drive improvement. Providing international standard trauma care will require investment in both emergency care and rehabilitation facilities. Some local centres will need to retain the capacity to stabilise major trauma even after networks are set up, and regions should avoid swamping specialist centres with unnecessary cases.

Further information
Major trauma care in England, NAO, February 2010.

Critical care

Critical care comprises intensive and high-dependence care services. A modernisation programme for critical care has integrated services for critically ill patients wherever they are in the health system. Key objectives were to:
- increase capacity
- develop services supporting critically ill patients throughout the hospital – not necessarily restricted to critical care 'units'
- provide an integrated critical care organisation within and between hospitals working in collaborative networks
- provide comprehensive information and data on critical care.

NHS CONFEDERATION

The number of adult critical care beds in January 2010 increased to 3,685 – 1.3 per cent more than a year earlier; capacity is now more than 50 per cent greater than in 2000. However, high levels of respiratory illness have increased demand for such beds.

Further information
Comprehensive critical care – a review of adult critical care services, DH, May 2000.

Maternity services

The NHS is striving to offer a wider choice of type and place of maternity care and birth. A 2005 DH survey found 80 per cent of women were pleased with maternity care but would have preferred more choice about type of care and where to have their baby. Services should be accessible to all women and be designed to take full account of their individual needs, including different language, cultural, religious and social needs or particular needs related to disability, including learning disability.

Four national 'choice guarantees' were introduced in 2009 so that all women can choose:
• how to access maternity care – by going straight to a midwife or a GP
• type of antenatal care – either midwifery or care provided by a team of maternity health professionals, including midwives and obstetricians
• place of birth – either at home, supported by a midwife; in a local midwifery unit or birth centre, which might be in the community or in a hospital, supported by a midwife; or in a hospital supported by a maternity team that may include midwives, obstetricians, paediatricians and anaesthetists
• postnatal care – either at home or in a community setting, such as a Sure Start children's centre.

Further information
Towards better births: a review of maternity services in England, Healthcare Commission, July 2008.
Maternity matters: choice, access and continuity of care in a safe service, DH, April 2007.

Mental health

One sixth of the population suffers from a mental health problem every day. Mental illness accounts for a third of all illness and 40 per cent of all disability in Britain. By 2026, the number of people with a mental health problem is forecast to rise by 14.2 per cent to 9.88 million. Mental health services absorb 13.8 per cent of the NHS budget: from 2001/02, spending on adult mental health services increased by 50 per cent in real terms to £5.89 billion in 2008/09, making them among the best-resourced in Europe, according to the World Health Organisation. New services and staff were introduced as a result of the mental health national service framework in 1999 and the NHS Plan in 2000. Since 1997 the number of consultant psychiatrists has risen by 64 per cent, clinical psychologists by 71 per cent and mental health nurses by 21 per cent.

Today, the principles guiding mental healthcare are:
- care provided closer to home
- earlier intervention
- 24/7 home treatment
- care tailored to individuals' needs
- better access to modern drugs
- care provided by multi-disciplinary teams
- more use of talking therapies.

Further information
Fact sheet: Key facts and trends in mental health, Mental Health Network/NHS Confederation, November 2009.

Key organisation: National Mental Health Development Unit
NMHDU consists of a small central team and a range of programmes funded by the DH and the NHS. It provides national support for implementing mental health policy by advising on best practice. It commissions or provides:
- specialist expertise in priority areas
- expertise on research, evidence and good practice
- translation of national policies into practical initiatives
- coordination of national activity to help regional and local implementation.

Launched in 2009, it replaced the National Institute for Mental Health. **www.nmhdu.org.uk**

Organising mental health services
Mental health services are provided as part of primary and secondary care, with responsibility split between the NHS, social care and the independent and voluntary sectors. However, PCTs are responsible for commissioning all mental health services, sometimes jointly with local authorities. There are 59 specialist mental health trusts and 14 PCT providers, which provide acute inpatient care, community and rehabilitation services, residential care centres, day hospitals and drop-in centres. About 80,000 staff work in statutory mental health services, and 1.2 million people were in contact with mental health services in 2008/09.

Primary and community services
Of people who receive help for mental health problems, 90 per cent are dealt with in primary care. In a typical PCT serving 330,000 people, about 40,000 will suffer from depression, anxiety or other so-called mental disorders. Another 800 will have a psychotic illness such as schizophrenia. Of GP consultations, 30 per cent have a significant mental health component.

Nevertheless, 80 per cent of NHS spending on mental health is devoted to inpatient services. Less than half of GPs have postgraduate training in psychiatry and only 2 per cent of practice nurses have mental health training, although about half of GP surgeries provide counselling. The GMS contract (see page 215) gives GPs an incentive to provide care for the physical health of people with severe mental illness. GPs usually refer patients they cannot help directly to the local community mental health team (CMHT) or to a psychiatric outpatient clinic.

CMHTs – sometimes known as primary care liaison teams – are the main source of specialist support for those suffering severe and enduring mental health problems. They assess and monitor mental health needs using two specialist systems – the care programme approach or care management. These require that everyone seen by specialist mental health services should have their need for treatment assessed, a care plan drawn up and a named mental health worker to coordinate their care, including a regular review of their needs. They aim to help provide continuity of care across different services, promote multi-professional and inter-agency working, and ensure appropriate care for people diagnosed with serious mental illness on discharge from hospital.

CMHT members include community psychiatric nurses, social workers, psychologists, occupational therapists, doctors and support workers. Patients will regularly meet the psychiatrist from their mental health team at a psychiatric outpatient clinic for review of their treatment.

Providing mental health services in the community has prompted new approaches to care to avoid hospital admission. For example, there are:

- 166 early intervention teams, which aim to treat psychotic illness as quickly and effectively as possible, especially during the critical period after its onset
- 251 assertive outreach teams to provide intensive support for severely mentally ill people who are difficult to engage in more traditional services
- 343 home treatment and crisis resolution teams to provide flexible acute care in patients' own homes with a 24-hour service to help with crises.

The availability of 'talking treatments' such as cognitive behavioural therapy (CBT) is being extended for the 6 million people with depression and anxiety disorders. The Improving Access to Psychological Therapies (IAPT) programme is encouraging provision outside hospital, in people's homes, GP practices, Job Centres and other community settings. After piloting in 13 PCTs, IAPT is gradually expanding, with £173 million investment over three years.

By the end of 2009, 100,000 people had benefited from IAPT services, with a recovery rate of 47 per cent. The intention is now to broaden the scope of IAPT services to include more non-CBT treatments, such as interpersonal therapy, couples therapy, brief dynamic therapy, counselling and collaborative care.

Further information

Realising the benefits: IAPT at full roll out, DH, February 2010.
Refocusing the care programme approach: policy and positive practice guidance, DH, March 2008.
Briefing 157: Improving access to psychological therapies, PCT Network/NHS Confederation, February 2008.

Key organisation: NHS Stressline

The NHS Stressline (0300 123 2000) offers practical advice and emotional support from trained health advisers between 8am and 10pm. Callers suffering stress, anxiety or depression are directed to a package of financial and mental health support. Launched at the beginning of 2010, it is expected to be particularly helpful to those worried about debt, which a quarter of people with mental health problems experience.

Hospital services

Psychiatric hospital services have been progressively scaled down over the past 30 years, as many services are now provided in the community. Admissions fell 17 per cent between 2004 and 2009. However, numbers of patients detained under the Mental Health Act have been rising, intensifying pressure on beds and stress on staff: 32 per cent of inpatients were detained in 2008/09. One result has been a significant increase in pressure on hospital services, with psychiatric beds experiencing high occupancy rates – more than one-third of wards exceed capacity. Acute inpatient services deal mainly with patients suffering severe mental illness.

A Care Quality Commission survey in 2009 found 'too great a proportion' of mental health inpatients felt let down by aspects of their care: only 45 per cent said they always felt safe on the ward, and less than half who wanted talking therapies received any.

Further information

National NHS patient survey programme: mental health acute inpatient service users survey 2009, CQC, September 2009.

Child and adolescent mental health services

One in ten children has a clinically significant mental health problem. Child and adolescent mental health services (CAMHS) cater for young people and children with all types of mental disorder, including hyperkinetic disorders. Services are arranged into four tiers, which should be closely linked:

- tier 1 includes services contributing to mental healthcare of children and young people, but whose primary function is not mental healthcare (for example, schools and GPs)
- tier 2 includes mental health professionals assessing and treating those who do not respond at tier 1

- tier 3 includes teams of mental health professionals providing multi-disciplinary interventions for more complex problems
- tier 4 includes the most severe and complex problems that cannot be dealt with at tier 3, including inpatient and specialist services such as eating disorders.

Mental health trusts are the principal providers of CAMHS, although PCTs, local authorities and the independent sector also provide services. Since 2006 all areas have been required to have 'comprehensive CAMHS', including out-of-hours emergency cover as well as adequate provision for all young people up to the age of 18 with mental health problems. However, many are still far from meeting this requirement.

A national review of CAMHS during 2008 called for 20 changes over the next five years, to include:
- children's mental health and psychological well-being services to be viewed as a single service
- in all services, staff trained to promote mental health and psychological well-being, intervene early and be aware of how to call on more specialised services
- easy-to-access, readily available and evidence-based specialist services.

The DH and DCSF have set up a National Advisory Council for Children's Mental Health and Psychological Wellbeing to monitor implementation of the review recommendations.

Further information

Keeping children and young people in mind: the Government's full response to the independent review of CAMHS, DCSF/DH, January 2010.

Improving access to child and adolescent mental health services: reducing waiting times policy and practice guide (including guidance on the 18 weeks referral to treatment standard), DCFS/DH, August 2009.

The National CAMHS Support Service (NCSS) – 2009/10 business plan, DCSF/DH, July 2009.

Children and young people in mind: the final report of the national CAMHS review, DCSF/DH, November 2008.

Forensic services

Forensic mental health services deal with mentally ill people who may need a degree of physical security and have shown challenging behaviour beyond the scope of general psychiatric services. Some may be mentally disordered offenders.

Services fall into three categories:

- low-security services tend to be based near general psychiatric wards in NHS hospitals
- medium-secure services often operate regionally and usually consist of locked wards with a greater number and a wider range of staff
- high-security services are provided by the three special hospitals (Ashworth, Broadmoor and Rampton), which have much greater levels of security and care for people who pose an immediate and serious risk to others.

In addition, new services are developing to meet the needs of mentally disordered offenders in the community. A strategic advisory body, the National Oversight Group, advises on policy development, commissioning and performance management for high-security services in England and Wales, taking into account the needs of the wider NHS and the criminal justice system.

Further information
National Oversight Group annual report 2008–09, DH, July 2009.

Reforming services

The national service framework for mental health, published in 1999, set out a ten-year programme to introduce new standards of care that people could expect in every part of the country. It emphasised mental health promotion, primary care and access, effective services for people with severe mental illness, caring about carers and reducing suicide by at least one-fifth by 2010. Eight years later, the national director for mental health noted that focus had shifted from specialist mental health services to whole-community mental health. Policy emphasis is now on breaking down traditional boundaries – between professional groups, between primary and secondary care, between the NHS and the independent sector and between health services and other agencies such as education and employment.

A cross-departmental strategy on mental health, New Horizons, has been launched to succeed the NSF. Its twin aims are to improve the population's general mental health and well-being and to improve service quality and accessibility. It contains no new targets or funding commitments, and envisages that public service agreements, local area agreements and the NHS operating framework will be used to achieve its aims.

Employment and housing initiatives are highlighted as priority areas: employment is seen as good for individual well-being, for successful recovery from mental illness and for the wider economy. Key measures include moves to encourage higher rates of employment and retention in work for people in contact with secondary mental health services and promoting employment support, such as employment specialists in PCTs and mental health teams. Tackling the stigma of mental illness is another priority.

Prevention, early intervention and personalisation are all cited as ways to drive up quality and efficiency of services. Improving access for socially excluded or high-risk groups is a major theme – including homeless people, those with learning difficulties, military veterans, rural communities, older people, black and minority ethnic communities and lesbian, gay, bisexual and transgender people.

Further information
New Horizons: a shared vision for mental health, HM Government, December 2009.
Briefing 196: New Horizons: the next phase of mental health policy, MHN/NHS Confederation, December 2009.
A future vision for mental health, Future Vision Coalition, July 2009.
Breaking down barriers – clinical case for change: report by Louis Appleby, national director for mental health, DH, May 2007.
Mental health ten years on: progress on mental health care reform, DH, April 2007.
www.newhorizons.dh.gov.uk

Key organisation **Mental Health Network**
The Mental Health Network was established as part of the NHS Confederation to provide a distinct voice for mental health and learning disability service providers. Launched in 2007, membership includes mental health and learning disability trusts, independent sector members and PCTs that deliver NHS mental health services. The network aims to improve the system for patients and staff by raising the profile of mental health issues and increasing the influence of mental health and disability providers.
www.nhsconfed.org/mhn

Delivering race equality in mental healthcare

One in five mental health inpatients comes from a black and minority ethnic (BME) background, compared to about one in ten of the population as a whole. This initiative was launched in 2005 and outlines a five-year action plan for achieving equality and tackling discrimination in mental health services in England and for all people of black and minority ethnic status. Delivering race equality (DRE) is part of a wider programme of action to develop greater equality in health and social care. The programme is based on three building blocks:

• providing more appropriate and responsive services and improving clinical services for groups such as older people, asylum seekers, refugees and children
• engaging communities in planning services, supported by 500 new community development workers
• improving ethnicity monitoring, dissemination of information and knowledge about effective service, including a regular census of mental health patients.

The intention is that mental health services will be characterised by 'less fear' among BME communities and service users; increased satisfaction with services; a reduced rate of admission of people from BME communities to psychiatric inpatient units; a reduction in the disproportionate rates of compulsory detention of BME service users in inpatient units and a more balanced range of culturally appropriate and effective therapies.

Eighteen focused implementation sites have been established across the country to help identify and spread best practice. The evaluation of these sites is informing national implementation. A BME mental health programme board, directly accountable to ministers, is overseeing this action plan and the wider BME mental health programme.

Further information

Briefing 158: Delivering race equality in mental health care, MHN/NHS Confederation, March 2008.
Delivering race equality in mental health care: progress review of focused implementation sites – national summary, National DRE Programme, January 2007.
www.mentalhealthequalities.org.uk

Revising mental health law: the Mental Health Act 2007

The Mental Health Act 2007 updates the Mental Health Act 1983 through seven major amendments, while an eighth amendment updates the Mental Capacity Act 2005. These provide better safeguards for service users, with new rights to advocacy, a say in who their nearest relative is and the right to refuse electro-convulsive therapy and other treatments.

The seven major amendments are:
- a simplified definition of mental disorder
- a wider definition of medical treatment
- the introduction of supervised community treatment after initial detention and treatment in hospital
- additional safeguards for service users
- changes to professional roles to allow a wider range of staff to adopt the functions traditionally delivered by approved social workers and medical professionals
- improved access to review tribunals
- abolition of finite restriction orders.

Further information
Briefing 175: Mental Capacity Act 2005 deprivation of liberty safeguards, MHN/NHS Confederation, March 2009.
Briefing 171: Implementing the Mental Health Act 2007: what boards need to know, MHN/NHS Confederation, September 2008.

Care for special groups

Healthcare for people with learning disabilities

There are 985,000 people in England with a learning disability – 2 per cent of the population – and numbers will increase significantly in the next 15 years, especially among older age groups. But only 177,000 are known to use learning disability services. People with learning disabilities have greater health needs than the general population, being more likely to experience mental illness and more prone to chronic health problems such as epilepsy, cerebral palsy and other physical disabilities. They are also 58 times more likely to die before the age of 50. But many have difficulty accessing healthcare and are less likely to seek routine screening. All too often they have been effectively invisible to mainstream NHS services.

When they do access health services they may be subject to 'diagnostic overshadowing' bias – clinicians' tendency to overlook symptoms of mental health problems among people with learning disabilities, attributing them to the disability. Therefore, people with learning disabilities may need support when using mainstream services, including longer appointments and help with communication.

The 2001 learning disability white paper, *Valuing people*, was based on four key principles that still apply:
• legal and civil rights – people with learning disabilities have the right to a decent education, to grow up to vote, marry and have a family, and express their opinions, with help and support where necessary
• independence – individuals' needs will differ, but the presumption should be one of independence rather than dependence, with public services providing the support needed to maximise this
• choice – everyone should be able to make choices, including people with severe and profound disabilities, with help and support
• inclusion – people with learning disabilities should be able to do ordinary things, make use of mainstream services and be fully included in the local community.

Despite progress since the white paper, the 2008 Michael Inquiry found much remained to be done and a follow-up white paper, *Valuing people now*, set out plans for addressing the inquiry's recommendations. Priorities for 2009/10 included:
• an effective learning disability partnership board in every local authority area
• SHAs and PCTs leading work on securing access to, and improving healthcare
• increasing the range of housing options for people with learning disabilities and their families
• ensuring all local authority services and developments for people with learning disabilities and their carers are underpinned by person-centred planning
• increasing employment opportunities.

The Ombudsman highlighted several cases – thought not to be isolated incidents – where health and social care failings had led to the premature and avoidable deaths of people with learning disabilities. The Ombudsman recommended all NHS and social care organisations urgently review their effectiveness and capacity for helping people with learning disabilities.

A National Learning Disabilities Programme Board is monitoring progress and will link to new regional learning disability boards and, through them, to all local partnership boards. It is hoped this structure will improve the local partnership boards, which were set up after 2001 to bring together relevant local agencies and stakeholders, giving a voice to people with learning disabilities and their carers. In practice, their membership, governance, responsibilities, accountability and effectiveness have varied, with few operating as envisaged: most have focused on process and engagement rather than improving outcomes. Nevertheless, they are crucial to achieving the aims of *Valuing people now*.

Further information

World class commissioning: improving the health and wellbeing of people with learning disabilities, DH, November 2009.

Good learning disability partnership boards: 'making it happen for everyone', DH, October 2009.

Briefing 174: Commissioning healthcare for people with learning disabilities, PCT Network/ NHS Confederation, March 2009.

Six lives: the provision of public services to people with learning disabilities, Parliamentary and Health Service Ombudsman, March 2009.

Valuing people now: a new three-year strategy for people with learning disabilities, HM Government, January 2009.

Valuing people now: the delivery plan, HM Government, January 2009.

Healthcare for all: report of the independent inquiry into access to healthcare for people with learning disabilities, DH, July 2008.

Valuing people: a new strategy for learning disability for the 21st century, DH, March 2001.
http://valuingpeople.gov.uk

Prison healthcare

People in prison have generally poorer health than the population at large: 71 per cent have two or more mental disorders, and 70 per cent have a concurrent drug and/or alcohol programme; 10 per cent suffer from psychosis, while 80 per cent smoke. Since 2006, PCTs have been responsible for commissioning healthcare for prisons. The aim is to provide prisoners with access to the same quality and range of healthcare services as the public receives from the NHS. Schemes to tackle smoking and drug misuse and vaccinate against hepatitis B have since begun. Prisons have also implemented a new care-planning system for prisoners at risk of suicide. The Enhancing the Healing Environment Programme, run by the King's Fund and the DH, is working in 20 prisons to improve facilities.

A national partnership agreement between the DH and the Home Office on behalf of the Prison Service underpins the local partnership arrangements between PCTs and public sector prisons.

Improving the outcomes of prison healthcare is important for successful rehabilitation and reducing re-offending rates. After Lord Bradley's 2009 independent review of the needs of people with mental health problems or learning disabilities in the criminal justice system, an action plan to improve the health of offenders in prison and the community was devised. *Improving health, supporting justice* proposes:
- liaison and diversion services to assess individuals' health needs in all courts over the next five years
- training criminal justice staff to identify health issues and share information across the system
- giving offenders access to the same level of healthcare as everyone else
- improving continuity of care by developing care pathways that enhance health and social care provision.

Further information
Briefing 197: Improving health, supporting justice: the national delivery plan of the Health and Criminal Justice Programme Board, MHN/NHS Confederation, December 2009.
Improving health, supporting justice: the national delivery plan of the Health and Criminal Justice Programme Board, DH, November 2009.
Commissioning healthcare in prisons, Healthcare Commission/HM Inspectorate of Prisons, February 2009.
Good practice in prison health, DH, July 2007.
National partnership agreement between the Department of Health and the Home Office for the accountability and commissioning of health services for prisoners in public sector prisons in England, DH, January 2007.

Defence Medical Services
The Defence Medical Services (DMS) comprise the Surgeon General's Department, the Joint Medical Command including the Defence Dental Services, and the medical services of the Royal Navy, the Army and the Royal Air Force. The DMS are headed by the Surgeon General and over 7,000 regular uniformed medical personnel from all three services belong to them, working alongside the Ministry of Defence's civilian medical and dental staff.

The DMS run the Royal Centre for Defence Medicine in Birmingham and five other Ministry of Defence hospital units based in the NHS, 15 rehabilitation units across the UK and Germany and 15 military departments of community mental health. They also provide primary care to serving personnel and some dependants in the UK and to 250,000 serving personnel and entitled dependants abroad – the latter mainly in Germany, Cyprus and Gibraltar.

The DMS interact with the NHS at many levels: for example, DMS healthcare professionals train in the NHS, while 1,600 NHS staff belong to the British Reserve Forces. A partnership of seven NHS trusts provides inpatient mental healthcare to serving personnel across the UK under contract to the Ministry of Defence.

The NHS and the Ministry of Defence have launched six community mental health pilot sites (including one in Scotland) designed to make available, within the NHS, expert assessment and treatment for veterans with mental health problems. Since 2008 all military veterans have been entitled to priority access to NHS secondary care for any conditions thought to be related to their service. There are about 5 million veterans in England. They are most likely to make use of audiology, mental health and orthopaedic services.

In future, personnel who are seriously injured will receive a comprehensive assessment of their long-term needs before they leave the armed forces and then a regular review of their needs by an NHS case manager. SHAs will identify a director, and PCTs a champion, to ensure the needs of the armed forces, veterans and their families are reflected in local plans and service provision. The transfer of medical records to the NHS will be improved so that GPs are more aware of a new patient's veteran status to ensure they receive priority access.

Further information
Meeting the healthcare needs of armed forces personnel, their families and veterans, DH, December 2008.
Seventh report of session 2007/08: medical care for the armed forces, House of Commons defence committee, February 2008.
www.mod.uk/DefenceInternet/microsite/dms

Healthcare for asylum seekers and refugees

People with an outstanding application for refuge in the UK are entitled to use NHS services without charge. Although the High Court ruled in 2008 that failed asylum seekers may still be deemed 'ordinarily resident' in the UK and so also entitled to free NHS treatment, this judgement was overturned by the Court of Appeal in 2009. The DH has since proposed that failed asylum seekers who cannot return home should be exempt from charges.

Asylum seekers are often from very different cultures, may not understand the principles behind the NHS, may not speak English and may have complex healthcare requirements.

The DH's Asylum Seeker Coordination Team (ASCT) coordinates healthcare policy for asylum seekers and refugees. ASCT works across the DH and other government departments, and with health workers and service planners in the field. In particular, it liaises with the Home Office to try to ensure health and social care needs are met during the asylum process and taken into account in policy planning.

Asylum seekers usually stay in a network of induction centres on their arrival. Here they undergo an initial health assessment, normally by a nurse with access to a GP. Each asylum seeker is issued with a national hand-held health record.

The best model of healthcare for asylum seekers is integration into existing mainstream services. Where this is not possible immediately, the NHS locally may have to consider dedicated initiatives appropriate for asylum seekers new to an area. Some PCTs ensure there is space on GMS surgery lists for asylum seekers; others use personal medical services to set up surgeries for local vulnerable populations, which may include asylum seekers. PCTs and local councils are responsible for ensuring adequate access to interpreters for asylum seekers within their own area.

Further information

Unheard voices – listening to the views of asylum seekers and refugees, Commission for Patient and Public Involvement in Health, May 2006.
Caring for dispersed asylum seekers: a resource pack, DH, June 2003.

04 Policy and strategy: creating a 'vision' for the NHS

Making and implementing policy is a key strand of the Department of Health's work, and during a government's term of office it will publish a plethora of major policy documents designed to improve health and social care, turning political vision into action.

Policy and strategy are aimed at the long term – for example, setting out a 'vision' of how the NHS might look in ten years' time – the medium term, such as the three-year cycle of the NHS's operational plans, and the short-term, such as the annual operating framework. And apart from initiatives specific to the health and social care system, the NHS is influenced by cross-government policy and strategy frameworks such as the comprehensive spending review and public service agreements.

NHS system reforms can improve management but need time to deliver significant benefits for patients, according to a study by the Audit Commission and Healthcare Commission. By 2008 they found some reforms beginning to work, with better financial management and a more business-like approach encouraged by payment by results and foundation trusts. Evidence suggested competition from independent organisations had improved services in places and standards were improving across the NHS. But other changes needed more time to deliver significant results, with limited progress on moving care out of hospitals and closer to home. The commissions advised further nationally imposed structural changes should be avoided as progress had been hampered by two major reorganisations since the reforms were introduced. Underdeveloped commissioning and weak monitoring had also hindered progress.

Further information
Is the treatment working? Progress with the NHS system reform programme, Audit Commission and Healthcare Commission, June 2008.

Envisaging the future
The coalition Government's plans for the NHS are contained in the Health Bill 2010.

Health Act 2009
The Health Act 2009 enshrines in law many of the recommendations of the Labour Government's Next Stage Review (see page 127) and sets out a framework for how the NHS Constitution will operate. Key measures include:
• a duty on all NHS bodies, private and third sector providers of NHS services to have regard to the NHS Constitution

- providers of NHS care to produce 'quality accounts' containing detailed information about the quality of their services
- patients to be given direct payments as part of their personal budgets for choosing care for long-term conditions (see page 90)
- innovation prizes to encourage enterprise and innovation in the NHS
- the appointment of a trust special administrator to an NHS trust, PCT or de-authorised foundation trust that is failing and unsustainable
- powers for the Secretary of State to suspend chairs, vice-chairs and non-executive directors of SHAs, special health authorities and other NHS bodies where concerns about their performance arise
- greater powers to PCTs to commission pharmacy services and ensure pharmacies are performing adequately
- end the display of tobacco products and banning cigarette vending machines.

The planning framework

The Labour Government set long-term strategy for public services every few years during a comprehensive spending review (CSR). It also decided the financial settlement for every government department and published public service agreements that contained its priority outcomes for the CSR period. In turn, the Department of Health published its priorities in its business plan, while the NHS operating framework outlined priorities for the health service over a three-year planning cycle.

Comprehensive spending review

The CSR is a long-term and fundamental review of all Government expenditure. The first was held in 1998 and the second in 2007. The next will take place in autumn 2010.

The 2007 CSR contended that far-reaching social, economic and technological changes – as well as shifts in public expectations and attitudes – have transformed the environment in which public services operate. It stated that 'public services need to be ready to respond to these trends', and said the new model of public service delivery should be based on excellent outcomes, personalisation and value for money. It defined personalised services as those that are flexible and tailored to individuals' needs, that treat people with care, respect their preferences and appreciate the value of their time. The 2007 CSR also set the NHS's financial allocation for the subsequent three years up to April 2011.

Further information

The 2007 comprehensive spending review and pre-Budget report, HM Treasury, October 2007.

Key text: NHS Constitution

'The NHS belongs to the people...' The NHS Constitution, which applies only to the health service in England, comprises:

- seven key principles that govern how the NHS operates, such as providing a comprehensive service and value for money
- 37 rights and pledges to patients and the public about matters such as access, quality, respect, choice and complaints
- nine responsibilities that patients and public owe the NHS, such as keeping appointments and treating staff with respect
- ten staff rights concerning issues such as working environment, fair pay, representation and equal treatment (see page 218)
- 11 staff responsibilities, including patient confidentiality and professional accountability
- six values, including respect and dignity, commitment to quality and compassion.

The Constitution attempts a balance between the need for clarity and avoiding litigation, between enshrining enduring values and principles while ensuring the NHS has flexibility to change. The Health Act 2009 places a duty on all NHS organisations, private and third sector providers in England to take account of the Constitution. By law the Government must renew the Constitution every ten years, so that changes cannot take place without debate.

The DH has proposed that, from 2010, the NHS Constitution would give patients the legal right to maximum waiting times to start treatment by a consultant within 18 weeks of GP referral, and to be seen by a cancer specialist within two weeks of GP referral. If the NHS could not meet this, it would have to take all reasonable steps to find alternative providers that could, including private providers at NHS prices. Guaranteeing in legislation what patients can expect is a significant departure.

Another proposal is to give everyone aged 40–74 the right to an NHS health check every five years to assess their risk of heart disease, stroke, diabetes and kidney disease. The DH has also consulted on including more rights in the Constitution in future, including the right to NHS dentistry and to die at home.

In 2009 the NHS Constitution State of Readiness Group called for the 'passion and enthusiasm' felt at the DH to be more strongly shared on the front line, warning of a need for clarity about the Constitution's purpose and how its aims would be achieved.

Further information

The NHS Constitution for England, NHS, March 2010.
The handbook to the NHS Constitution for England, DH, March 2010.
Final report, NHS Constitution State of Readiness Group, November 2009.
The NHS Constitution: a consultation on new patient rights, DH, November 2009.
The NHS Constitution: all you need to know about how the NHS Constitution affects you as a provider or commissioner of NHS care, DH, May 2009.
The statement of NHS accountability for England, DH, January 2009.

Public service agreements (PSAs)

Before 2007, each government department drew up a public service agreement with the Treasury setting out what it was expected to provide with its resources over a three-year period. After the last CSR, the Labour Government published a set of 30 PSAs cutting across departments. Each PSA is underpinned by a single delivery agreement shared across all contributing departments, which sets out plans for achieving the PSA targets and the role of key partners. The DH is leading two PSAs:
• PSA 18 – promoting better health and well-being for all
• PSA 19 – ensuring better care for all.

At the end of 2009 the DH reported 'some progress' on PSA 18, with three of the five measures against which it is judged showing improvement; progress on PSA 19 was 'strong', with six out of eight measures improving.

Ten other PSAs are relevant to the NHS:
• improving the health and well-being of children and young people
• improving children's and young people's safety
• increasing the number of children and young people on the path to success
• addressing the disadvantage individuals experience because of their gender, race, disability, age, sexual orientation, religion or belief
• increasing the proportion of socially excluded adults in settled accommodation and employment, education or training
• tackling poverty and promoting greater independence and well-being in later life

- reducing the harm caused by alcohol and drugs
- leading the global effort to avoid dangerous climate change
- securing a healthy natural environment for today and the future
- reducing poverty in poorer countries through quicker progress towards the millennium development goals.

The DH's own priorities for 2009–11 include:
- strengthening midwifery and maternity services
- Olympic and paralympic health programme
- implementing the NHS Constitution
- health and social care integration
- expanding clinical research networks across the NHS
- developing high-quality informatics to support improved access to data.

Further information
Department of Health autumn performance report 2009, CM7776, TSO, December 2009.
Department of Health business plan 2009–11, DH, June 2009.

NHS priorities 2008–11

The NHS's programme is set out in the operating framework for 2010/11, although it will be revised by the coalition Government. As with PSAs, the DH is keen to give NHS organisations some local flexibility over their priorities. The operating framework therefore combines a small number of compulsory national priorities with areas where PCTs can decide themselves how they meet the target. They also have the chance to add their own priorities.

The compulsory national priorities were established in the operating framework for 2008/09 and remain:
- improving cleanliness and reducing healthcare-associated infections
- achieving the maximum 18-week referral to treatment waiting time and improving access to GPs
- improving the health of adults and children, and reducing health inequalities
- improving patient experience, staff satisfaction and engagement
- preparing to respond in a state of emergency, such as the outbreak of a new pandemic.

In developing their own local priorities after consultation with their communities and partners, PCTs are expected to pay particular attention, among other things, to:
- eradicating variations in cancer, stroke, heart disease and maternity services
- ensuring services are in place to meet anticipated demand after NHS health checks are introduced for people aged 40–74
- supporting health research
- eliminating mixed-sex accommodation
- cooperating with the military to ensure their needs are met.

Setting the context for the framework, the NHS chief executive calls 2010/11 a 'pivotal year' in which the NHS 'is about to enter perhaps the toughest financial climate it has ever known' as it searches for £20 billion or more in savings by 2014. PCT allocations will increase by an average 5.5 per cent this year, but funding for frontline services will then be frozen and the rest will face cuts. The NHS's task is to improve quality and productivity simultaneously, making full use of innovation and prevention. To this end the framework contains some new financial levers (see page 192). If successful, the NHS will be characterised by:
- more care closer to home
- fewer acute beds
- reduced unit costs
- reduced variation
- more standardisation of pathways
- early and more upstream intervention
- people taking greater ownership of their health.

Drawing on the Next Stage Review, the framework stipulates that four key principles should govern change in the NHS:
- clinical ownership and leadership of decisions
- co-production – all parts of the system need to work together
- subsidiarity – to ensure decisions are taken at the right level and as close to the patient as possible
- system alignment – all parts pulling in the same direction.

Further information
Briefing 192: The operating framework for the NHS in England 2010/11, NHS Confederation, January 2010.
The operating framework for the NHS in England 2010/11, DH, December 2009.
Operational plans 2008/09–2010/11: national planning guidance and 'vital signs', DH, January 2008.

The new NHS – modern, dependable

The Labour Government's first health white paper after coming to power, published in December 1997. It announced the setting up of primary care groups (forerunners of PCTs), NICE, the Commission for Health Improvement (forerunner of the Care Quality Commission) and NHS Direct, describing reforms that would be 'a new model for a new century'.

The NHS Plan

The NHS Plan was the foundation of the Government's reforms for modernising the health service, and linked change explicitly to extra investment announced in the March 2000 Budget. Published in July 2000 and intended as an ambitious ten-year programme, the Plan set out to tackle 'systematic problems, which date from 1948 when the NHS was formed'.

Shifting the balance of power within the NHS

Two documents – *Securing delivery* (July 2001) and *The next steps* (January 2002) – outlined the rationale behind devolving power from Whitehall to frontline NHS organisations, in particular PCTs. They announced that SHAs were to replace the existing 95 health authorities and that the DH would have a reduced role in directly managing the NHS.

Delivering the NHS Plan: next steps on investment, next steps on reform

This document, published in April 2002, introduced plans to reform the NHS's financial flows through payment by results, brought new emphasis to patient choice and underlined commitment to promoting diversity in supply of healthcare through joint ventures with the private sector.

The NHS Improvement Plan: putting people at the heart of public services

Published in June 2004, this 'supports the ongoing commitment to a ten-year process of reform first set out in the NHS Plan' but added some new priorities to be achieved by 2008: giving patients more information and extending patient choice through 'personalised care', improving support for people with long-term conditions and stronger emphasis on disease prevention.

Creating a patient-led NHS: delivering the NHS Improvement Plan
In March 2005, the Labour Government revealed it wanted 'some radically different types of provision' that would 'involve freeing up the entrepreneurialism within primary care and developing new types of provider organisations'.

Our health, our care, our say
Published in January 2006, this white paper set out the Labour Government's vision for more effective health and social care services outside hospital, calling for closer integration between health and social services, better access to GPs, improved care for people with long-term conditions and further effort to combat health inequalities.

Health reform in England: update and commissioning framework
In July 2006, six years after the NHS Plan, this document reported progress and set out commissioning arrangements for hospital services covered by choice and payment by results.

Our NHS, our future: NHS Next Stage Review – interim report
Issued to coincide with the comprehensive spending review in October 2007, this stressed that the NHS should complete current reforms, not do something different. It called for improved access to GPs and screening of all admissions for MRSA. It described a vision of the NHS as fair, personalised, effective and safe.

High quality care for all: NHS Next Stage Review final report
Coinciding with the NHS's 60th anniversary in July 2008, this report and a suite of others accompanying it sought to plot a direction for the next ten years, emphasising services that were personalised and locally led, and proposing an NHS Constitution.

NHS 2010–2015: from good to great. Preventative, people-centred, productive
Published in December 2009 as the general election approached, this sought to guard the NHS's performance gains as it searched for major efficiency improvements.

Equality and diversity

Eliminating discrimination and disadvantage in the healthcare workforce and reducing health inequalities in the population are major policy aims of the DH and the NHS.

To that end, the DH has devised a Single Equality Scheme (SES) for 2009–12, superseding a previous scheme from 2007 and detailing how it plans to meet its obligations under equality legislation. The SES states: 'All public organisations, including the Department of Health and public providers and commissioners of health and social care services, have a duty to promote equality. The fulfilment of these duties is a necessary part of the health and social care system's mission to offer services that deliver high quality care for all.'

The scheme covers the DH's responsibility for the health and social care system and as an employer in its own right. It is based on six strands:
• race
• gender
• disability
• age
• sexual orientation
• religion and belief.

These reflect the fact that inequality and prejudice are often perceived and experienced on many levels. Within the DH, the equality and human rights group (EHRG) aims to:
• give strategic leadership on equality and human rights
• champion equality and human rights within the DH
• challenge discrimination across the DH, NHS and social care
• advise on proposed legislation
• devise innovative change programmes
• develop partnerships with stakeholders, regulators, patients and staff.

In addition, the national director for equality and human rights works across the DH, NHS and adult social care, while the DH's equality and inclusion team provides support for the SES. In 2009 the DH set up an Equality and Diversity Council chaired by the NHS chief executive and with members from patient groups, NHS staff, social care and voluntary organisations. It reports on equality and diversity issues to the NHS management board, championing improvement and campaigning for change.

The Pacesetters programme is a partnership between the DH, NHS and local communities experiencing health inequalities. It aims both to reduce health inequalities and produce working environments that are fair and free of discrimination. Six strategic health authorities and three trusts within each SHA area are working with the EHRG on issues that include promoting dignity and respect, tackling bullying and improving the health status of Gypsies and Travellers.

Individual NHS trusts are also encouraged to develop their own single equality schemes, bringing together their responses to all three duties covering race, disability and gender and also addressing other areas such as religion, belief, age and sexual orientation.

After the Equality Bill becomes law, age discrimination against adults will be banned in public services from 2012. This has implications for health and social care since age can be a factor in decisions about treatments and services. A review of age equality in the NHS and social care found no areas should be wholly exempt from the legislation and where possible, age as a criterion for assessing care provision should be replaced by more pertinent and individualised evidence.

Further information

Achieving age equality in health and social care: a report to the Secretary of State for health by Sir Ian Carruthers OBE and Jan Ormondroyd, COI, October 2009.
Department of Health single equality scheme 2009–2012, DH, June 2009.
Briefing 60: Managing diversity: making it core business, NHS Employers, April 2009.
Briefing 58: Monitoring for equality and diversity: what healthcare employers need to know and do, NHS Employers, January 2009.
Sexual orientation: a practical guide for the NHS, DH, February 2009.
Religion or belief: a practical guide for the NHS, DH, January 2009.
Trans: a practical guide for the NHS, DH, November 2008.
Making the difference: the Pacesetters beginner's guide to service improvement for equality and diversity in the NHS, DH, July 2008.
A dialogue of equals: the Pacesetters programme community engagement guide, DH, January 2008.
www.nhsemployers.org/equality

In 2004 the NHS was set a target that by the end of 2008 no one should wait more than 18 weeks from the time they are referred to the start of their hospital treatment, unless it is clinically appropriate or they choose to wait longer. This was one of the major workforce challenges facing the NHS, but it was achieved on time. By early 2009, the average wait for treatment for admitted patients was 8.6 weeks.

Although the 18-week target is being met by all organisations, it is not being met in all specialties. The 2010/11 operating framework states: 'We know this can be achieved and expect it to happen.' However, the target may be reviewed by the coalition Government.

From 2010 patients have a legal right under the NHS Constitution to treatment within 18 weeks (two weeks for cancer patients).
www.18weeks.nhs.uk

05 Quality and safety

The NHS is committed to providing high-quality care, which means continually striving to improve clinical standards, using resources efficiently and ensuring patients' safety. Quality and safety criteria are set and monitored nationally, with every organisation's performance assessed and made public. Recent concerns about healthcare-acquired infections have brought renewed emphasis on patient safety.

Ensuring quality

The Labour Government's first health policy white paper, *The new NHS: modern, dependable*, published in 1997, promised that the service 'will have quality at its heart'. Eleven years later, the Next Stage Review's *High quality care for all*, declared: 'Enabling all parts of the NHS to focus consistently and systematically on improving the quality of care is a major challenge. It requires a long-term transformation that touches all parts of the system, starting from the front line.' The review insisted that quality be understood from the patient's perspective, and defined it as comprising:
• patient safety
• patient experience
• effectiveness of care.

Little more than a year later, the strategy document *NHS 2010–2015* was demanding 'an acceleration of the improvements in quality we seek', while the NHS operating framework for 2010/11 sought to 'ensure a relentless focus on quality'. Like the Next Stage Review (see page 127), both emphasised 'quality as the organising principle' of the NHS, 'at the heart of all that we do'.

NHS organisations have a statutory duty to ensure the quality of their services, just as they have always had to keep their organisations financially solvent. Indeed, by law they now have to publish 'quality accounts' (see page 137). Other recent measures designed to foster quality include CQUIN (see page 138), adjustments to the tariff system to link increases in payments to specific quality goals (see page 192) and registration with the Care Quality Commission (see page 174).

Trust chief executives are accountable for clinical standards, and each trust has a designated senior clinician who must make sure clinical governance systems are functioning properly. Primary care trusts have to nominate a senior health professional, usually a GP, to lead on clinical standards and professional development. As commissioners, PCTs are held to account for the quality of health outcomes they achieve for their populations, including the most vulnerable or excluded people with complex needs. Each strategic health authority is setting up a 'quality observatory' to enable services to be benchmarked, develop ways of measuring quality and help staff improve services.

Further information
Briefing 198: Commissioning for quality – delivering national priorities, PCT Network/NHS Confederation, February 2010.

Key organisation: National Quality Board
An initiative of the Next Stage Review, the NQB is intended to provide strategic oversight and leadership in quality across the service and is chaired by the NHS chief executive. Other members include the NHS medical director, chief medical and nursing officers and the chairs of the Care Quality Commission, NICE and Monitor, as well as leaders from the charity and third sectors, academe, social care and the Royal Colleges.

The board's role is to 'align quality at all levels in the NHS', from clinical teams to SHAs. It oversees work to improve quality indicators, advises the Secretary of State on priorities for clinical standards set by NICE and reports annually on the state of quality using internationally agreed measures.

Following an NQB recommendation, organisations with the highest MRSA infection rates must make the biggest reductions in 2010/11, while the best performers must maintain their low rates and strive for further improvements.

Further information
Annual report 2009/10, National Quality Board, February 2010.

Clinical governance
Clinical governance is an explicit framework for making all NHS staff accountable for quality improvement and safeguarding standards, ensuring that quality remains a priority. The chief medical officer's definition of clinical governance is:

> a system through which NHS organisations are accountable for continuously improving the quality of their services and safeguarding high standards of care, by creating an environment in which clinical excellence will flourish.

It seeks to transform the culture, ways of working and systems of every health organisation so that patient safety, quality assurance and improvement are an integral part of their everyday work. Its main features are a coherent approach to quality improvement, clear lines of accountability for clinical quality systems and effective processes for identifying and managing risk and addressing poor performance.

Its essential components are:
- the patient's experience – of access to services, organisation of care, humanity of care and the care environment
- the organisation's use of information
- consultation and patient involvement
- risk management
- clinical audit
- effectiveness and research
- staffing and staff management
- education, training and continuing professional development
- leadership
- direction and planning, accountability and structures
- partnership with the public
- partnership with the local health economy.

For clinical governance to work properly and quality to flourish, NHS organisations must foster a culture of openness and participation, value education and research, and encourage people to learn from failures. Good practice and new approaches should be shared readily and received willingly.

The Essence of Care guidelines enable NHS organisations to benchmark the fundamentals of good-quality care. They cover topics such as the care environment, communication, food and drink, personal hygiene, record-keeping, respect, safety and self-care. In 2009 the DH launched the twelfth in the series, on pain management, and reviewed existing benchmarks.

Further information
Essence of care: a consultation on the reviewed original benchmarks, DH, June 2009.
Improving quality and safety – progress in implementing clinical governance in primary care: lessons for the new primary care trusts, National Audit Office, January 2007.

Clinical audit

Clinical audit is an important instrument of clinical governance, providing rich data to support service improvement, better information for patients and revalidation of clinicians. It 'aims to assess the extent to which care is consistent with best practice and/or achieves expected outcomes'. With education and research it is one of the medical profession's three core responsibilities, but unlike them has lacked a national strategy and coherent programme – despite participation being mandatory for all doctors since 1989.

In 2006 the chief medical officer called for clinical audit to be reinvigorated, and a National Clinical Audit Advisory Group was set up as a 'wide and inclusive' forum to enhance the existing programme of national clinical audits and support NHS staff involved in audits in their own organisations. It also seeks to improve connections between national clinical audits regardless of how they are funded, between audit and IT, revalidation and research and development.

NCAAG also acts as the steering group for the National Clinical Audit and Patients' Outcomes Programme, which commissions national audits, consults those with an interest in audit and develops resources for them. NCAPOP is administered by the Healthcare Quality Improvement Partnership (HQIP), a consortium of the Royal College of Nursing, Academy of Medical Royal Colleges and National Voices.

In 2008, for the first time, the NHS in England released survival rates for four common cardiac and orthopaedic operations for each trust, published on the NHS Choices website. The figures revealed all hospitals were performing acceptably and five were above average. Data for a wider range of elective and emergency surgery will be made available in due course.

Further information

What is clinical audit?, DH, October 2009.
National Clinical Audit Advisory Group annual report 2008–09, DH, July 2009.
Trust, assurance and safety – the regulation of health professionals in the 21st century, TSO, February 2007.
Healthcare Quality Improvement Partnership **www.hqip.org.uk**

Developing integrated governance

NHS boards' decisions must take note not only of clinical governance but of corporate governance, research governance, information governance and financial governance. As the NHS engages with a wider range of partners than ever before, governance between organisations has become crucial too. These strands of governance have developed independently from each other, and do not necessarily align or inter-relate: for example, financial allocations may not always take fully into account the pressures of clinical governance. But in reality, these domains all complement and impact on one another. Creating different structures to manage and monitor them can lead to duplication and wasted effort, overburdening staff with demands for data.

Some NHS organisations have begun to streamline their governance activities. However, integrating the strands of governance is not easy, and much detail remains to be worked out.

Further information
Integrated governance handbook, DH, February 2006.

National service frameworks

National service frameworks (NSFs) – or, as new ones are to be known, 'national clinical strategies' – are evidence-based programmes setting quality standards and specifying services that should be available for a particular condition or care group across the whole NHS. They are intended to eradicate local variations in standards and services, raise standards generally, promote collaboration between organisations and contribute to improving public health. Each identifies key interventions, puts in place a strategy to support implementation and establishes an agreed timescale.

Each NSF is developed with assistance from an external reference group of health professionals, service users and carers, health service managers, partner agencies and other advocates. The DH supports the groups and manages the overall process.

Usually only one new NSF is released in a year. The programme so far covers:
• paediatric intensive care, January 1997
• mental health, September 1999
• coronary heart disease, March 2000
• cancer, September 2000; cancer reform strategy, December 2007

- older people, March 2001
- diabetes: standards, December 2001; delivery strategy, January 2003
- renal services: part one, January 2004; part two, February 2005
- children, young people and maternity services, September 2004
- long-term conditions, March 2005
- national clinical strategy for chronic obstructive pulmonary disease, pending.

Quality accounts

Under the Health Act 2009 all providers of NHS care must publish annual 'quality accounts' indicating the quality of the care they provide. These require boards to consider the quality of their services, their priorities for improvement and how they intend to achieve them. They are not intended to be a comprehensive assessment of every service, nor to supply patients with information they need to make an informed choice about services.

Quality accounts must include:
- a statement of accountability from the provider
- priorities for improvement and reporting arrangements to track progress
- a review of quality performance, confirming the organisation has set indicators for patient safety, effectiveness of care and patient experience, is developing a quality improvement plan and participates in clinical audit
- research and innovation, confirming the organisation participates in clinical research and uses CQUIN (see page 138)
- what others say about the provider, such as reports from the Care Quality Commission, local involvement network and PCT
- data quality – a simple data quality score.

Boards are free to decide any other content. In 2010/11, only NHS trusts, foundation trusts, private or voluntary sector providers need provide a quality account. Other organisations will follow in due course.

Further information

The framework for quality accounts: response to consultation, DH, February 2010.
Discussion paper 4: Scoping 'quality accounts' in mental health, MHN/NHS Confederation, April 2009.
Making the most of your Quality Accounts, Foundation Trust Network/NHS Confederation, June 2009.
Quality Accounts 2: reviewing NHS foundation trusts' 2009 experiences and plans, Foundation Trust Network/NHS Confederation, February 2010.

NHS CONFEDERATION

CQUIN

The Commissioning for Quality and Innovation (CQUIN) payment framework makes part of a provider's income conditional on quality and innovation. It is intended to ensure contracts include quality improvement plans by allowing PCTs to link a specific proportion of providers' contract income to achieving locally agreed goals. For example, if the PCT has concerns about stroke services, the provider could undertake to increase the percentage of stroke patients with access to scanning within three hours of admission – a process known to improve outcomes – to an agreed level.

In 2010/11, the amount that can be earned under CQUIN will treble to 1.5 per cent of contract income. All CQUIN schemes will be required to include a patient experience element. SHAs are responsible for ensuring schemes adhere to the guidance. From 2011/12, PCTs will be able to withhold a significant proportion of contract payment, rising to 10 per cent over time, if providers fail to meet agreed patient satisfaction goals on a service-by-service basis.

Further information
Using the Commissioning for Quality and Innovation (CQUIN) payment framework, DH, December 2008.

Quality and Outcomes Framework

The QOF is an incentive scheme to encourage high-quality services in general practice, and was introduced as part of the new general medical services contract in 2004. It sets out a range of national standards based on the best available research evidence. The standards are divided into four domains:
- clinical standards linked to the care of patients suffering from chronic disease
- organisational standards relating to records and information, communicating with patients, education and training, medicines management and clinical and practice management
- additional services, covering cervical screening, child health surveillance, maternity services and contraceptive services
- patient experience, including assessing access to GP appointments measured by the GP patient survey.

A set of indicators – reviewed annually by NICE – has been developed for each domain to describe different aspects of performance. Practices are free to choose the domains they want to focus on and the quality standards to which they aspire. They receive payments against the indicators, which are adjusted according to list size and prevalence of disease. About 15 per cent of practice payments nationally are made through QOF.

NICE quality standards

NICE (see page 172) is developing a library of 150 quality standards to clarify the clinical evidence and guidance available to clinicians, commissioners and patients. They will be a 'final distillation' of clinical best practice, derived from the best available evidence from NICE guidance or other sources accredited by NHS Evidence (see page 226) to provide a set of specific, concise quality statements and associated measures. Produced in collaboration with health and social care professionals, each will make clear what quality care looks like, to help end variations in care quality. The first four cover stroke care, venous thromboembolism (VTE) prevention, dementia and neonatal care.

Indicators for Quality Improvement

NHS clinical teams have access via the Information Centre's website to more than 200 indicators generally accepted as effective measures of high-quality care. They can use these to assess local quality improvement. The Indicators for Quality Improvement have been selected with the Royal Colleges, and they cover ten care pathways using the three key dimensions of quality – safety, effectiveness and patient experience. Coverage will be expanded over the next two to four years, and most data will eventually appear on the NHS Choices website. The long-term aim is to build an extensive menu of indicators to help all the NHS understand and improve the quality of services.
Information Centre **www.ic.nhs.uk/mqi**

Eradicating mixed-sex accommodation

To protect patients' privacy and dignity, men and women ought not to have to share sleeping areas, bathrooms or toilets when admitted to hospital. Despite repeated initiatives, this has remained a stubborn problem in the NHS. Until recently, nearly a quarter of patients reported being in a mixed-sex sleeping area when first admitted to hospital – although 99 per cent of trusts say they have same-sex sleeping accommodation and 97 per cent have same-sex toilets and bathrooms.

In 2009 the NHS undertook a six-month intensive drive to 'all but eliminate' mixed-sex accommodation, backed by a £100 million 'privacy and dignity fund'. More than 1,157 projects were planned across 396 sites belonging to over 200 organisations for completion by mid-2010. In addition to new and refurbished same-sex sanitary facilities such as bathrooms, work included erecting separating walls, providing same-sex lounges and improved partitions, as well as implementing approved bed-management systems.

From 2010, trusts will be financially penalised for mixed-sex accommodation that is not clinically justified – for example, where a patient needs very urgent treatment, one-to-one nursing or very specialised or high-tech intensive care. But no specialty has a blanket exception. The Delivering Same-Sex Accommodation programme intends to continue 'in the coming months and years'.

Further information
Briefing 195: Delivering same-sex accommodation in mental health and learning disability services, MHN/NHS Confederation, January 2010.
Delivering same-sex accommodation progress report: the story so far, DH, December 2009.
Action to deliver same-sex accommodation: root cause analysis, National Patient Safety Agency/DH, September 2009.
Briefing 186: Same-sex accommodation: your privacy, our responsibility, NHS Confederation, June 2009.
www.dh.gov.uk/Samesexaccommodation

Patient surveys
Listening to patients' views is essential for a patient-centred health service. To deliver improvements, the NHS has to know what people need and expect from it, and how well they think the service has responded to

their needs and expectations. The programme of national patient surveys has three aims:
- to provide feedback for local quality improvement
- to assess users' experience for performance ratings, inspections and reviews
- to monitor patients' experience nationally.

The NHS national patient survey programme is the longest established and one of the largest patient survey programmes in the world: since 2002, several million patients have taken part in surveys. The Care Quality Commission (see page 171) is now responsible for carrying out national survey programmes. Surveys have included adult inpatients in acute hospitals, primary care trusts and community mental health services. For example, in 2008 a total of 72,000 adult patients from 165 acute and specialist NHS trusts took part, and 79 per cent rated their care excellent or very good.

The DH launched an annual GP patient survey in 2006. Now conducted quarterly, it is sent to 1.4 million patients from GP practices throughout England. It asks about issues such as how easy or difficult it is for patients to make an appointment, as well as satisfaction with opening hours and quality of care from their GP and practice nurses.

Each trust is required to obtain feedback from its own patients about their experiences of care. These surveys are intended to:
- track changes in patients' experience at trusts, year on year
- provide information for local quality improvement initiatives
- inform each trust's performance ratings and the performance indicators.

Trusts can seek support in carrying out their surveys from the NHS Survey Coordination Centre, run by Picker Institute Europe on behalf of the CQC, which can also help patients who are taking part in surveys.

Patients may also rate the service they received in hospital or at a GP practice using the NHS Choices website.

Further information
The key findings report for the 2008 inpatient survey, Picker Institute Europe, June 2009.
NHS Survey Co-ordination Centre **www.nhssurveys.org**
GP Patient Survey **www.gp-patient.co.uk/surveyresults**

PROMs

Assessing effectiveness of care means understanding success rates from different treatments, including clinical measures such as mortality or survival rates and measures of clinical improvement. But the patient's perspective is just as important. Patient-reported outcome measures (PROMs) are a method for collecting information on the clinical quality of care as reported by patients themselves. Since 2009 all providers of hip replacements, knee replacements, groin hernia surgery and varicose vein surgery must invite patients undergoing one of these procedures – more than 200,000 a year – to complete a pre-operative PROMs questionnaire. Some months after their operation patients are sent a follow-up questionnaire. The comparable data on their quality of life is then used to calculate a numerical value for the improvement to their health.

Further information
Guidance on the routine collection of patient reported outcome measures (PROMs), DH, December 2008.
NHS redress: statement of policy, DH, November 2005.

Spotlight on policy: Dignity in Care campaign

The Dignity in Care campaign aims to raise care standards and encourage people to become 'dignity champions', spreading best practice and giving advice to other health and social care workers. High-quality services that respect people's dignity should:
• have zero tolerance of all forms of abuse
• treat people as individuals by offering a personalised service
• enable people to exercise maximum independence, choice and control
• listen and support people to express their needs and wants
• respect people's right to privacy
• ensure people feel able to complain without fear of retribution
• engage with family members and carers as care partners
• assist people to maintain confidence and self-esteem
• act to alleviate people's loneliness and isolation.

By the beginning of 2010, 12,000 dignity champions had been recruited.

Further information
Final report on the Department of Health Dignity in Care campaign, Opinion Leader, November 2009.
www.dhcarenetworks.org.uk/dignityincare

Assessing performance

The NHS performance framework applies to all NHS trusts (but not foundation trusts) and PCTs. It is intended to support them in achieving high-quality care, identify those that are underperforming and stipulate when intervention should occur.

It is intended to be:
- transparent – clear and predetermined performance measures and interventions
- consistent – a uniform approach across England at different levels of the system and across different types of provider
- proactive – identifying underperformance early in order to address it
- proportionate – relating intervention to risk
- focused on recovery – including action to address root causes of problems.

Organisations are categorised as 'performing', 'performance under review' or 'underperforming'. An organisation that persistently underperforms or that needs more intensive support for recovery may be categorised as 'challenged'. An organisation's overall performance category is determined by its lowest score across four key domains:
- finance
- operational standards and targets
- quality and safety
- user experience.

Remedial action for providers categorised as 'performance under review' is led by the relevant PCT as commissioner, overseen by the SHA. Where organisations are deemed to be 'underperforming', SHAs lead the intervention, as they do – on the DH's behalf – for 'challenged' organisations.

The DH publishes results from the performance framework in *The Quarter*. For example, the second quarter results for 2009/10 identified 52 trusts as 'performing', 31 with 'performance under review' and seven as 'underperforming'.

The framework is closely aligned to the Care Quality Commission's 'annual health check' of NHS organisations (including foundation trusts), which rates them for the quality of their services and use of resources, for the purposes of registration (see page 174).

Monitor reports quarterly on foundation trusts, assessing their governance and financial performance as well as their progress on targets such as reducing healthcare-associated infections and achieving maximum 18-week waiting times. It assigns each a risk rating for governance and finance. For governance, a green rating indicates the trust is complying with its terms of authorisation; amber that concerns exist; and red that it may be in 'significant breach' of its terms. Financial risk is scored from 1 to 5, with 1 the highest risk of a breach in terms of authorisation. In the second quarter of 2009/10, of the then 122 foundation trusts, 70 were rated green for governance and 13 red; 11 were rated 5 for finance and two judged to be at highest risk.

Monitor can de-authorise a foundation trust where there are serious concerns that it has breached its terms of authorisation. The Secretary of State can request that Monitor triggers this process. De-authorisation results in it becoming an NHS trust and becoming directly accountable to the Secretary of State. This power was added to the Health Act 2009 after investigations at Mid Staffordshire NHS Foundation Trust found major shortcomings in its emergency care.

Further information
The Quarter: quarter 2, 2009/10, DH, December 2009.
NHS foundation trusts: review of six months to 30 September 2009, Monitor, December 2009.
Response to 'Consultation on the de-authorisation of NHS foundation trusts', DH, October 2009.
NHS performance framework: implementation guidance, DH, April 2009.
Investigation into Mid Staffordshire NHS Foundation Trust, Healthcare Commission, March 2009.

Key text: *State of care* report
The Care Quality Commission publishes an annual report to Parliament. Its first, released in February 2010, looked simultaneously across health and social care – the first time a report by an independent regulator had done so, according to the CQC. *The state of health care and adult social care in England: key themes and quality of services in 2009* applauded overall improvements in recent years but cautioned that some services were lagging behind and warned of areas of common concern across health and social care, notably keeping people safe and staff training. It concluded that rising demand and pressure on finances made reform essential.

Ensuring patient safety

The NHS's first priority is its patients' safety. No healthcare system can be entirely risk-free but it must do everything possible to minimise unintended harm, whether from healthcare-associated infections or medical accidents. Failure to do so rapidly undermines public confidence in the system.

Key organisation: Central Alerting System

The web-based Central Alerting System (CAS) distributes all patient safety alerts and related guidance to the NHS and other health and social care providers. These include emergency alerts, drug alerts, 'Dear Doctor' letters and medical device alerts issued on behalf of the Medicines and Healthcare Products Regulatory Agency, National Patient Safety Agency, and the DH. The public can access CAS, although part of the site is open only to registered NHS users.
www.cas.dh.gov.uk

Combating healthcare-associated infections

HCAIs are infections acquired in hospitals or as a result of healthcare interventions. They are caused by a wide variety of micro-organisms, often by bacteria that normally live harmlessly in or on the body. While HCAIs are most likely to be acquired during treatment in acute hospitals, they can also occur in GP surgeries, care homes, mental health trusts, ambulances and at home. They can have severe consequences for patients as well as costs for the NHS. An HCAI adds on average three to ten days to a patient's stay in hospital and costs between £4,000 and £10,000 to treat.

HCAIs are a worldwide problem. Since the mid-1980s, prevalence in hospitals worldwide has been 5 to 10 per cent; in England it had reached 8.2 per cent by 2004. For most patients, the risk of acquiring an infection is low (one case per 1,450 admissions for MRSA), and lower still for those who spend only one or two days in hospital.

Despite overall prevalence of HCAI remaining relatively constant during the last 25 years, the organisms themselves have changed, with new strains developing and others being controlled. The NHS faces particular problems with MRSA and C. *difficile*. MRSA can infect surgical wounds and ulcers, and if it enters the bloodstream cause chest infections. It is usually spread through skin-to-skin contact, or by touching materials and surfaces contaminated from someone infected with MRSA. Measures such as hand washing and using alcohol handrub can help reduce the spread, as can isolating infected patients.

Toxins released by C. *difficile* cause diarrhoea, which can be severe and life-threatening. In most cases, the infection develops after cross-infection from another patient. Over 80 per cent of cases occur in people aged over 65. Alcohol handrubs are ineffective for C. *difficile*. Isolation of infected patients coupled with thorough hand-washing before and after contact, use of gloves and aprons and cleaning the ward are usually successful in prevention and control.

The DH introduced a target to reduce MRSA across all NHS trusts by 50 per cent by 2008 and C. *difficile* by 30 per cent by 2010/11. By 2008, MRSA had been reduced by 57 per cent and C. *difficile* by 41 per cent. By the end of 2009, MRSA had been reduced by 76 per cent nationally.

Although a quarter of trusts reduced MRSA by more than 80 per cent, in 12 per cent of trusts MRSA infections increased. C. *difficile* was reduced by more than 50 per cent in 29 per cent of trusts, but it increased in 19 per cent.

The NHS has two national targets to reduce HCAIs:
• maintaining the annual number of MRSA bloodstream infections at less than half the 2003/04 number; from 2010, organisations worse than the median are required to reduce rates to the median or by 20 per cent, whichever is greater
• reducing the number of C. *difficile* cases by 30 per cent nationally by 2011 compared to 2007/08; a new minimum standard to come into force from April 2011 is pending.

Nationally the total number of MRSA cases reported for July to September 2009 was 465, mostly in people aged 65–70. The total number of C. *difficile* cases was 6,423, of which 3,100 occurred in trusts.

The DH's HCAI and cleanliness strategy involves a wide range of measures to tackle HCAI, including:
• investing £270 million a year in infection prevention and control and improving cleanliness
• encouraging hospitals to employ two infection control nurses, two isolation nurses and an anti-microbial pharmacist

- all non-emergency patients admitted to hospital are now screened for MRSA, and all emergency patients will be screened by 2011
- annual infection control inspections of all acute trusts by specialist inspectors
- a bare-below-the-elbows dress code for hospital staff
- a deep clean for every hospital (completed March 2008)
- a hygiene code contained in the Health Act 2006, stipulating that all trusts must establish appropriate systems, assess and manage risks, implement clinical care protocols, ensure healthcare workers' access to occupational health services and provide induction and training
- giving matrons powers to report safety concerns direct to the Care Quality Commission
- a National Patient Safety Forum to set the agenda and check progress
- patient safety action teams in all strategic health authorities
- a patient safety charter agreed and signed by over 20 organisations
- a national 'cleanyourhands' campaign run by the NPSA since 2004, to which every acute trust has signed up and now extended to primary care, mental health, ambulance trusts and the independent sector.

An HCAI technology programme has been designed to accelerate development and adoption of new technologies to help fight infection. It includes the Showcase Hospitals scheme, comprising seven hospitals that trial innovative products to reduce and prevent HCAI. As part of a Design Bugs Out project, designers have been challenged to devise new furniture, equipment and services for hospital wards that will enhance cleanliness. In addition, the Health Protection Agency (see page 62) supports a range of activities related to identifying, investigating, monitoring and managing HCAIs. However, the Care Quality Commission noted in its annual performance ratings for 2008/09 that 48 acute trusts failed to meet at least one infection control standard compared to 44 the previous year.

Further information
The Health and Social Care Act 2008: code of practice for health and adult social care on the prevention and control of infections and related guidance, DH, December 2009.
The Government response to the health select committee report 'Patient safety', TSO, October 2009.
Sixth report of session 2008–09: Patient safety, House of Commons health committee, July 2009.
Reducing healthcare associated infections in hospitals in England, NAO, June 2009.
www.clean-safe-care.nhs.uk

An organisation with a memory
Compiled by an expert group led by the chief medical officer (CMO) and published in June 2000, this recommended a mandatory reporting scheme for adverse healthcare events and near-misses. It set out to encourage a reporting and questioning culture in the NHS to replace blame with a proper understanding of the underlying causes of failures.

Winning ways
Launched by the CMO in December 2003, this required chief executives to ensure that infection control teams work with bed managers to optimise bed use, while implementing procedures to minimise the risk of infection.

Safety first – a report for patients, clinicians and healthcare managers
Commissioned by the CMO and published in December 2006, this updates progress since *An organisation with a memory* and says more remains to be done to ensure patient safety. Its recommendations include a patient safety forum, refocusing the National Patient Safety Agency's role, setting up local patient safety action teams and ensuring national priorities take explicit account of patient safety from 2008.

Being open: communicating patient safety incidents with patients, their families and carers
Published in November 2009 by the NPSA's National Reporting and Learning Service, this best-practice guide outlines ten principles healthcare staff should use when communicating with patients and their families after a patient safety incident in which the patient was harmed. It supports a culture of openness, honesty and transparency, and includes apologising and explaining what happened.

Key organisation: National Patient Safety Agency
NPSA is responsible for promoting patient safety throughout the UK
wherever the NHS provides care. NHS staff anonymously report incidents
that did or could have affected patient safety to NPSA.

NPSA has three divisions:

- **National Reporting and Learning Service (NRLS)** – collects, analyses and
  prioritises data on patient safety incidents in the NHS, making
  recommendations to reduce risk. In the year to June 2009, there were
  945,518 incidents reported in England, most causing no harm but 3,735
  reported to have caused death. From 2010 it will be mandatory for all
  trusts in England to report patient safety incidents, and the information
  will be shared with the Care Quality Commission as part of the registration
  system. By 2012 the ruling will also cover all independent providers.
- **National Clinical Assessment Service (NCAS)** – provides confidential
  advice and support where the performance of doctors and dentists is
  causing concern. Employing organisations, managers or practitioners
  themselves can contact NCAS for advice. The service also covers the
  independent sector.
- **National Research Ethics Service (NRES)** – promotes ethical research to
  maintain a review system that protects the safety, dignity and well-being
  of research participants. It provides support for research ethics
  committees that assess and oversee research projects.

NPSA commissions and monitors the three national confidential inquiries
into patient outcome and death, maternal and child health, and suicide
and homicide by mentally ill people.

Further information
Large scale workforce change: Briefing 51: Improving patient safety and information
governance, NHS Employers, November 2008.
Briefing 161: Act on reporting: five actions to improve patient safety reporting, NHS
Confederation/NPSA, June 2008.
www.npsa.nhs.uk

Reforming clinical negligence procedures

Although the NHS provides high-quality healthcare for millions of people every year, occasionally patients do not receive the treatment they should, or mistakes are made. In the UK and other developed countries, about 10 per cent of hospital admissions may result in some kind of adverse event, and a third of these patients will suffer severe illness or die. In NHS primary care, research suggests about 600 errors a day occur, mainly in diagnosis and treatment, of which a fifth will cause harm.

Anyone who suffers harm as a result of treatment must receive an apology, a clear explanation of what went wrong, proper treatment and care and, where appropriate, financial compensation. The NHS must ensure it learns from such experiences.

But legal proceedings for medical injury are slow, complex and costly. They divert clinical staff from providing care, and can damage morale as well as public confidence. The system encourages defensiveness and secrecy, which hampers the NHS from learning and improvement. The NHS Redress Act 2006 – yet to be implemented – provides an alternative to litigation for less severe cases, aimed at shifting emphasis from attributing blame towards preventing harm, reducing risks and learning from mistakes. It does not fundamentally alter the existing legal system but provides an additional mechanism.

The intention is that the scheme would deal with less costly claims, avoiding the courts altogether. Compensation would be roughly equal to what a court might order but a patient accepting compensation under the scheme would be barred from taking legal proceedings. The Act applies only to NHS hospital care and excludes GP practices, dental surgeries and private healthcare. The NHS Litigation Authority would decide liability and compensation, as well as instituting and investigating claims. The scheme does not include an appeals process, but if a patient was dissatisfied with the outcome, they could begin legal proceedings.

However, in 2009 ministers said the scheme could only be enacted through secondary legislation, and would require extensive consultation before draft proposals could be brought before Parliament. They preferred to focus on reforming the complaints system (see page 166), which they said would allow the same principles to be applied across a wider number of cases, but once this was established they would consider implementing the redress scheme.

The Act applies to England and contains framework powers for Wales only. The scheme cannot apply in Scotland or Northern Ireland. The Welsh Assembly Government has consulted on proposals with a view to implementing a redress scheme in 2010. The Scottish Government is investigating the introduction of a no-fault compensation scheme.

Further information

NHS redress: statement of policy, DH, November 2005.
NHS redress: improving the response to patients, DH, October 2005.

Spotlight on policy: 'Never events'

'Never events' are serious and largely preventable patient safety incidents. Originally a US concept, they were highlighted by the Next Stage Review (see page 127) as another way for the NHS to raise quality. The NPSA drew up a list of never events for the NHS:
- wrong-site surgery
- retained instrument post-operation
- wrong route administration of chemotherapy
- misplaced naso or orogastric tube not detected before use
- inpatient suicide using non-collapsible rails or while on one-to-one observation
- transferred prisoners absconding from medium or high-secure mental health services
- in-hospital maternal death from post-partum haemorrhage after elective caesarean
- intravenous administration of mis-selected concentrated potassium chloride.

PCTs must monitor their occurrence in services they commission, reporting them to the NPSA and to the public. From 2010, PCTs will not pay providers where treatment results in a never event. The NPSA is consulting on whether more ought to be added to the list.

Further information

Never events framework 2009/10: process and action for primary care trusts, NRLS/NPSA, February 2009.

Key organisation: NHS Litigation Authority

NHSLA, set up in 1995, handles negligence claims against NHS bodies in England, and operates a risk management programme to help raise standards and reduce incidents leading to claims. It also monitors human rights case law and coordinates equal-pay claims on the NHS's behalf.

In 2008/09 NHSLA received 6,088 claims for clinical negligence and paid out £807 million in damages and costs. At March 2009 it had 17,899 live claims. Fewer than 50 clinical negligence cases a year are contested in court, and 96 per cent of the NHSLA's cases are settled out of court. Claims are settled on average in a year and a half. Of all clinical claims handled since 1997:
• 41 per cent were abandoned by the claimant
• 42 per cent were settled out of court
• 4 per cent were settled in court
• 13 per cent are outstanding.
www.nhsla.com

06 Accountability and regulation

Primary care trusts and NHS trusts are accountable outwards to their local communities and upwards through their strategic health authority to the Department of Health, which in turn is accountable through its ministers to Parliament and the electorate. Foundation trusts are also accountable to their local communities (with local members and governors forming an integral part of their governance structure) and to Parliament and the electorate, but not to SHAs or directly to the DH. Foundation trusts are also accountable to the independent regulator, Monitor. Primary care trusts are soon to have directly elected members on their boards.

NHS organisations must demonstrate strategic and operational accountability: they must have a clear and well-evidenced long-term plan, and show transparency in their day-to-day decisions. They are accountable to local people who are consumers of their services and taxpayers who fund the NHS: therefore, they have a duty to maintain the highest standards of quality and safety, as well as to balance the books and provide value for money.

NHS organisations are immediately accountable to independently appointed boards, and they have a duty to involve and consult patients and the public. They can also be called to account by their local authority, and must answer to a variety of national regulators and inspectorates. The healthcare professions too are subject to their own regulatory bodies.

The role of boards

Duties and responsibilities
NHS boards' roles and responsibilities are broadly the same throughout the UK. They take corporate responsibility for their organisation's strategies and actions. With current policy emphasis on decentralisation, local leadership and autonomy, their role is more important than ever.

Boards generally consist of five executives (including the chief executive and finance director) and five non-executives plus a chair. The chair and non-executives are lay people drawn from the local community, and are accountable to the Secretary of State.

A board's role is:
• formulating the organisation's strategy
• holding the organisation to account for achieving the strategy and ensuring that systems of control are robust and reliable
• shaping a positive culture for the board and the organisation.

An effective board:
- is informed by the external context in which it operates
- is informed by and shapes information about the organisation's performance, as well as local people's needs and the market
- builds a healthy dialogue with patients, public and staff, and feels accountable to all of them.

Legally, there is no distinction between the board duties of executive and non-executive directors: they both share responsibility for the organisation's direction and control. The board is expected to bring about change by making best use of all its resources – financial, staffing, physical infrastructure and knowledge – and working with staff and partner organisations to meet the public's and patients' expectations. As leaders, board members are expected to understand opportunities for improving services and motivate others to bring them about.

Boards make plans to achieve the Government's objectives for healthcare, guided by long-term strategy and shorter-term aims such as the NHS's operating framework. Boards have increasing scope to pace their plans to reflect local circumstances, and have a large say over how to achieve them – in theory at least. All boards sign off an annual business plan setting out the year's objectives, and it is the whole board's function to ensure progress.

NHS boards are obliged to ensure their organisations have an ethos and culture of public service that reflects and respects public expectation. The need for accountability means boards must conduct business in an open and transparent way that commands public confidence. Boards have different ways of ensuring this transparency and accountability, and ensuring that they command the confidence of their key stakeholders, including the local community.

Trust boards should be more challenging of the information they receive, according to the Audit Commission, which examined how boards assured themselves that internal controls were in place and operating effectively. It found 'significant gaps' between the processes on paper and the rigour with which they were applied. Data received by boards was not always relevant, timely or fit for purpose. Board members should understand, question and assess risk on an informed and ongoing basis, the Commission said.

On rare occasions it is necessary to remove a chair or non-executive from their post if they prove unable to meet the requirements of public office. In a foundation trust, the board of governors has the power to remove the chair or non-executive directors, and Monitor can intervene to remove a chair, non-executive or executive director. In NHS trusts, the Secretary of State may suspend a chair while an investigation takes place.

Further information
The healthy NHS board: principles for good governance, National Leadership Centre, February 2010.
Taking it on trust: a review of how boards of NHS trusts and foundation trusts get their assurance, Audit Commission, April 2009.
Reputation management: a guide for boards, NHS Confederation, February 2009.
Adding value to a 21st century health service: a review of the NHS public appointments process, Appointments Commission, November 2007.
Codes of conduct and accountability for NHS boards, Appointments Commission/DH, July 2004.

The chair
The chair's role is to:
- ensure the board develops a vision, strategies and clear objectives to deliver organisational purpose
- hold the chief executive to account for achieving the strategy
- ensure board committees that support accountability are properly constituted
- provide visible leadership in developing a positive culture for the organisation, and ensure this is reflected and modelled in their own and the board's behaviour and decision-making
- lead and support a constructive dynamic within the board, enabling contributions from all directors
- provide a safe point of access to the board for whistle-blowers
- ensure all board members are well briefed on the organisation's external context
- ensure requirements for accurate, timely and clear information to the board directors (and for foundation trusts, governors) are clear
- play a key role as an ambassador and build strong partnerships with patients and public; clinicians and staff; key institutional stakeholders and regulators (and for foundation trusts, members and governors).

In general, a strong correlation exists between the quality of the chair's and chief executive's leadership and the organisation's success. Where an organisation is not delivering, questions can legitimately be asked about the quality of the board leadership.

Non-executive directors

Non-executive directors should:
- bring independence, external skills and perspectives to strategy development
- hold executives to account for achieving the strategy
- offer purposeful, constructive scrutiny and challenge
- chair or participate as members of key committees that support accountability
- actively support and promote a positive culture for the organisation and reflect this in their own behaviour
- provide a safe point of access to the board for whistle-blowers
- satisfy themselves of the integrity of financial and quality intelligence
- ensure the board acts in the best interests of the public
- ensure a senior independent director is available to members (and in foundation trusts, governors) if there are unresolved concerns.

There are about 3,000 chairs and non-executives in NHS organisations in England, excluding foundation trusts. During 2008/09, 767 appointments and re-appointments were made to local NHS bodies, and 332 to national health and social care bodies. Women make up 33.7 per cent of appointments to local NHS bodies, while people from black and minority ethnic groups account for 11.7 per cent.

Remuneration for chairs and non-executives

	Chairs	Non executives	Audit committee chairs
Strategic health authorities	£42,033–£63,049	£7,882	£13,136
Primary care trusts	£31,525–£42,033	£7,882	£13,136
NHS trusts	£18,437–£23,366	£6,096	£6,096

Source: Appointments Commission

Non-executives work two-and-a-half days a month, while chairs are expected to work three to three-and-a-half days a week.

In foundation trusts, the rates for chairs and non-executives are set by the trust's own remuneration committee, which comprises elected and appointed governors.

Further information
Are there any women on board? A review of recruiting and retaining women in public appointments in 2009, Appointments Commission, 2009.

The chief executive
The chief executive is responsible for ensuring the board is empowered to govern the organisation and its objectives are accomplished through effective and properly controlled executive action. A chief executive's main responsibilities are:
• leading strategy development
• leading the organisation in achieving the strategy
• establishing effective performance management arrangements and controls
• acting as the organisation's accountable officer
• providing visible leadership in developing a positive culture for the organisation, and ensuring this is reflected in their own and the executive's behaviour and decision-making
• ensuring all board members are well briefed on the organisation's external context
• ensuring provision of accurate, timely and clear information to board directors (and in foundation trusts, governors)
• playing a key role as an ambassador and building strong partnerships with patients and public; for foundation trusts, members and governors; clinicians and staff; key institutional stakeholders and regulators.

Board committees
NHS boards may delegate some of their powers to formally constituted committees. Some are set up to advise the board on a permanent basis, such as the:
• audit committee
• remuneration and terms of service committee
• clinical governance committee
• risk management committee.

PCT boards and PECs

Like other NHS organisations, PCTs are overseen by a board consisting of a lay chair and a majority of non-executives, although they must include a director of public health. The coalition Government plans to introduce elections for some posts on PCT boards. In addition, to reflect the importance of clinical leadership in PCTs, each has a professional executive committee (PEC), which may include GPs, nurses, social workers, allied health professionals, dentists, pharmacists, optometrists and consultants; clinicians must be in a majority but PECs should not be dominated by one professional group. Since 2007 PCTs have been free to decide how many members their PEC has and how much it pays them, based on guiding principles from the DH. PECs are responsible for guiding the PCT board through detailed thinking on priorities, service policies and investment plans.

Further information
Fit for the future, DH, March 2007.

Foundation trust boards

Foundation trusts have distinctive governance arrangements which reflect their independence from central government control. Staff, patients and local people can join the foundation trust and become members. Membership entitles them to vote at elections for the board of governors and to stand for election to the board. According to Monitor, foundation trusts had recruited over 1.5 million members by the end of 2009 and there are over 3,800 governors.

The board of governors includes those elected by the trust members and staff, as well as people appointed by PCTs, local councils and other local stakeholders. Governors elected by patients and the public must be in the majority, while at least three governors must be elected by staff. The statutory duties of the board of governors are to:
- appoint, reappoint and if appropriate, remove the chair or non-executive directors
- decide the remuneration, allowances and terms and conditions of office of the chair and non-executive directors
- approve the appointment of the chief executive
- appoint, reappoint or remove the trust's auditor
- receive the trust's annual accounts, auditors' report and annual report
- provide feedback to the board of directors on the content of the forward plan.

Each foundation trust has a board of directors made up of non-executives appointed by the governors and executive directors appointed by the non-executives. The board of directors leads the organisation, sets its strategy and ensures its delivery. The board of governors ensures that the voice of the community is heard, and holds the chair to account for the effectiveness of foundation trust performance.

Further information
Developing the role of NHS foundation trust governors, Monitor, June 2008.
Membership governance in NHS foundation trusts: a review for the Department of Health, University of Birmingham/Mutuo, March 2008.
New voices, new accountabilities: a guide to foundation trust wider governance, Foundation Trust Network, August 2005.

Key organisation: Appointments Commission
The Appointments Commission specialises in finding people for board-level public appointments to the NHS and other public bodies in England. It recruits through advertising campaigns in national and local papers. Short-listed candidates are interviewed by panels that include an independent assessor.

The Commission's role is to:
• manage recruitment, selection and appointment of chairs and non-executives
• provide year-long induction training
• set minimum standards and advise on appraisal
• promote good governance through advice, guidance and policy development
• support and advise chairs through regionally based commissioners.

The Commission was set up in 2001 and employs 60 people based in Leeds. It aims to ensure all appointments are made on merit and follow an open, fair and impartial process. Before it existed, health ministers were responsible for appointing all non-executive directors. The Commission's board meets monthly to consider panel recommendations and make appointments. It is directly accountable to the Department of Health.
www.appointments.org.uk

Engaging patients and the public

Engaging patients and the public in health services can be interpreted in different ways.

- Individual patients may be involved together with health professionals in making decisions about their own care.
- Organisations may seek direct feedback from patients about their experiences of using services: patient experience is now one of the three measures of quality – along with safety and effectiveness – against which services are judged, and part of the payment-by-results tariff (see page 192) is linked to it.
- Users of a particular service may be involved as a group in advising how it might be improved: world-class commissioning emphasises the importance of using patient feedback to design better services.
- Members of the public may be involved in making strategic decisions about how or where services are to be provided, and about future priorities.

Empowering both individuals and communities to play a greater role in shaping health and social care services has become a central aim of policy: not only have people said they want more influence over these services, but it can help organisations provide a better service if they understand what patients and the local community want and their experience of using services. It also strengthens accountability, and helps build a relationship of confidence and trust between the NHS and the people it serves.

Since the NHS Plan of 2000, the health service has had an explicit duty to ensure patients and the public have a real say in how services are planned and developed. The NHS Act 2006 places a duty on strategic health authorities, primary care trusts, NHS trusts and foundation trusts to 'involve and consult' patients and the public. They were already required by law to consult on substantial variations and developments to services; under the Act, they must arrange to involve and consult patients and the public in:

- planning and provision of services they are responsible for
- developing and considering proposals for changes in the way those services are provided
- decisions to be made that affect how those services operate.

Under the Local Government and Public Involvement in Health Act 2007, strategic health authorities, PCTs, NHS trusts and foundation trusts have a strengthened duty to involve service users or their representatives. This came into force in 2008. In addition, from 2010 a new 'duty to report on consultation' applies to PCTs and SHAs, requiring them to report on how people's views have shaped the decisions they make when commissioning services. All NHS trusts, foundation trusts and PCTs will have to prepare a 'statement of involvement' from September 2011.

The NHS Constitution establishes as an underlying principle that the health service will involve individual patients and the wider community, and be accountable to the public, communities and patients. It includes specific rights for patients to be involved in discussions and decisions about their healthcare, in planning healthcare services and in decisions about proposed changes and how services are run. The NHS also pledges to provide the information needed to enable this to happen.

PCTs are also expected to 'proactively seek and build continuous and meaningful engagement with the public and patients to shape services and improve health' as part of the world-class commissioning assurance framework (see page 40). Comprehensive area assessments (see page 54) add further impetus to effective engagement by judging how people are served by their local public services and how these address the local community's priorities – as well as by directly assessing whether organisations have met their duty to consult.

All this means discussing with patients and the public their ideas, the organisation's plans, patients' experiences, why services need to change, what people want from services and how to make best use of resources. Boards must consider patient and public engagement (PPE) issues on their agendas, include among their membership an individual to champion these issues and designate a staff member responsible for the activity. They must commit resources to PPE, and ensure all staff are trained in it.

Since the NHS Plan, every trust has had to obtain feedback from patients about their experiences of care. Information from patient surveys is used in assessing trusts' performance. Many acute trusts and other service providers are seeking direct patient feedback, including 'real-time' feedback, to improve their understanding of people's experiences of care. A DH report reviewing lessons from the investigation into Mid Staffordshire NHS Foundation Trust emphasises that organisations should take note of early, 'soft' and informal information that reveals consistent concerns from patients and the public.

Since 2008, new PPE bodies, local involvement networks, have been established in every PCT/local social care authority (see LINks below). In addition, local authority overview and scrutiny committees (see page 175) are intended to ensure elected councillors have a say in the NHS in their area, while the public can become members of foundation trusts and elect representatives to the board of governors (see page 159).

Further information
The heart of the matter: patient and public engagement in today's NHS, NHS Confederation, February 2010.
Real accountability: demonstrating responsiveness and accountability – guidance on the NHS duty to report on consultation, DH, November 2009.
Putting people at the heart of care: the vision for public and patient experience and engagement in health and social care, DH, September 2009.
Helping the NHS put patients at the heart of care: the patient and public engagement support programme 2009–10, DH September 2009.
Understanding what matters: a guide to using patient feedback to transform services, DH, May 2009.
Mid Staffordshire NHS Foundation Trust: a review of lessons learnt for commissioners and performance managers following the Healthcare Commission investigation, Dr David Colin-Thomé, DH, April 2009.

Local Involvement Networks (LINks)
In 2008, LINks replaced 400 patient and public involvement forums (PPIFs) as the main vehicles for involving patients and the public in the NHS. Unlike PPIFs, the 150 LINks cover all publicly funded health and social care services in a local authority area, irrespective of who provides them. They have the power to investigate concerns, demand information, enter and view services, make reports and recommendations and refer issues to local councillors on overview and scrutiny committees (see page 175) – which have the power to summon NHS managers.

LINks are made up of individuals, groups and organisations – such as voluntary organisations, community groups, faith groups, residents' associations and youth councils – with an interest in local services, although they do not have to adopt a particular structure. They:
• help commissioners understand the services people want to receive
• monitor services
• provide a means for the NHS and social care to reach out to their communities and seek their views.

Membership of a LINk

Youth councils
Individuals
Foundation trust governors
Tenants' groups
Minority ethnic groups
Patients' groups
Faith groups
Neighbourhood renewal networks   LINks
Carers' networks
Patient transport groups
Local business groups
Older people's forums
Self-advocacy groups
Support groups for specific service users

Source: Department of Health

Each LINk is supported and guided by a host organisation contracted by the local authority. The Labour Government earmarked £84 million over three years for setting up LINks, most of which is going to local authorities. The DH has urged health and care professionals to promote participation in LINks among users, and to regard LINks as a 'vital service planning and delivery tool'.

Before the advent of PPIFs in 2003, community health councils acted as patient and public representatives in England. These continue in Wales with new powers. NHSScotland has replaced its local health councils with a single Scottish Health Council that has local offices in each board area, while Northern Ireland has replaced its four health and social service councils with a single Patient and Client Council.

Further information
Listening and responding to communities: a brief guide to local involvement networks, DH, September 2008.
What you said: response to the consultation on regulations for local involvement networks (LINks), DH, August 2008.
The LINks Exchange **www.lx.nhs.uk**
www.nhs.uk/links

Human rights and healthcare

Human rights are based on the 'FREDA' values of fairness, respect, equality, dignity and autonomy. The Government has incorporated into UK law most of the rights defined in the European Convention through the Human Rights Act 1998. This was intended to bring about a culture of human rights in public services. Putting human rights at the heart of how health services are designed and delivered can improve experience and outcomes for patients and staff. It also supports aspirations for a personalised service.

The Act provides a framework that can help NHS organisations ensure individuals receive fair, dignified and equitable treatment. Of the 15 rights defined in the Act, most relevant to healthcare are the rights:
• not to be treated in an inhuman or degrading way
• to respect for private and family life, home and correspondence
• to liberty and the right to life
• not to be discriminated against.

Examples of human rights issues in practice include 'do not resuscitate' orders, unsanitary conditions, excessive force in restraint, staff disciplinary procedures, privacy on wards and family visits. NHS organisations can take a human rights-based approach by ensuring accountability and empowerment, by encouraging participation and involvement and by paying attention to vulnerable groups, ensuring they are not discriminated against.

Further information
Human rights in healthcare – a short introduction, DH, October 2008.
Human rights in healthcare – a framework for local action, DH, October 2008.
Equality and human rights in the NHS: a guide for NHS boards, Appointments Commission/DH, April 2007.

Patient advice and liaison services

Every NHS trust and PCT should have a patient advice and liaison service (PALS) providing on-the-spot help and information about health services. PALS aim to:

- resolve concerns before they become major problems
- provide information to patients, carers and their families about local health services and put people in contact with local support groups
- tell people about the complaints procedure and independent complaints advocacy support
- act as an early-warning system by monitoring trends, highlighting gaps in service and making reports for action to trust managers.

The National PALS Network aims to promote PALS and support the professional development of PALS staff, as well as acting as a national voice for the service.

Further information

National evaluation of PALS: briefing for chief executives, University of the West of England/DH, September 2006.
www.pals.nhs.uk

Complaints

Reforming complaints procedures

Since 2009, a single complaints system has existed for all health and local authority adult social care services in England. The new unified arrangements aim to:

- resolve complaints locally in a more personal and flexible way
- ensure early and effective resolution and robust handling of all cases, not just the more complex
- make sure people with complaints have access to effective support, particularly those who find it difficult to make their views heard
- give people the option of going direct to their PCT with a complaint about their GP, NHS dentist or pharmacist instead of complaining directly to the practice
- give people the option of going direct to their local authority where their care has been arranged by the local authority
- ensure organisations improve services by routinely learning from people's experiences.

Kennedy Report

The inquiry into the deaths of child heart patients at Bristol Royal Infirmary between 1984 and 1995 was chaired by Professor Sir Ian Kennedy and made many important recommendations for change in the NHS, not least that there should be representation of patient interests on the inside of the NHS and at every level. The inquiry ran from 1998 to 2001, and its report was published in 2001.

www.bristol-inquiry.org.uk

Francis Report

Robert Francis QC's independent inquiry into failures in patient care at Mid Staffordshire NHS Foundation Trust between 2005 and 2009 made 18 recommendations, all of which the Labour Government accepted when his report was published in February 2010. Among the shortcomings he found were:

- corporate focus on process at the expense of outcomes
- failure to listen to patients by properly considering their complaints
- staff disengaged from management
- insufficient attention to professional standards
- lack of support for staff through appraisal, supervision and professional development
- weak professional voice in management decisions
- some treatment of elderly patients tantamount to abuse of vulnerable people
- lack of external and internal transparency
- false reassurance taken from external assessments
- disregard for the significance of mortality statistics.

Key recommendations included:

- reviewing arrangements for the appointment, training, support and accountability of trust executive and non-executive directors
- setting up a working group to examine methodologies for compiling mortality statistics
- a further inquiry into why the commissioning, supervisory and regulatory bodies did not detect the trust's failings earlier.

The range of measures available locally to resolve complaints include:

- robust risk assessment to deal quickly with serious complaints, such as those involving abuse or unsafe practice
- a plan, agreed by the complainant, outlining how the complaint is going to be tackled, who will be involved and their roles, timescales and how the complainant will be kept informed of progress
- involvement of the most senior managers or clinicians at an early stage where appropriate
- early face-to-face meetings between everyone concerned to make sure the circumstances giving rise to the complaint are clearly understood
- independent mediators when the relationship between the complainant and the NHS body has broken down
- people independent of the service provider, commissioning organisation or the locality to investigate where complaints cannot be resolved satisfactorily or complex issues are involved
- specialist advocates to help people with complex needs voice their complaint effectively and understand the organisation's response
- clear, effective leadership from the most senior managers to ensure complaints arrangements meet people's needs and services are improved as a result.

Local organisations must make every effort to resolve the complaint, but if complainants are dissatisfied with the local response they may go directly to the Ombudsman (see page 173).

In 2008/09, NHS trusts received 89,139 complaints, a 2 per cent increase on the previous year; 73 per cent were resolved within 25 days. Complaints included:

- 37,149 about aspects of clinical treatment
- 12,102 about delays and cancellations of appointments
- 11,332 about the attitude of staff.

Complaints about primary care totalled 48,597, an 11 per cent increase on the previous year.

Further information
Briefing 178: A new complaints procedure for health and social care, NHS Confederation, March 2009.

Independent Complaints Advocacy Services (ICAS)

ICAS are available across the country to help individuals pursue complaints about the NHS. Complainants can contact their local ICAS office direct, or through complaints managers at hospitals, PCTs and GP practices, NHS Direct or the patient advice and liaison service. ICAS aims to ensure complainants have access to the support they need to articulate their concerns and navigate the complaints system. It can simply offer advice or write letters and attend meetings to speak on the complainant's behalf. Since 2006 three independent organisations with experience of advocacy have delivered ICAS under contract across England.

Spotlight on policy: Freedom of information (FOI)

The Freedom of Information Act 2000 requires every public authority to adopt a 'publication scheme' that specifies the classes of information the authority publishes, the form it takes and whether it charges for the information. Each scheme must be approved by the Information Commissioner, an independent public official responsible for overseeing operation of the Act, who also has powers of enforcement.

Since January 2005, NHS organisations must answer requests for information within the terms of the individual right of access given by the Act. This applies to all types of recorded information held by the organisation regardless of its date, although the Act specifies some exemptions – such as information where the patient is identifiable. Anyone making a request must be told whether the organisation holds the information and, if so, be supplied with it – generally within 20 working days. Organisations also have a duty to provide advice or help to anyone seeking information. Where a request for information is denied, it may be possible to appeal against the decision.

In 2008, NHS organisations received an average of 173 FOI requests, with the largest number coming from journalists.

Further information

Briefing 180: Freedom of information in the NHS, NHS Confederation, June 2009.
Freedom of Information publication scheme – guide to information, DH, December 2008.
Information Commissioner **www.ico.gov.uk**

Regulation and inspection

NHS organisations and the healthcare professions are all subject to stringent regulation, audit and inspection to ensure they maintain high service standards and provide value for money.

The regulators

Many national bodies are responsible for regulating, auditing and inspecting various aspects of NHS services – some long-established, others more recent. This has led to NHS organisations feeling overburdened by the demands of different regulatory authorities, in particular preparing for numerous inspections by different bodies and dealing with broadly similar information requests in different formats or covering different time periods. At the peak of this trend, the NHS Confederation identified more than 50 bodies inspecting trusts.

In response the Labour Government pledged to reduce the number and improve the coordination of data requests to those on the front line of healthcare. In 2007, it set a target to reduce the data burden from central departments on frontline staff by 30 per cent by 2010. By December 2009 it had achieved a 23.6 per cent decrease. The Information Centre (see page 245) is pursuing further initiatives to streamline data collection requests. In 2009 the Care Quality Commission replaced the Healthcare Commission, Commission for Social Care Inspection and Mental Health Act Commission, to provide 'joined-up' regulation of health and social care for the first time. The CQC works with other regulators to improve coordination of regulation through collaborative reviews. It also has specific 'gatekeeping' powers to reduce duplication.

There are different regulators for Scotland (NHS Quality Improvement Scotland, see page 251), Wales (Health Inspectorate Wales, see page 283) and Northern Ireland (Regulation and Quality Improvement Authority, see page 294).

Further information

Simplification plan: year four, DH, December 2009.
What's it all for? Removing unnecessary bureaucracy in regulation, Independent Healthcare Advisory Service/NHS Confederation, June 2009.
Review of health and social care burdens final report – recommendations, Lifting the Burdens Taskforce/Local Government Association, September 2008.
The bureaucratic burden in the NHS, NHS Confederation, March 2007.

The following are among the major national bodies regulating and inspecting the NHS:

Care Quality Commission
Operating since April 2009, the CQC regulates health and adult social care services, whether provided by the NHS, local authorities, private companies or voluntary organisations. Its functions are:
- registering health and adult social care providers to ensure they meet essential common safety and quality standards
- monitoring and inspecting all health and adult social care, including how the Mental Health Act is working
- using enforcement powers, such as fines, public warnings or closures, if standards are not met
- assessing commissioners' and providers' performance, and carrying out special reviews of particular services, pathways of care or themes where concerns about quality exist
- reporting the outcomes of its work to the public and professionals.

Since 2010, health and adult social care providers must register with the CQC in order to provide services (see page 174).

The CQC's performance ratings (see page 175) assess NHS trusts and PCTs against core standards, national priorities, financial management and their use of the Mental Health Act and Mental Capacity Act. Commissioners are judged using the world-class commissioning assurance system and 'vital signs' indicators. In 2008/09 the CQC rated:
- 15 per cent excellent
- 47 per cent good
- 33 per cent fair
- 5 per cent weak.

The coalition Government has said it will strengthen the CQC's role.

Further information
Our strategy for 2010–2015, CQC, February 2010.
www.cqc.org.uk

Monitor

Established in 2004, Monitor authorises and regulates foundation trusts. It receives and considers applications from NHS trusts, and if they meet its criteria, grants them foundation status. It then monitors their activities to ensure they comply with their terms of authorisation. Monitor has power to intervene in the running of a foundation trust in the event of failings in its healthcare governance or financial performance, or other aspects of its activities. Ultimately it can de-authorise a foundation trust. It is independent of Government and accountable to Parliament. The coalition Government intends to develop Monitor into an 'economic regulator' overseeing 'aspects of access, competition and price-setting in the NHS. www.monitor-nhsft.gov.uk

National Institute for Health and Clinical Excellence (NICE)

Set up in 1999, NICE provides guidance in three areas:
• public health – promotion of good health and the prevention of ill health for those working in the NHS, local authorities and the wider public and voluntary sector
• health technologies – the use of new and existing medicines, treatments and procedures within the NHS
• clinical practice – the appropriate treatment and care of people with specific diseases and conditions within the NHS.

The DH commissions NICE to examine specific topics, which may be suggested by patients, the public, health professionals or the national clinical directors. Health professionals and the NHS are expected to take NICE guidance fully into account, although it does not override their responsibility to make appropriate decisions based on individual patients' circumstances. Local government and NHS organisations must take account of NICE public health guidance in working towards the targets in the *Choosing health* white paper (see page 55) and in local area agreements.

NICE's 30-strong citizens council keeps the organisation informed on what the public thinks about the use of treatments and NHS care. Members are drawn from all age groups, social circumstances, ethnic backgrounds, regions and abilities. NICE's partners council is appointed by the Secretary of State and meets annually to review the annual report. It includes patients and representatives of patient organisations, professional organisations and healthcare industries.

In 2009 NICE took measures to speed up access to new treatments. It devised a faster system for referring drugs for appraisal, and increased investment in horizon scanning to identify new drugs early on. It also changed the way it appraises drugs that may extend the life of patients with a short life-expectancy. Under the NHS Constitution, patients have a right to treatments NICE has recommended. The coalition Government intends to 'reform' NICE.
www.nice.org.uk

The Ombudsman

The office of the Parliamentary and Health Service Ombudsman (sometimes referred to as the Health Service Commissioner) undertakes independent investigations into complaints about the NHS in England, as well as government departments and other public bodies. It is completely independent of the NHS and Government. In the NHS, the Ombudsman investigates complaints that a hardship or injustice has been caused by its failure to provide a service, by a failure in service or by maladministration. The Ombudsman looks into complaints against private health providers only if the treatment was funded by the NHS.

Complainants can only take their cases to the Ombudsman if they fail to achieve a resolution with the organisation or practitioner they are complaining against – for example, because of delays in dealing with a complaint locally or failure to get a satisfactory answer. The Ombudsman can consider complaints from a patient; a close member of the family, partner or representative, if the patient is unable to act for themselves; or from someone who has suffered injustice or hardship as a result of the actions of the NHS. A complaint will normally only be considered within a year of the events which gave rise to it, and only if the Ombudsman believes the NHS has not acted properly or has provided a poor service.

The Ombudsman publishes detailed reports of investigations, which identify common themes in complaints. The reports are intended to be used as training tools to improve services, and chief executives are asked to ensure all clinical directors and complaints managers are aware of them. They are also considered by the House of Commons public administration committee (see page 17).
www.ombudsman.org.uk

Spotlight on policy: Registration with CQC

From 2010, the Care Quality Commission is registering all providers of health and adult social care services against a single set of requirements for quality and safety of care. The process covers initial registration, monitoring and checking ongoing compliance, inspection and enforcement. Without registering, it will be illegal for organisations to provide certain services – called 'regulated activities' – within the scope of the new regulations. To maintain their registration, providers must demonstrate a continuing ability to meet all the requirements.

For the NHS, these requirements replace the Standards for Better Health, and for adult social care and independent healthcare they replace the National Minimum Standards. The new requirements allow providers flexibility in how they meet essential levels of quality and safety. They are intended to reflect differences in the nature of services – for example, between hospitals and residential care homes.

In order to register, organisations must comply with 16 core quality and safety regulations that apply to all providers. Other regulations apply to different types of provider. The regulations are grouped into six key areas:
• involvement and information
• personalised care, treatment and support
• safeguarding and safety
• suitability of staffing
• quality and management
• suitability of management.

Organisations must pay an annual fee to register as well as fees when there are changes to their registration, such as providing new services or merging with another provider.

Registration has applied to the NHS since April 2010, and will come into force for independent and voluntary healthcare and adult social care providers in October 2010. Primary dental care providers and private ambulances will be brought into registration in 2011 and primary medical care providers in 2012.

If organisations fail to meet the regulatory requirements, the CQC can take enforcement action. This includes levying fines, imposing conditions on registration, suspending or cancelling registration or prosecution for certain offences.

Further information
Briefing 159: Future registration framework for health and social care, NHS Confederation, May 2008.

Audit Commission
The Audit Commission is an independent public body responsible for ensuring that public money is spent economically, efficiently and effectively. As well as the NHS it covers local government, housing, criminal justice and fire and rescue services. In particular, it is dedicated to raising the standards of financial management and challenging public bodies to deliver better value for money. It is the lead body for comprehensive area assessment (see page 54).
www.audit-commission.gov.uk

National Audit Office
Headed by the Comptroller and Auditor General, the NAO's role is to report direct to Parliament on how public bodies have spent central government money, conducting financial audits and assessing value for money. It works closely with the Commons public accounts committee (see page 16).
www.nao.org.uk

Overview and scrutiny committees (OSCs)
The Health and Social Care Act 2001 gave local authorities specific powers to scrutinise local health services and health organisations. These powers formally rest with authorities that have social care responsibilities (county, unitary, metropolitan, London borough authorities), but there are provisions for joint or delegated scrutiny with borough or district councils.

OSCs are made up of elected council members not on the authority's executive or cabinet. They are able to call chief executives of local health organisations to attend a scrutiny hearing at least twice a year. OSCs can:
• refer contested service changes to the Secretary of State
• report their recommendations locally
• insist on being consulted by the NHS over major changes to health services.

NHS organisations must consult OSCs on any proposals that would lead to 'substantial developments and variations' in health services.

The Centre for Public Scrutiny helped to foster local authorities' role in scrutinising health services by running a support programme. It has published a guide for health OSCs, clarifying their distinct roles.

The CQC is keen to develop an 'ongoing dialogue' with OSCs, which, it says, in many ways operate like a local regulator, holding services to account. It wants to receive information from OSCs throughout the year and use it in its key assessments as well as routine monitoring of services.

Further information
Health on the frontline – district councils and health scrutiny, CfPS, January 2009.
Centre for Public Scrutiny **www.cfps.org.uk**

Professional regulation
NHS patients need to know that the staff who care for them are well trained and competent. Professional self-regulation has been a cornerstone of the NHS since it began, yet events over the last decade or so – such as the Bristol Inquiry into the deaths of child heart patients (1998–2001), the Alder Hey cases in which organs from dead children were retained without their families' knowledge (2001), and Dr Harold Shipman's conviction for multiple murders (2000) – highlighted the need for reform.

Professional regulation covers education, registration, training, continuing professional development and revalidation. It includes setting standards for deciding who should enter and remain members of a profession and determining their fitness to practise. Its underpinning principles are:
• clarity about standards
• maintaining public confidence
• transparency in tackling fitness to practise
• responsiveness to and protection of patients.

The DH has an ongoing professional standards programme that aims to raise further the standards of all who work in health and social care. Its key components are:
• increasing public and professional trust in the professional regulatory bodies
• revalidation to ensure professionals remain up to date
• improvements to local appraisal and clinical governance

- fair and effective local systems to identify those who fall short of professional standards, plus appropriate remedial, performance or regulatory action
- extending regulation to unregulated professionals and health and social care workers
- reforming the national regulatory systems for investigating complaints about health professionals.

The programme works closely with Scotland, Wales and Northern Ireland to ensure a coherent system of assurance across the UK: professional regulation issues and initiatives are usually UK-wide.

Professional regulatory bodies

The NHS Plan (see page 126) stipulated that regulatory bodies had to reform to become smaller, with much greater public and patient representation, faster, more transparent procedures and more meaningful accountability to the public and the health service. This was reinforced by the Kennedy Report on the Bristol Royal Infirmary a year later (see page 167).

Regulators have been instructed to develop common systems across the professions and agree standards that put patients' interests first. Professional regulatory bodies must be open and make improvements based on feedback from patients, their representatives and the public. They must deal with complaints quickly, thoroughly, objectively and in a way that is responsive to the complainant while treating fairly the health professional complained against.

Updated regulatory bodies have been introduced for medicine, nursing, midwifery and health visiting, the allied health professions and pharmacy:
- The Nursing and Midwifery Council replaced the UK Central Council in 2002 as the body responsible for governing nurses, midwives and health visitors.
- The Health Professions Council is responsible for the professions previously regulated by the Council for Professions Supplementary to Medicine, and includes groups of healthcare professionals not previously covered by formal statutory regulation.
- The General Medical Council is the regulatory body for doctors. It receives about 5,000 complaints a year, of which about 1,700 result in investigation. Since November 2009, all doctors must be both registered and hold a licence to practise; they will be required to renew their licence periodically.

- The General Dental Council and General Optical Council regulate the dental and optometry professions.
- The General Pharmaceutical Council replaces the Royal Pharmaceutical Society of Great Britain from 2010 as the regulator for pharmacists and pharmacy technicians. This development separates professional leadership from regulation, in line with other professions.

Further information
Briefing 62: Better, safer doctors: implementing medical revalidation, NHS Employers, June 2009.
Nursing and Midwifery Council **www.nmc-uk.org**
Health Professions Council **www.hpc-uk.org**
General Medical Council **www.gmc-uk.org**
General Dental Council **www.gdc-uk.org**
General Optical Council **www.optical.org**
General Pharmaceutical Council **www.pharmacyregulation.org**

Reforming professional regulation

Following the Shipman Inquiry, the chief medical officer reviewed the regulation of the medical profession, and a parallel review of non-medical professional regulation also took place. The Labour Government subsequently published its proposals in a white paper, *Trust, assurance and safety: the regulation of health professionals in the 21st century*, now being implemented. Key changes include:

- measures to make regulators more independent, such as professional members no longer forming the majority on regulatory bodies, and an independent adjudicator for doctors
- measures to ensure healthcare professionals are objectively revalidated throughout their career and remain up to date with clinical best practice
- moving from the criminal standard of proof to the civil standard in fitness-to-practise cases
- a stronger role for the medical Royal Colleges in revalidation
- introducing a system of regional GMC affiliates who will help local employers address concerns about doctors
- establishment of a General Pharmaceutical Council
- developing a comprehensive strategy for prevention, treatment and rehabilitation services for all health professionals.

Milestones in reforming professional regulation

Since 2001, developments in professional regulation have included:

2001	new multi-professional Health Professions Council
	reform of the Dentists Act 1984
2002	new Nursing and Midwifery Council
	overhaul of GMC structure and fitness-to-practise process
2003	Council for Healthcare Regulatory Excellence established
	introduction of statutory regulation for operating department practitioners
	European Qualifications Regulations
2004	further overhaul of GMC structure and fitness-to-practise process
2005	reform of the Opticians Act 1989
2007	reform of pharmacy regulation
	reform of the GMC's registration processes
	Trust, assurance and safety white paper published
2008	Health and Social Care Act takes forward white paper proposals
2009	GMC introduces licence to practise
	practitioner psychologists regulated by Health Professions Council
2010	launch of the General Pharmaceutical Council
	Office of the Health Professions Adjudicator established.

At the same time the Labour Government published its response to the final report of the Shipman Inquiry. Key changes include:

- measures to ensure patients registering concerns are taken seriously
- more systematic use of information about the clinical outcomes of individual practitioners and teams
- bringing together information from different sources for a fuller picture about professionals
- all primary care organisations to adopt best practice in investigating and acting on concerns.

Progress by the end of 2009 included:

- each regulator having a fully appointed council, with parity between lay and professional members
- new council members recruited by the Appointments Commission against specific criteria relating to their skills and expertise
- smaller, more board-like councils making it easier for regulators to act strategically.

NHS CONFEDERATION

Council for Healthcare Regulatory Excellence

CHRE is a statutory body responsible to Parliament and independent of the Department of Health. It covers all the UK, promoting best practice and consistency in professional self-regulation in nine bodies:

- General Medical Council
- General Dental Council
- General Optical Council
- General Osteopathic Council
- General Chiropractic Council
- Health Professions Council
- Nursing and Midwifery Council
- General Pharmaceutical Council
- Pharmaceutical Society of Northern Ireland.

CHRE's council is its governing body and consists of nine members: seven non-executives and two executives. With parliamentary approval, CHRE can force a regulator to change its rules. It also has the power to refer unduly lenient decisions about professionals' fitness to practise to the High Court for review.
www.chre.org.uk

Office of the Health Professions Adjudicator

From 2011 OHPA will adjudicate on fitness-to-practise cases brought before it by the General Medical Council and the General Optical Council. The GMC and GOC will continue their current role regarding doctors, dispensing opticians and optometrists, in setting standards of practice, investigating complaints and deciding whether to refer concerns about a professional's fitness to practise to an OHPA panel for a hearing. This separation is designed to ensure decisions are fair and effective, separate from the regulators, the professions and Government.

Recent proposals for further reforming professional regulation have included:
- strengthening local NHS arrangements for identifying poor performance among healthcare workers and taking effective action
- alternatives to statutory regulation for currently unregulated health and occupational professions, such as some healthcare scientists, psychotherapists and counsellors, which include licensing and a 'gatekeeper' role for an advisory body for future regulation.

Further information

Extending professional and occupational regulation: the report of the working group on extending professional regulation, DH, July 2009.
Tackling concerns nationally: establishing the Office of the Health Professions Adjudicator, DH, March 2009.
Tackling concerns locally: report of the working group, DH, March 2009.
Trust, assurance and safety: the regulation of health professionals in the 21st century, DH, February 2007.
Learning from tragedy, keeping patients safe: overview of the Government's action programme in response to the recommendations of the Shipman Inquiry, DH, February 2007.
Fifth report – safeguarding patients: lessons from the past – proposals for the future, Shipman Inquiry, December 2004.

Continuing professional development

In *A first class service*, the DH defined continuing professional development (CPD) as:

> a process of lifelong learning for all individuals and teams which meets the needs of patients and delivers the health outcomes and healthcare priorities of the NHS, and which enables professionals to expand and fulfil their potential.

In a climate of constant change, it is important that members of all professions demonstrate that they are keeping their knowledge and skills up to date: it is no longer sufficient simply to establish competence at the beginning of a career. Many professions, not just in healthcare, have adopted mandatory CPD. For individuals, CPD should:

* maintain professional competence and enable them, their teams and organisation to meet patients' needs, carry out their work with confidence and assist them in the event of an untoward incident
* provide them with the professional and personal satisfaction that they are working to the best of their ability and for the greater benefit of patients, colleagues and their employer
* help sustain motivation and interest in their work
* help meet career aspirations and learning needs, support flexible career pathways and allow them to take on wider responsibilities if necessary
* help them keep their jobs or enhance the possibility of finding another job
* help them identify the skills and knowledge they need to develop, preparing them for future opportunities.

CPD is a cyclical process involving four components:

Assessment
of individual and
organisational
needs

Evaluation
of effectiveness of
CPD intervention,
and of benefit to
patient care

Planning
personal
development plan
requirements

Implementation

Source: Department of Health

CPD is as important for NHS organisations as it is for individuals. A professional's failure to keep up to date could have serious results, while allowing their skills and knowledge to become obsolete is to waste the investment in their education and training. In *Continuing professional development – quality in the new NHS* (July 1999) the DH stated that 'every health organisation needs to develop a locally managed, systematic approach to CPD'. The core principles are that CPD should be:

- purposeful and patient-centred
- participative, fully involving the individual and other relevant stakeholders
- targeted at identified educational need
- educationally effective
- part of a wider organisational development plan supporting local and national service objectives
- focused on the development needs of clinical teams across traditional professional and service boundaries
- designed to build on previous knowledge, skills and experience
- designed to enhance the skills of interpreting and applying knowledge based on research and development.

Code of conduct for NHS managers

Just as doctors, nurses and other health workers have codified ethics, so since 2002 have NHS managers. Written by senior managers in collaboration with the DH, the code states that all NHS managers must:

- make the care and safety of patients their first concern and act to protect them from risk
- respect the public, patients, relatives, carers, NHS staff and partners in other agencies
- be honest and act with integrity
- accept responsibility for their own work and the proper performance of the people they manage
- show their commitment to working as a team member by working with all their colleagues in the NHS and the wider community
- take responsibility for their own learning and development.

NHS organisations must incorporate the code in the contracts of chief executives and directors, and investigate alleged breaches. Those who break the code can be dismissed from the NHS and barred from re-employment within it.

A DH advisory group concluded in 2010 that the code and other existing measures were insufficient to guarantee the calibre of NHS managers. It recommended clarifying standards; strengthening recruitment, vetting and employment procedures; enhancing corporate governance; and considering a system of licensing, accrediting or regulating managers.

Further information

Assuring the quality of senior NHS managers: report of the advisory group on assuring the quality of senior NHS managers, DH, February 2010.
Briefing 78: Managing for excellence in the NHS and the code of conduct for NHS managers, NHS Confederation, February 2003.
Code of conduct for NHS managers, DH, October 2002.
www.nhsemployers.org/managementstandards

Put these dates in your diary

NHS Confederation annual conference and exhibition

23 – 25 June 2010, Liverpool
6 – 8 July 2011, Manchester
20 – 22 June 2012, Manchester
www.nhsconfed.org

NHS Employers annual conference and exhibition

16 – 18 November 2010, Liverpool
15 – 17 November 2011, Liverpool
www.nhsemployers.org

07   Financing the NHS

NHS car parking: consultation on improving access for patients, DH, December 2009.
Fair for all, not free-for-all: principles for sustainable hospital car parking, NHS Confederation, April 2009.

Recovering the costs of personal injury

Since the 1930s hospitals have been entitled by law to collect money for treating road traffic accident victims from drivers' insurance companies. Since 2007 the NHS has been able to recover costs from insurance companies for treating patients in all cases where personal injury compensation is paid. In the first nine months of 2009/10, the injury costs recovery scheme raised almost £133 million in England, Scotland and Wales. The Compensation Recovery Unit, part of the Department for Work and Pensions, collects the charges on the DH's behalf. They are:
• use of an NHS ambulance: £171
• flat rate for treatment without admission: £566
• daily rate for treatment with admission: £695
• maximum in any one case: £41,545.

Further information
Injury costs recovery scheme, DH, January 2007.
Compensation Recovery Unit **www.dwp.gov.uk/cru**

Overseas visitors

Anyone who is lawfully 'ordinarily resident' in the UK is entitled to free NHS treatment in England, regardless of nationality. UK residents may be absent from the country for up to six months in a year before being considered for charges for NHS hospital treatment. British citizens who do not normally live in the UK may have to pay charges for NHS treatment, regardless of whether they have paid UK taxes and national insurance contributions, unless they are eligible for certain exemptions. British state pensioners who split their time between the UK and another European Economic Area member state are exempt from charges. Responsibility for deciding who is entitled to free treatment rests with the hospital providing the treatment. Asylum seekers whose application for refuge in the UK is outstanding are entitled to use NHS services without charge, as are those refused asylum but unable to return home due to 'recognised barriers'. Unaccompanied children, including those in local authority care, are also exempt from charges. In any case, treatment in an A&E department or walk-in centre, family planning services, compulsory psychiatric treatment and treatment for certain communicable diseases are free to all.

The DH is consulting on proposals that visitors with significant debts to the NHS should be refused permission to enter or remain in the UK, and on the longer-term feasibility of introducing health insurance requirements for visitors.

Further information
Review of access to the NHS by foreign nationals: consultation on proposals, DH, February 2010.

Other sources
Other sources of NHS funding come from land sales and income generation schemes. For example, income from hospital car-parking fees has risen from £59.5 million in 2001/02 to £180 million. In addition, the Big Lottery Fund has provided funding for health (as well as education and the environment). UK-wide it distributed £300 million to help set up healthy living centres, and gave over £360 million for coronary heart disease, stroke and cancer services. It also allocated £84 million for palliative care and support and information services for people with cancer and other life-threatening conditions.

Further information
www.biglotteryfund.org.uk

Resource allocation

The Treasury is responsible for overall public expenditure. Every two to three years it conducts a spending review of all government departments covering three years (see page 121). After each review, the Department of Health – like all government departments – draws up a public service agreement with the Treasury, setting out what it is expected to provide with its new resources over a three-year period. The DH in turn issues priorities and planning guidance to the NHS in the annual operating framework. The Treasury makes block grants to the Scottish Parliament, the Welsh Assembly and the Northern Ireland Assembly, from which they allocate funds for the NHS.

Spending on the NHS divides into these main sectors:

- *hospital and community health services and discretionary family health services* (HCFHS). This covers hospital and community health services, prescribing costs for drugs and appliances and discretionary general medical services (which include reimbursements of GMS GPs' practice staff, premises, out-of-hours and IT expenses). It also includes other centrally funded initiatives, services and special allocations managed centrally by the DH (such as education and training, and research and development).
- *non-discretionary family health services* (FHS). This covers demand-led family health services, including the remuneration of GPs for items such as capitation payments, health promotion and basic practice allowance, the cost of general dental and ophthalmic services, dispensing remuneration and income from dental and prescription charges.
- *central health and miscellaneous services* (CHMS). This includes, for example, certain public health functions and support to the voluntary sector.

Role of PCTs
Since 2003/04 the DH has made 'unified allocations' covering a three-year period direct to primary care trusts. PCTs now control 82 per cent of the NHS budget, and have to plan the use of their resources over the three years as agreed with their strategic health authority. However, they must manage within their annual resource limit total for each year, although they can carry forward planned underspends of up to 0.25 per cent. These unified budget allocations cover:

- commissioning hospital, mental health and learning disability services
- PCT running costs
- GP and community nurses' prescribing costs
- primary care infrastructure.

Provided they are achieving the targets in their local delivery plan and keep sufficient in reserve to pay GPs, PCTs can use their resources as they see fit.

PCTs are responsible for funding the healthcare of all patients registered with GPs in their area. Under practice-based commissioning (see page 48), PCTs delegate budgets to GP practices to commission acute, community and emergency care. PCTs' and practices' agreements with providers – NHS trusts, foundation trusts and independent providers – may no longer set activity levels, which are now decided by patient choice and funded through payment by results (see page 192). However, all contracts and agreements do contain planned activity levels profiled across the year.

NHS trusts derive most of their income by providing services in this way, although they also earn some by providing private healthcare and are funded separately for training health professionals. They may also generate some income from shops or car parks on hospital premises.

All providers of NHS services have to publish their costs for individual procedures on a consistent basis in the national schedule of reference costs. This gives details of the unit costs for a range of procedures and treatments, from x-rays to lung transplant surgery and from a visit by a district nurse to a home delivery by a midwife. Commissioners can use the information when negotiating agreements, and identify areas for improving efficiency. The DH, with help from the Audit Commission, is reviewing its reference cost collection process to improve the accuracy of submissions and increase the usefulness of the information provided.

Deciding allocations

Four factors are taken into account in allocating resources to PCTs:

- weighted capitation targets – set according to a national formula, which calculates a PCT's target share of resources based on its population and their health needs due to deprivation or high mortality and morbidity levels, as well as a 'market forces factor' to account for unavoidable geographical variations in the cost of providing services; the intention is that every PCT should be able to commission similar levels of health services for populations in similar need
- recurrent baselines – representing the actual allocation a PCT received in the last allocation round, plus any recurrent adjustments
- distance from target – the difference between target and recurrent baseline
- pace-of-change policy – decided by ministers for each allocation round, this determines the level of increase all PCTs get and the extra for under-target PCTs to move them closer to their weighted capitation targets.

The DH's Advisory Committee on Resource Allocation (ACRA) revised the weighted capitation formula in 2008 to better target funds, improve assessment of need and include a new market forces factor. ACRA recommended use of a separate formula to take account of health inequalities; ministers decided to apply this formula to 15 per cent of allocations for 2009/10 and 2010/11. The coalition Government is committed to reviewing the allocation mechanisms for public health services.

NHS CONFEDERATION

Payment by results

In a far-reaching change to the way money flows through the NHS in England between commissioners and providers, a system of payment by results has been gradually introduced. The aim is to ensure funding follows the patient and underpins policy on increasing patient choice, providing a transparent system for paying trusts which encourages activity and so helps keep waiting times short.

PCTs commission the volume of activity they require for their populations, but instead of drawing up block agreements with NHS trusts as previously, providers are paid for the activity they undertake. A tariff derived from national reference costs has removed prices from local negotiation, so that commissioners focus instead on gains in patient choice, quality, shorter waiting time, volumes of activity and efficiency. However, after 2010/11 tariffs will represent the maximum price for a service, a measure intended to provide commissioners with a lever in negotiations to get better value but which will challenge organisations with high costs.

Payment by results began in a limited way in 2003/04, and has been gradually extended. Each year, changes to the tariff are 'sense-checked' for anomalies that could lead to perverse incentives and 'road-tested' before their introduction to enable the service to get used to the new tariff.

Changes in 2010/11 include a zero per cent uplift in tariff prices and a 3.5 per cent efficiency requirement to cover pay and price inflation. Unplanned emergency activity will only attract 30 per cent of its tariff price. 'Best practice tariffs', structured and priced to incentivise and adequately reimburse the costs of high-quality care, have been introduced for four high-volume areas with significant unexplained variation in practice and clear consensus of what clinical best practice constitutes. In addition, under CQUIN (see page 138) part of a hospital's income will depend on patient satisfaction. Payment by results will be extended to mental health and community health services beginning in 2011/12.

A code of conduct for payment by results sets out core principles, ground rules for organisational behaviour and expectations of how the system should operate – and is intended to minimise disputes.

Further information
Code of conduct for payment by results, DH, February 2010.

In 2010/11 the average allocation growth for PCTs is 5.5 per cent, with minimum growth of 5.1 per cent. Planned growth for 2011/12 and 2012/13 is that the 95 per cent of the NHS budget spent on 'frontline' patient services will rise in line with inflation; other spending will be subject to cuts.

Further information
Resource allocation: weighted capitation formula – sixth edition, DH, December 2008.
Report of the Advisory Committee on Resource Allocation, DH, December 2008.

Capital

Capital investment is expenditure – typically on buildings or large items of equipment – that will continue to provide benefits into the future. To count as NHS capital, spending must generally be on assets that individually cost £5,000 or more and are recorded on the balance sheet as fixed assets.

The NHS's main sources of capital are Government funds, receipts from land sales and the private finance initiative.

Allocating capital

The DH allocates operational capital to PCTs according to a national needs-based formula. They can spend it as they choose, but it is mainly used for maintaining buildings and replacing equipment.

Vital statistics: NHS capital 2009/10 (£m)

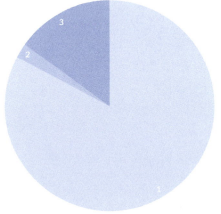

1   Government spending: 5,434
2   Receipts from land sales: 146
3   PFI investment: 992
    Total: 6,572

Government-funded capital and land sales receipts were distributed as follows:
PCT allocation: 800
NHS trusts and foundation trusts: 2,900
Central budgets: 1,800

Source: Department of Health

Strategic capital is allocated to SHAs according to a weighted capitation formula to fund schemes they decide are priorities for bringing about major change.

Foundation trusts do not rely on allocations of operational or strategic capital but are free to reinvest all cash generated from their activities to maintain and replace their assets. They may also borrow capital, from commercial banks or the DH, under 'prudential borrowing' arrangements if their projections of future cash flows show they would be able to afford to pay back the sum with interest. Monitor assigns each foundation trust a 'prudential borrowing limit', fixing the amount of debt it may take on.

Since 2007 NHS trusts may also borrow capital under a similar regime to that for foundation trusts, but approved by SHAs and the DH: access to capital funding is decided by the affordability of proposed investments and financed by loans and borrowing subject to a 'prudential borrowing regime'. However, NHS trusts' first source of capital financing is internally generated cash. Since 2008, PCTs have also been free to set their own local investment plans subject to agreement with their SHA. In 2010/11, £565 million is available for this.

Capital to fund some specific policy initiatives is still allocated centrally. These 'programme budgets' include:
• community hospital development
• fluoridation
• substance misuse
• learning disability service reprovision
• mental health facilities
• energy efficiency.

Capital funding (excluding PFI) for 2010/11 is planned to decrease to £4.67 billion. In the NHS operating framework for 2010/11, the DH warns that 'all organisations should be preparing for a period of capital constraint'.

Private finance initiative (PFI)
PFI involves a public–private partnership between an NHS organisation and a private sector consortium that makes private capital available for health service projects. All major NHS capital projects are expected to consider whether PFI could represent a value-for-money solution.

The private sector consortium will usually include a construction company, a funding organisation and a facilities management provider. Contracts for major PFI schemes may be for 30 years or more and are typically DBFO (design, build, finance and operate) projects. This means the private sector partner is responsible for:
- designing the facilities (based on the requirements specified by the NHS)
- building the facilities (to time and at a fixed cost)
- financing the capital cost (with the return to be recovered through continuing to make the facilities available and meeting NHS requirements)
- operating the facilities (providing facilities management and other support services).

PFI schemes must demonstrate value for money, which is usually achieved by the PFI partner assuming risks which would otherwise have been borne by the public sector, and by efficiency savings. The PFI contract sets out the performance standards required of the consortium. The NHS makes no payments until services are provided to the agreed standard, and then they must be maintained to ensure full payment.

The aims of PFI are to increase innovation and reduce the overall risks associated with procuring new assets and services for the NHS, as well as to improve the quality and cost-effectiveness of public services. Because the PFI partner's capital is at risk, they have an incentive to perform well throughout the life of the contract, while private sector management, commercial and creative skills are harnessed for the NHS's benefit.

Critics have questioned whether PFI will really provide long-term value for money for the NHS, and have claimed services have been cut in some cases to make schemes affordable. The National Audit Office found that when PFI contracts had to be altered due to new policy initiatives or changing local circumstances, the changes often did not offer value for money.

Government guidance said: 'PFI is only a procurement tool – not an end in itself – and will only be used in cases where it offers value for money to the taxpayer and the NHS.' It is not advised in projects involving rapid change, such as IT. As the NHS is undergoing a period of rapid change, it can be argued that PFI will need to adapt to accommodate the changes.

The Treasury report, *PFI: strengthening long-term partnerships*, confirmed the commitment to a PFI investment programme for public services and describes the steps it is taking to strengthen PFI with measures to increase flexibility and reinforce the requirement for value for money.

With policy emphasising the shift of services from acute to community health and primary care settings, DH and local reviews of PFI schemes over the last five years have resulted in 11 schemes being cancelled and the capital cost of the programme falling from £12 billion to £7.6 billion. However, the banking crisis has made the future of PFI uncertain as banks' reluctance to lend money meant they were unwilling to finance PFI schemes.

By the end of 2009, of the PFI schemes that had been approved since 1997:
• 87 were operational
• 14 were under construction
• 1 was in procurement
• 8 were preparing for procurement.

Of schemes funded by public capital:
• 29 were operational
• 4 were under construction
• 4 were awaiting construction.

Further information

Making changes in operational PFI projects, National Audit Office, January 2008.
Rebuilding the NHS: a new generation of healthcare facilities, DH, June 2007.
PFI: strengthening long-term partnerships, HM Treasury, March 2006

NHS Local Improvement Finance Trust (LIFT)

NHS LIFT aims to encourage investment in primary care and community-based facilities with the aim of refurbishing or replacing them. It is similar to PFI, except that it is a joint venture between PCTs, the private sector partner, local authorities and GPs.

Community Health Partnerships (from 2001 to 2007 known as Partnerships for Health), a public–private partnership between the DH and Partnerships UK, was set up to invest money in NHS LIFT and help attract additional private funding; the DH became the sole owner in 2006. At local level, NHS LIFT is not a single trust but a series of local public–private partnerships between PCTs, the private sector, CHP and local authorities. The resulting partnership is a LIFT company, which is a local joint venture.

More than 250 new community facilities have either opened or are under construction as part of the LIFT programme, which seeks investment in primary care developments by bundling them together. So far, 48 local LIFT schemes are renting accommodation to GPs, pharmacists, opticians, dentists and others on a lease basis. Schemes may now include clinical and facilities management services as well as buildings and maintenance. The total value of the LIFT programme is £2 billion. It covers all ten SHAs and 58 per cent of PCTs.

Since 2008 PCTs can extend LIFT schemes to enable them to manage PCTs' entire estates. The Express LIFT framework, introduced in 2009, reduces the time and cost of setting up a scheme by offering a choice of seven pre-approved partners for local procurements by PCTs and local authorities, completing contracts within three or four months rather than two years.

Further information
Innovation in the NHS: local improvement finance trusts, National Audit Office, May 2005.
www.communityhealthpartnerships.co.uk

NHS spending

The era of growth
From the time the NHS was founded until the end of the 1990s, its annual average increase in funding was just over 3 per cent – slightly more than the real growth in the economy as a whole. However, from the early 1980s, real spending changes were erratic. Taking into account the level of inflation in the NHS rather than in the general economy, annual average growth was about 0.9 per cent from 1983 to 1987, 2 per cent from 1987 to 1992 and 1.4 per cent from 1992 to 1997. In 2000 the Labour Government announced its intention to raise the share of national income spent on health to the European average: it then ranked 14th out of the 15 EU countries.

In 2001 Derek Wanless was commissioned to produce the first evidence-based assessment of the NHS's long-term resource requirements (see page 199). He produced a similar report for NHS Wales in 2003 (see page 280), while in Northern Ireland the Appleby Report of 2005 (see page 296) sought to predict future needs and resources.

Vital statistics: UK health spending (public and private) as a percentage of GDP

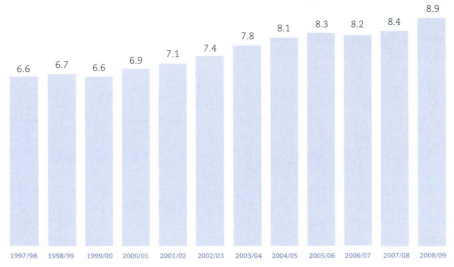

1997/98	1998/99	1999/00	2000/01	2001/02	2002/03	2003/04	2004/05	2005/06	2006/07	2007/08	2008/09
6.6	6.7	6.6	6.9	7.1	7.4	7.8	8.1	8.3	8.2	8.4	8.9

Source: HM Treasury

As a result of Wanless's report on the English NHS, the 2002 Budget heralded major increases in net spending until 2007/08: from £53.7 billion to £85.6 billion in England alone. These were the largest sustained increases in any five-year period in NHS history: an annual average increase of 7.4 per cent in real terms between 2002/03 and 2007/08, a total increase of 43 per cent in real terms over the period. This translated into a rise in NHS spending per head from £890 in 2001/02 to £1,676 in 2007/08. The aim was to put the health service on a 'sound long-term financial footing', making significant investment in IT, buildings and equipment, and raising NHS spending to the EU average. To help pay for these increases, national insurance contributions were raised by 1 per cent from April 2003.

NHS spending was long planned to increase at the slower rate of 4 per cent a year in real terms for three years from 2008/09, taking the total budget to £110 billion in 2010/11.

Wanless Report

In 2001 the then Chancellor commissioned Derek Wanless, former chief executive of NatWest Bank, to examine demand and cost pressures in the NHS over the next 20 years and recommend the spending needed for a 'publicly funded, comprehensive, high-quality service available on the basis of clinical need and not ability to pay'.

In his April 2002 report, Wanless found that although an ageing population would be an important influence, this would not be the main factor driving up costs. Patients were likely to demand more choice and higher-quality services. Improving information and communication technology would be key to achieving this, while the NHS would have to change its skill-mix and ways of working, and enhance the role of primary care.

Wanless concluded that spending would need to rise between 9.4 per cent and 11.3 per cent of GDP by 2021, with the fastest growth before 2008. He warned: 'Both additional resources and radical reform are vital: neither would succeed without the other.'

Wanless's figures assumed that plans for huge expansion of the workforce would be achieved, that IT spend could be doubled and used productively while the NHS fulfilled commitments on waiting times and national service frameworks. If productivity improvement fell short of 2 per cent a year, spending would need to rise to an even higher proportion of GDP.

Reviewing progress after five years, Wanless noted significant improvements in staffing, equipment, infrastructure, waiting times and care for coronary heart disease, cancer, stroke and mental health. But he was disappointed that increased funding had not resulted in the increased productivity envisaged. In particular, he was alarmed at delays to the IT programme and at the dramatic rise in obesity. He criticised the introduction of policies and structural changes without adequate preparation, and concluded the NHS was no longer on course to achieve a 'world-class' service by 2021. Nevertheless, he said: 'Despite these concerns we conclude that the broad direction of Government health policy is the right one.'

Further information

Our future health secured? A review of NHS funding and performance, King's Fund, September 2007.

Securing our future: taking a long-term view. Final report, HM Treasury, April 2002.

Dealing with the downturn

In the words of the NHS chief executive in 2009: 'We are at a critical juncture in the history of the NHS. After a decade of investment and reform that has helped drive real improvements for our patients, the NHS, along with other public services, is about to enter perhaps the toughest financial climate it has ever known.'

The banking crisis and subsequent world recession increased UK public sector net debt to £845 billion by the end of 2009 – 60.2 per cent of GDP (compared to the Government's previous ceiling of 40 per cent). Efforts to reduce the deficit will inevitably put huge pressure on public finances.

Although the NHS budget will grow as planned by 5.5 per cent in 2010/11, between 2011 and 2014 the health service has to find an unprecedented £15–20 billion in efficiency savings, and possibly more. However, savings will be reinvested in the NHS. The coalition Government has guaranteed 'real terms' increases for the NHS above inflation for the next five years.

As an interim, by 2012/13 the NHS is expected to have achieved £10 billion in savings, including:
• £1.5 billion from cutting procurement costs
• £100 million from the National Programme for IT – part of a total £600 million reduction in NPfIT costs
• £60 million from reducing energy use and cutting carbon emissions by 10 per cent
• £70m from more efficient use of estates
• £555m by reducing staff sickness absence, as suggested in the review of staff health and well-being (see page 220).

Management and administrative support costs in PCTs and SHAs must fall by 30 per cent by 2013/14. Other measures are a 1 per cent cap on public sector pay rises for 2011/12 and 2012/13 and a pay freeze for senior groups including senior NHS managers, consultant doctors, GPs and chief executives of non-departmental public bodies. But an additional pressure is a 1 per cent increase in employers' national insurance contributions from 2011.

The Budget in March 2010 suggested longer-term NHS savings would include:
- £3.5 billion from improving staff productivity and reducing dependency on agency staff
- £2.7 billion from achieving best practice in care planning and case management for people with long-term conditions, empowering patients to self-care, reducing emergency admissions and providing more efficient, integrated community services
- £1.5 billion from reducing unnecessary referrals and prescribing, and improving mental health services
- £2 billion from better procurement, savings in management and back-office costs and more efficient use of the hospital estate.

The 2009/10 SHA and PCT surplus will be carried forward to 2010/11, and SHAs must agree with the DH how this is to be used. SHAs and PCTs are expected to end 2010/11 with an aggregate surplus of £1 billion, to be spent during the next spending review period.

The 'quality and productivity challenge' that the NHS will face in the next five years presents a daunting task, all the more so given that management capacity itself is to be cut. Much will depend on how quickly and successfully services can be redesigned. This is not a new aim, yet progress so far has been slow. The Audit Commission noted: 'PCTs made little or no inroad in 2008/09 to transferring care from hospitals to the community.'

Further information

Pre-Budget report – securing the recovery: growth and opportunity, HM Treasury, December 2009.

Putting the frontline first: smarter government, HM Government, December 2009.

Health briefing: More for less – are productivity and efficiency improving in the NHS?, Audit Commission, November 2009.

Dealing with the downturn paper 4: The greatest ever leadership challenge for the NHS?, NHS Confederation, June 2009.

Discussion paper 5: Commissioning in a cold climate, PCT Network/NHS Confederation, June 2009.

Spotlight on policy: Quality, innovation, productivity and prevention (QIPP)
The QIPP programme aims to achieve major efficiency savings forced on the NHS by the economic downturn without compromising the quality of service. It is headed by the NHS national director for improvement and efficiency, and is focusing on three key areas divided into 12 workstreams, each led by NHS and DH experts. These are:

Commissioning and pathways
- safe care
- right care
- long-term conditions
- urgent care
- end-of-life care

Provider efficiency
- back-office efficiency and optimal management
- procurement
- clinical support
- supporting staff productivity
- medicines use and procurement

System enablers
- primary care contracting and primary care commissioning
- technology and digital vision.

Further information
The NHS quality, innovation, productivity and prevention challenge: an introduction for clinicians, DH, March 2010.

Where the money is spent
In England, NHS total expenditure (revenue and capital) including money available from charges and receipts, is expected to be over £107.9 billion in 2010/11. The largest part of NHS spending is on hospital and community health services, discretionary family health services and related services. For 2010/11, total planned revenue expenditure for hospital, community and family health services is £103.3 billion and total planned capital expenditure is £4.6 billion.

The domination of spending on acute services reflects the demand for emergency treatment and the continuing emphasis on reducing waiting lists and waiting times. Healthcare for people over 65 accounts for more than 40 per cent of the total expenditure.

Vital statistics: How hospital and community health service (HCHS) spending is divided

1 General and acute: 59%
2 Mental health: 14%
3 Community health services: 12%
4 Accident and emergency: 4%
5 Learning disability: 4%
6 Other: 4%
7 Maternity: 3%

Source: Department of Health

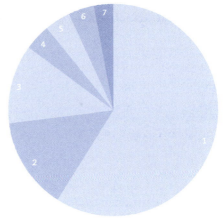

Measuring inflation

Increases in the cost of goods and services used by the NHS are measured by the health service cost index (HSCI). This weights together price increases for a broad range of items – for example: drugs, medical equipment, fuel and telephone charges. Pay inflation must also be taken into account to calculate the rate of inflation affecting the hospital and community health services.

Vital statistics: HCHS inflation (%)

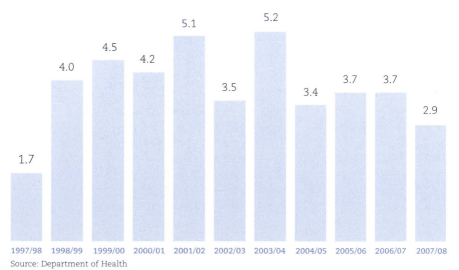

| 1997/98 | 1998/99 | 1999/00 | 2000/01 | 2001/02 | 2002/03 | 2003/04 | 2004/05 | 2005/06 | 2006/07 | 2007/08 |

1.7 / 4.0 / 4.5 / 4.2 / 5.1 / 3.5 / 5.2 / 3.4 / 3.7 / 3.7 / 2.9

Source: Department of Health

Commercial support units

CSUs will be centres of expertise in every region, providing commercial support to commissioners and providers, managing contracts and working with NHS Supply Chain to secure better value for money for goods and services bought by the NHS. CSUs are being set up at a cost of £20 million in 2009/10. They are intended to give healthcare suppliers a single, simple point of contact with the NHS. The DH says: 'Initially SHAs will play a key coordinating and supporting role but, over time, the ownership and development of CSUs will increasingly be in the hands of local commissioners and providers.'

NHS Shared Business Services

NHS Shared Business Services was launched as a joint venture between the DH and a private sector company in 2005, building on an earlier shared financial services initiative that used two purpose-built centres in Leeds and Bristol. SBS provides finance and accounting, payroll and e-procurement services so that frontline organisations can concentrate on patient care. It currently provides finance, accounting and payroll services to over 100 NHS organisations. With 1,000 employees at six locations in the UK and India, it processes 300,000 invoices each month and 100,000 payslips for NHS staff.
www.sbs.nhs.uk

NHS Business Services Authority

This special health authority was set up in April 2006 to be the main processing facility for payment, reimbursement, remuneration and reconciliation for NHS patients, employees and others. For example, it manages the NHS pension scheme, reimburses dentists and pharmacists, and administers the European health insurance card in the UK. It was formed from the Dental Practice Board, NHS Pensions Agency and the Prescription Pricing Authority.
www.nhsbsa.nhs.uk

NHS Supply Chain

NHS Supply Chain is a single organisation that provides procurement, logistics, e-commerce and customer and supplier support. Its 2,400 staff buy and deliver 620,000 products for more than 600 healthcare organisations. It aims to save £1 billion for the NHS, and is operated by DHL under a ten-year contract with the NHS Business Services Authority.
www.supplychain.nhs.uk

NHS Counter Fraud Service
The NHS Counter Fraud Service was established to tackle fraud and corruption throughout the NHS, whether involving professionals, staff, patients or contractors. The service has more than 300 trained and accredited counter-fraud specialists throughout the NHS in England and Wales. In the ten years to 2008, CFS brought 482 successful prosecutions and recovered £50.5 million. The NHS fraud and corruption reporting line is 0800 028 4060.
www.nhsbsa.nhs.uk/fraud

Buying goods and services

Pharmaceutical Price Regulation Scheme
The PPRS regulates the prices of branded medicines and the profits that manufacturers are allowed to make on their sales to the NHS. It is a voluntary agreement made between the DH and the Association of the British Pharmaceutical Industry. A series of voluntary agreements has limited branded medicine prices and profits since 1957, each lasting five years or so.

Agreements cover all licensed, branded prescription medicines sold to the NHS. They do not cover products without a brand name (generics) nor over-the-counter branded products except when prescribed by a doctor. The PPRS is a UK-wide scheme, and covers around 80 per cent by value of the medicines used in the NHS in both primary and secondary care. The total NHS drugs bill in England is over £10.9 billion a year, including both branded and generic medicines and drugs prescribed in the community as well as in hospital.

The PPRS seeks to achieve reasonable prices for the NHS, while recognising that the industry needs to earn the money to enable it to develop and market new and improved medicines. The last agreement secured for the NHS a 3.9 per cent price reduction for branded prescription medicines from February 2009 and a further 1.9 per cent cut from January 2010. The DH hopes these more flexible pricing arrangements will enable companies to supply drugs to the NHS at lower initial prices, with the option of higher prices if value is proven at a later date. NICE has taken measures to allow patients faster access to clinically proven new drugs.

The agreement included plans to consult on the introduction of generic substitution, subject to the outcome of discussions. In 2008, 83 per cent of prescriptions in primary care were dispensed generically. Of the remainder, only 5 per cent were prescribed by brand where a generic substitute was available.

A maximum price scheme for generics – on which the NHS spends £2 billion a year – was introduced in 2000 to restrain the drugs bill after steep price rises, saving around £330 million a year. Since 2004, where there is a limited number of manufacturers of a generic medicine or the supply is concentrated, manufacturers have to seek the DH's agreement to any price increase. Manufacturers and wholesalers must submit quarterly information on income revenues, cost of purchases and volumes of transactions.

Further information
The Pharmaceutical Price Regulation Scheme: tenth report to Parliament, DH, December 2009.
The Pharmaceutical Price Regulation Scheme 2009, DH, December 2008.
PPRS market study report, OFT, February 2007.

08 Staffing and human resources

As the UK's largest employer – indeed, one of the largest employers in the world – the NHS attaches special importance to good human resources policy and practice. Staff costs account for about 75 per cent of hospital expenditure. Effective recruitment, retention and remuneration of a well-trained and well-motivated workforce are seen as crucial factors in achieving ambitions for patient care.

The era of funding growth saw significant expansion in the NHS workforce and revised contracts to reflect changing patterns of care. Improving staff productivity and efficiency as spending diminishes is now a key theme. Organisations must also do their utmost to engage staff in designing ways of improving services. NHS commitments to staff and their responsibilities form a major part of the NHS Constitution (see page 218).

Workforce planning

Workforce planning in the NHS is undertaken on several levels. Strategic health authorities will coordinate overall plans for their area and retain the lead role for education commissioning. Primary care trusts will link workforce planning to health needs, and providers will integrate workforce and service plans locally. The Centre for Workforce Intelligence is being established to provide high-quality intelligence and evidence to inform workforce planning and strengthen decision-making.

Further information
Briefing 47: NHS Next Stage Review: workforce issues, NHS Employers, July 2008.
A high quality workforce: NHS Next Stage Review, DH, June 2008.
www.nhsemployers.org

Staff numbers
The NHS workforce in England grew 30.4 per cent between 1999 and 2009, with staff numbers reaching 1.4 million. This follows a substantial rise in funding over the last decade and headcount may be reduced as the NHS responds to a tighter financial situation.

Social Partnership Forum

The NHS Social Partnership Forum, set up in 2007, brings together NHS unions, NHS Employers and the DH to discuss current issues and develop joint initiatives to tackle national problems.

Key areas of the SPF's work currently include:
- workforce planning – including maximising opportunities for newly qualified healthcare professionals
- partnership working
- knowledge and skills framework
- staff engagement and the NHS staff survey
- the staff passport – policy on the employment standards for the wider NHS.

In 2009/10 the Labour Government made available a £500,000 fund to promote and develop partnership working between employers and trade unions locally and regionally, building on the SPF model.

Further information
Briefing 66: Leading the NHS workforce through to recovery, NHS Employers, November 2009.
NHS Social Partnership Forum review – final report, Involvement and Participation Association, April 2009.
Partnership agreement: an agreement between DH, NHS Employers and NHS trade unions, DH/NHS Employers/NHS trade unions, February 2007.
www.socialpartnershipforum.org

NHS Careers

NHS Careers is a service providing information on careers in the NHS in England. It consists of a telephone and email helpline, website, literature and supporting services for NHS employers, schools, colleges and careers advisers. Launched in 1999, it aims to raise awareness among the potential future workforce of the 350 careers the NHS offers. It has developed a service for 14–19-year-olds to find out what working in the NHS is like, and another where undergraduates on clinical and non-clinical courses in England can look at their options for a career in the NHS.
www.nhscareers.nhs.uk
www.stepintothenhs.nhs.uk
www.whatcanIdowithmydegree.nhs.uk

NHS Employers represents trusts in England on workforce issues and helps employers to ensure the NHS is a place where people want to work. It reflects employers' views and acts on their behalf in four priority areas:

- pay and negotiations
- recruitment and planning the workforce
- healthy and productive workplaces
- employment policy and practice.

NHS Employers, set up in 2004, is part of the NHS Confederation. The DH sets the broad framework within which it operates, but employers themselves drive the agenda. Its policy board plays an important role in making decisions about the work, position and direction of the organisation, with members drawn from across the NHS.
www.nhsemployers.org

NHS Jobs

NHS Jobs is an online recruitment service offering details of job vacancies throughout the NHS in England and Wales. Launched in 2003, it provides employers with online tools to manage every stage of the recruitment cycle. Each month it carries details of around 20,000 career opportunities in the NHS, attracts 6 million visits and receives job applications from more than 150,000 jobseekers. Of all NHS job applications, 90 per cent are made through the website. Almost all job applicants for the NHS are made through this website. Every NHS trust in England and Wales is registered to advertise with NHS Jobs, which is estimated to have saved the NHS about £240 million in advertising and recruitment administration costs since its launch.

Further information
Briefing 65: Talent for tough times: how to identify, attract and retain the talent you need, NHS Employers, November 2009.
Briefing 54: NHS Jobs – delivering the future for NHS recruitment, NHS Employers, November 2008.
www.jobs.nhs.uk

Training

New ways of working, new treatments and procedures and the shift of services from hospitals to the community all have implications for training the healthcare workforce. Responsibility for undergraduate and postgraduate medical education will be transferred to the General Medical Council. Medical Education England (see below) now also has a key role. The Deaneries oversee the placing of students in training within hospitals.

Modernising careers

Pre-registration education and training for nurses, midwives and healthcare scientists are changing to reflect their evolving roles – a trend boosted by the renewed focus on strong clinical leadership. This means greater flexibility and more emphasis on practice during learning, and makes the education system more responsive to the NHS's needs.

Modernising Medical Careers (MMC) introduced a major reform of postgraduate medical education and training from 2005 with new foundation and specialty training programmes. Difficulties experienced with recruitment to specialty training programmes in 2007 prompted an independent review of MMC by Sir John Tooke, which led to further reform to the structure of postgraduate training.

Medical Education England provides independent advice to ministers and contributes to policy-making on the content and structure of professional education and training for doctors, dental teams, healthcare scientists and technologists and pharmacy teams. Set up in 2009, it also advises on the quality of workforce planning for these groups at a national level. MEE intends to develop a long-term strategic vision for professional education and training. Membership is drawn from employers, professional bodies, staff organisations, the DH and other interested organisations.

Under the Modernising Nursing Careers programme, the DH consulted on a new structure for nurses' careers based on five patient pathways:
• children, family and public health
• first contact, access and urgent care
• supporting long-term care
• acute and critical care
• mental health and psychosocial care.

The Nursing and Midwifery Council conducted a review of pre-registration nursing to ensure all those who qualify as new registrants are fit for practice. As a result, the profession will become all-graduate from 2013.

NHS apprenticeships
During 2009 £25 million was made available to create 5,000 NHS apprenticeships – in addition to the existing 1,500 – as part of a plan to increase apprenticeships across the public sector by 21,000. Apprenticeships include clinical support roles such as dental nurses and pharmacy support workers and non-clinical roles such as IT support, estates and facilities management and catering. Apprentices get practical experience while improving their qualifications and contributing to the NHS workforce through employer-based training and day-release education. Apprenticeships widen the range of young people who can work in clinical support roles, and offer potential to progress to a professional career. A National Apprenticeship Advisory Committee was set up to drive progress and promote recruitment and retention of apprenticeships in the NHS.
www.apprenticeships.org.uk
www.skillsforhealth.org.uk/apprenticeships

The NHS's 55,000-strong healthcare scientist workforce includes 50 scientific disciplines encompassing biology, genetics, physiology, physics and engineering. As science and technology advance, greater clinical scientific expertise will be required, and healthcare scientists will take on broader roles, including leadership, management and education. Existing training and career arrangements will therefore need to change. The DH has consulted on clearer pathways into healthcare science careers defined through three stages, with the ability to progress between them subject to entry requirements:

• healthcare science assistant
• healthcare scientist practitioner
• healthcare scientist.

Further information
Aspiring to Excellence – final report of the independent inquiry into modernising medical careers led by Professor Sir John Tooke, MMC Inquiry, January 2008.
Towards a framework for post-registration nursing careers: consultation response report, DH, July 2008.
The Government response to the health select committee report 'Modernising medical careers', TSO, July 2008.
Briefing 52: Medical training and careers – the employers' vision, NHS Employers, November 2008.

The future of the healthcare science workforce. Modernising scientific careers, the next steps: a consultation, DH, November 2008.

Implementing the Tooke report: Department of Health update, DH, November 2008.

Medical Education England **www.mee.nhs.uk**

Modernising Medical Careers **www.mmc.nhs.uk**

Nursing and Midwifery Council **www.nmc-uk.org**

Productivity

With the NHS's spending constrained from 2011, it faces greater pressure than ever to improve workforce productivity while maintaining or improving the quality of care. With the economic downturn its productivity improvements are expected to go even 'further and deeper' than they otherwise would.

Work to improve NHS productivity is now part of the QIPP framework (see page 202).

Pay and pensions

Pay accounts for about 40 per cent of NHS spending, and 65 to 70 per cent in acute and mental health trusts. The pay and conditions of NHS staff are developed mainly through collective bargaining between the NHS and staff organisations, which also represent staff on a wide range of other employment issues. Most staff are members of trade unions or professional associations, and the NHS seeks 'partnership working' on key employment issues. Most NHS staff organisations have a professional and collective bargaining role. NHS Employers negotiates conditions of service and national contracts with the unions on behalf of employers through the NHS Staff Council, and represents employers' views in the pay review process. GPs are mostly independent self-employed contractors, and the general medical services contract is negotiated by the British Medical Association and NHS Employers.

Agenda for Change

Agenda for Change is the most significant reform of NHS pay since the creation of the health service in 1948. It applies to 1.4 million NHS staff across the UK, with the exception of doctors, dentists and the most senior managers.

The system is underpinned by a job evaluation scheme specifically designed for the NHS and by the NHS Knowledge and Skills Framework, which supports personal development and career progression.

Agenda for Change was designed to:
- deliver fair pay for non-medical staff based on the principle of equal pay for work of equal value
- provide better links between pay and career progression through the NHS knowledge and skills framework
- harmonise terms and conditions of service such as annual leave, hours and sick pay, and more recently for work performed in unsocial hours.

Staff are placed in one of nine pay bands on the basis of their knowledge, responsibility skills and effort needed for the job rather than on the basis of their job title.

NHS Employers, the DH and trade unions – including Unison and the Royal College of Nursing – agreed a multi-year pay deal for staff on the Agenda for Change pay system for three years from 2008/09. Its main features are:
- all staff to get a pay increase between 7.6 and 7.9 per cent over the three years
- a 5.8 per cent increase in the NHS minimum wage to £6.77 per hour.

The terms and conditions of service for all staff directly employed by NHS organisations under Agenda for Change are set out in the NHS Staff Council's *NHS terms and conditions of service handbook*.

Further information
NHS terms and conditions of service handbook, NHS Staff Council, January 2010.
NHS pay modernisation in England: Agenda for Change, NAO, January 2009.
The NHS knowledge and skills framework (KSF): essential guide for NHS boards, NHS Employers, 2007.
The NHS knowledge and skills framework (KSF): essential guide for NHS staff, NHS Employers, 2007.
From pay reform to system improvement – making the most of Agenda for Change, NHS Employers, 2006.
www.nhsemployers.org/agendaforchange

Contract for GPs

A new GP contract for general medical services (GMS) was implemented across the UK in 2004, with revisions made after negotiations between NHS Employers and the British Medical Association's General Practitioners Committee (GPC). The contract aims to reward practices for providing high-quality care, improve GPs' working lives and ensure patients benefit from a wider range of services in the community.

The GMS contract:
- is between the PCT and the practice rather than with each GP. This is intended to give practices greater freedom to design services for local needs while encouraging better teamworking and skill-mix
- helps GPs to manage their workload by enabling practices to transfer some services – including out-of-hours services – to their PCT.

A key component of the GMS contract is the Quality and Outcomes Framework (QOF), which resources and rewards practices for delivering high-quality care (see page 138). QOF payments will increasingly reflect the prevalence of long-term health conditions, to help address health inequalities by ensuring proportionately greater funding for practices in deprived areas.

The coalition Government plans to renegotiate the GP contract.

Contracts for other doctors and dentists

The current consultants' contract, introduced in 2003, is designed to provide a more effective system of planning and timetabling consultants' duties and activities for the NHS. It gives NHS employers the ability to manage consultants' time in ways that best meet local service needs and priorities. For consultants, it means greater transparency about the commitments expected of them and greater clarity over the support they need from employers to make the maximum effective contribution to improving patient services.

The current contractual arrangements for doctors in hospital and public health training have been in force since December 2000. Junior doctors' hours have been reduced to levels set in the European working-time directive: a maximum of 48 hours per week averaged over 26 weeks.

A new contract for staff grade and associate specialist doctors was agreed in 2008. It applies to 13,000 non-consultant career grade NHS doctors and to all new entrants to the new specialty doctor grade. Annual appraisal, job planning and objective setting are essential components of the new contract.

A salaried dentists' contract was implemented in early 2008. The pay structure is supported by mandatory annual appraisals and job planning to assist career development. The coalition Government plans to introduce a new dentistry contract.

A new community pharmacy contract was implemented in England in 2005, allowing pharmacies to offer an expanded range of clinical services. The 2008 white paper, *Pharmacy in England: building on strengths, delivering the future*, identified further ways in which pharmacists and their teams may improve patient care through personalised pharmaceutical services.

Further information
A guide to the implications of the European working time directive for doctors in training, EWTD Reference Group, December 2009.
Briefing 53: The consultant contract programme, NHS Employers, November 2008.
Briefing 41: Contract proposals for specialty doctors and associate specialists – introduction for employers, NHS Employers, March 2008.
Fifty-ninth report of session 2006/07: Pay modernisation – a new contract for NHS consultants in England, House of Commons public accounts committee, November 2007.

NHS Pension Scheme
All NHS staff automatically become members of the NHS Pension Scheme, but they can choose not to join or leave at any time. The NHS Pension Scheme has undergone significant changes that became effective on 1 April 2008. The changes aim to ensure the scheme continues to meet the needs of a modern NHS and its staff, and is sustainable in the longer term. Employees in the scheme before 1 April 2008 will be able to choose whether to move to the new arrangements, with the transfer process lasting three years until July 2012. The coalition Government is reviewing the long-term affordability of public sector pensions.

Redundancy
Redundancy arrangements for all staff directly employed by NHS organisations, except very senior managers and staff covered by the doctors' and dentists' review body, are included in the *NHS terms and conditions of service handbook*.

Further information
Briefing 67: Pension choice? Career and retirement options for the NHS, NHS Employers, November 2009.
The NHS Pension Scheme and NHS Pension Choice Exercise
www.nhsba.nhs.uk/Pensions

The NHS as an employer

The NHS recognises staff as its greatest asset and knows that to recruit and retain the right people it needs to practise excellence in employment. This includes treating staff with respect and supporting them in their work; valuing equality and diversity; ensuring a healthy workplace; offering flexible working; and providing training and opportunities for development.

Staff 'engagement' is a high priority for the NHS as it can improve morale, productivity, organisational performance and patient experience. Research indicates that staff satisfaction – and retention, discretionary effort and productivity – are closely associated with how staff feel about their employer and their sense of engagement with their workplace. Increasing evidence shows direct links between staff satisfaction and the patient experience.

The results of the seventh national NHS staff survey were published by the Care Quality Commission in 2010. The survey, in which 290,000 staff were invited to take part and 55 per cent responded, found high levels of job satisfaction, with 90 per cent feeling they made a difference to patients. Two-thirds reported working more than their contracted hours. The 28 per cent who said they had suffered from work-related stress in the last year were the same as the previous year but fewer than in 2007 and 2006, when 33 per cent reported this. Slightly fewer staff reported bullying, harassment and abuse from patients or their relatives: 21 per cent in 2009 compared with 23 per cent in 2008 and 26 per cent in 2007.

Further information
Briefing 68: Improving staff engagement: a practical toolkit, NHS Employers, November 2009.
National survey of NHS staff 2008, Healthcare Commission, March 2009.
National NHS Staff Survey Advice Centre **www.nhsstaffsurveys.com**
www.nhsemployers.org/staffengagement

The NHS Constitution, which came into effect in January 2010, made four pledges to staff:

• to provide all staff with clear roles and responsibilities and rewarding jobs for teams and individuals

• to provide all staff with personal development plans, access to appropriate training and the support of line management to succeed

• to provide support and opportunities for staff to maintain their health, well-being and safety

• to engage staff in decisions that affect them and the services they provide individually, through representative organisations and through local partnership working arrangements. All staff will be empowered to put forward better ways to deliver better and safer services.

The Constitution places 11 responsibilities on staff. Key ones stipulate that staff should aim to:

• maintain the highest standards of care and service and take responsibility for their contribution to their team and the NHS as a whole

• take up training and development opportunities provided over and above those legally required of their post

• be open with patients and their families, including if anything goes wrong, be welcoming of feedback and address concerns promptly and in a spirit of cooperation.

These responsibilities are not legally binding but enable employers to have clear expectations of staff.

Equality and diversity

The NHS aims to incorporate equality and diversity into all its workforce strategies and to highlight how it can contribute to improved health and better access to health services. NHS Employers helps trusts to embed equality and diversity in their organisations so they are able to build, manage and retain a diverse workforce, reflecting the communities they serve. Key areas include guidance on meeting employers' legal and statutory responsibilities on equality and diversity and advice on diversity monitoring to help organisations benchmark and track progress. It helps organisations enhance their leadership and ability to make progress on the equality and diversity agenda, as well as providing practical tools on key areas such as developing single equality schemes.

Further information
Briefing 58: Monitoring for diversity: what healthcare employers need to know and do,
NHS Employers, January 2009.
Briefing 49: Equality impact assessments in the NHS – a guide for employers,
NHS Employers, January 2009.
Briefing 48: Single equality schemes in the NHS: the developing picture, NHS Employers,
November 2008.
www.nhsemployers.org/equalityanddiversity

Mental health
One in four people, at some point in their lives, will experience a mental
health problem. Mental ill health costs England over £77 billion every year,
of which the cost to employers is over £25 billion per year. In the NHS,
stress alone is estimated to cause 30 per cent of sickness absence and cost
up to £400 million a year. The 2009 NHS staff survey found 28 per cent of
staff had felt unwell because of work-related stress over the previous 12
months. NHS Employers is tackling stress and other forms of mental ill
health in its Open Your Mind campaign, launched in March 2010. The
campaign aims to reduce stigma and increase understanding of mental ill
health and employment in the NHS.
www.nhsemployers.org/openyourmind

Bullying and harassment
The 2009 staff survey found that 17 per cent of staff had experienced
bullying, harassment or abuse from either their line manager or other
colleagues. The NHS has taken strong steps to eliminate this kind of
behaviour in the workplace but it is clear that problems persist. In 2007
NHS Employers developed model policy, employer and staff guidance,
HR toolkits and communications materials for employers and staff to
tackle bullying.
www.nhsemployers.org/bullying

Policy for health and healthcare must be based on reliable evidence about the population's needs and what will work best to meet them. Such evidence originates from many types of research, covering prevention of ill health, promotion of health, disease management, patient care, delivery of healthcare and its organisation, as well as public health and social care. Conducting research to improve health and medical treatments was one of the NHS's founding principles, and the UK health research system has an even longer tradition of excellence: the Medical Research Council (MRC) has funded 29 Nobel prize-winners since it was founded in 1913. This reputation, combined with the existence of a national health service, attracts high levels of research and development (R&D) investment from the pharmaceutical and biotechnology industries – an important part of the UK 'knowledge economy'.

Several recent developments have been designed to ensure the UK maintains this pre-eminence. They include a strategy for research in the NHS in England, *Best research for best health*, new organisations to help achieve the strategy and the creation of the UK Clinical Research Collaboration and Office for Life Sciences. The ambition is for the NHS to foster a culture that pioneers new treatments so it becomes a hive of research activity attracting the best researchers in the world.

Government, strategy and infrastructure

Department of Health's role

The DH invests in research to support Government objectives for public health, health services and social care, as well as contributing to the Government science strategy. To deliver these objectives, the DH:
- identifies needs and priorities for R&D in health and social care
- persuades other organisations to fund R&D that falls within their remits
- provides support funding for non-commercial research in NHS organisations
- funds and manages R&D not picked up by others
- supports synthesis of research and dissemination of findings to users
- uses research in policy-making
- contributes to wider Government science and technology strategy.

The DH's current research priority areas are:
- cancer
- mental health
- coronary heart disease

- ageing and older people
- public health
- genetics
- diabetes.

Best research for best health

The DH's health research strategy, *Best research for best health*, sets the direction for NHS R&D in England. Launched in 2006, its five-year goals are to:

- establish the NHS as an internationally recognised centre of research excellence
- attract, develop and retain the best research professionals to conduct people-based research
- commission research focused on improving health and care
- strengthen and streamline systems for research management and governance
- act as sound custodians of public money for public good.

As part of the strategy:
- every patient in England will have access to clinical trials and the chance to take part in studies involving new medical therapies
- approval for research projects will be streamlined to avoid bureaucracy, and a national expert advice line will advise researchers on the law
- through the National Programme for IT (see page 234), data collected from the NHS will meet researchers' needs and enable patients to access opportunities to participate in clinical trials
- research programmes will be expanded and world-leading research centres established to drive progress in biomedicine and NHS service quality and safety
- researchers of all disciplines and levels will be supported by the National Institute for Health Research with mentoring and training for career development.

Further information
Best research for best health: a new national health research strategy – the NHS contribution to health research in England, DH, January 2006.

National Institute for Health Research

The National Institute for Health Research (NIHR) has been set up to deliver the Government's R&D strategy for England. Its goal is to create a health research system in which the NHS supports outstanding individuals working in world-class facilities and conducting leading-edge research focused on the needs of patients and the public. The NIHR:

- supports individuals carrying out and participating in research
- commissions and funds research
- provides facilities for a thriving research environment
- creates unified, streamlined and simple knowledge-management systems.

Its programmes are:

- applied research – grants for leading researchers with an impressive track record; the first were made in mental health, medicines for children, diabetes, stroke and dementias, neurodegenerative diseases and neurology
- research for patient benefit (RfPB) – addresses issues of importance to the NHS, including research into everyday practice
- invention for innovation research – aims to accelerate the NHS's take-up of proven new treatments and devices
- research for innovation, speculation and creativity (RISC) – for speculative and radical health research proposals that could lead to a step-change in patient care
- public health research (PHR) – on the benefits, costs, acceptability and wider effect of non-NHS interventions such as prevention of obesity in children and speed humps for preventing road accidents
- health services research (HSR) – intended to lead to improved service quality and patient safety through better planning and provision
- health technology assessment (HTA) – to ensure healthcare professionals, NHS managers, the public and patients have the latest information on the costs, effectiveness and impact of health technology developments
- service delivery and organisation (SDO) – research on the way health services are organised and delivered by the NHS
- NHS physical environment research and development – improving the way property and facilities are managed and maintained and promoting safe, high-quality and best-value design
- research capacity development – providing support, guidance and academic training for the next generation of researchers.

NIHR has set up clinical research networks to support clinical trials throughout England and promote patient and public involvement in health research. They have increased numbers taking part in clinical trials, and improved their speed, quality and coordination. The UK now has the highest national per capita rate of cancer trial participation in the world. There are six topic-specific networks for cancer, dementia and neurodegenerative diseases, diabetes, medicines for children, mental health and stroke. Another covers primary care. NIHR has also set up a comprehensive NHS research network covering all other diseases and areas of need.

NIHR is investing £450 million over five years in 12 biomedical research centres investigating major causes of illness and death such as cancer, heart disease, asthma, HIV, mental illness, blindness, childhood diseases and ageing. The centres are partnerships between the NHS and universities in London, Oxford, Cambridge, Manchester, Liverpool and Newcastle. They are complemented by 16 biomedical research units taking advances in medical research into the hospital. Their work focuses on areas traditionally receiving limited research funding, including gastrointestinal and liver disease, deafness, musculoskeletal disease and nutrition. Each will receive £3.75 million over four years.

NIHR's nine collaborations for leadership in applied health research and care (CLAHRCs) are partnerships between a university and the surrounding NHS organisations, focused on improving patient outcomes by applying health research. They began work in 2008, aiming to create and embed approaches to research and its dissemination that are specifically designed to take account of how healthcare is increasingly delivered across sectors and wide geographical areas. NIHR provides core funding – typically £5 million to £10 million over five years – which CLAHRCs must match.

NIHR's annual budget incorporates all previously existing funds for NHS research in England, as well as NHS funding that supports clinical research and academics.

Further information
Transforming health research: the first two years – National Institute for Health Research progress report 2006–2008, DH, January 2008.
www.nihr.ac.uk

NHS Evidence is a web portal providing access to authoritative clinical and non-clinical evidence and best practice. Launched in 2009 and hosted by NICE, NHS Evidence aims to be a 'one-stop shop' for health information for the NHS in England. Drawing on local, national and international sources, it covers primary research, summarised clinical evidence, policy documents, commissioning and drugs. Information from the British National Formulary is a key element. It awards an accreditation mark to organisations that meet high standards in developing health information. Through 'My Evidence' users can personalise a search and register to receive the latest information. NHS Evidence is designed for professionals but is accessible to the public, and is intended to be as easy to use as any internet search engine.
www.evidence.nhs.uk

Office for Strategic Coordination of Health Research (OSCHR)

The *Cooksey Report* (see page 229) recommended setting up OSCHR to take an overview of the budgetary division and research strategy of both the Medical Research Council (MRC) and NIHR.

OSCHR was established as a government office to work with the MRC and NIHR on developing a single integrated strategy covering all areas of health research. Key functions are to:

- work with officials to set the Government's health research strategy, taking into account advice on priorities and needs from NIHR, its equivalents in Scotland, Wales and Northern Ireland, the MRC and the NHS
- set a budget for the strategy and submit a single bid to the Treasury
- communicate the UK's health priorities to the pharmaceutical and bioscience sectors
- monitor delivery of the strategy against objectives and report to Parliament on progress
- encourage a stronger partnership between Government, health industries and charities.

Further information

OSCHR: chairman's first progress report, HM Government, November 2008.

Milestones in NHS research

During its 61-year history, the NHS has played a central role in health R&D. Major discoveries involving the NHS include:

- in 1950, Sir Richard Doll and Sir Austin Bradford Hill discovered a link between smoking and lung cancer; in 1954, 80 per cent of UK adults smoked – now only 21 per cent do
- in 1962, orthopaedic surgeon Sir John Charnley was the first to perform a total hip replacement at Wrightington Hospital, Wigan; the NHS now carries out more than 62,000 hip replacements a year
- in 1978, the world's first IVF baby, Louise Brown, was born in Oldham General Hospital; more than 1 million 'test tube babies' have been born since
- in the 1990s, Professor Lesley Regan of St Mary's Hospital, London, discovered that 15 per cent of women who suffered recurrent miscarriages carried antibodies in their blood that made it prone to clotting; she found that by treating such women with aspirin and heparin their rate of live births rose from 10 to 70 per cent.

Further information

60 years of research in the NHS benefiting patients, NIHR, June 2008.

Office for Life Sciences

The Office for Life Sciences (OLS) was established in January 2009 in recognition that more needed to be done to support a thriving UK environment for the life sciences: pharmaceuticals, medical technology and medical biotechnology. Life sciences are seen as one of the high-tech strategic industries important in driving growth and prosperity, continuing improvements in healthcare and meeting future challenges such as an ageing population and obesity. The *Life sciences blueprint* is a plan for achieving this ambition. OLS has four priorities:

- strengthening the NHS as an innovation champion
- building a more integrated life sciences industry
- ensuring access to finance and stimulating investment
- marketing the UK life sciences industry overseas.

In its first year, OLS has created an 'innovation pass', the UK Innovation Investment Fund, the Patent Box and an NHS Life Sciences Innovation Delivery Board. In early 2010 the UK Life Sciences Super Cluster was launched, and aims to boost collaboration and leadership in translational research by harnessing UK capabilities in areas of clinical need.

Further information
Life sciences 2010: delivering the blueprint, HM Government, January 2010.
Life sciences blueprint: a statement from the Office for Life Sciences, HM Government, July 2009.
www.dius.gov.uk/ols

Funding R&D

Who funds R&D?
The DH is the largest single public sector contributor, but it is not the only funder of UK health and social care research. The funding councils, research councils – especially the MRC – and research charities all play significant roles. Industry is a major investor in healthcare R&D. The health departments in Scotland, Wales and Northern Ireland also support health and social care R&D. Other government departments provide research funding too.

CSR funding
The comprehensive spending review in 2007 resulted in full funding for the *Cooksey Report* recommendations (see opposite). Public funding for health research will rise to £1.7 billion, with ring-fenced funding for NIHR of £1 billion by 2010/11. This level of funding is intended to support an unprecedented growth in the number of NHS clinical trials in England.

Programme grants for applied research
A key strand of the R&D strategy is to support applied health research addressing the NHS's priorities and needs. NIHR's programme grants for applied research make available funding up to £2 million over three to five years from the scheme's annual budget of £75 million. The aim is to:
- provide evidence to improve health outcomes through promoting health, preventing ill health, and disease management, particularly for conditions causing significant disease burden, where other research funders may not be focused or insufficient funding is available
- enable NHS trusts to tackle areas of high priority or need for health
- provide stable funding to support long-term development of top-quality applied research groups in the NHS.

Sir David Cooksey's report in 2006 reviewed the institutional arrangements for health research and highlighted a number of health challenges facing the UK and the rest of the world, including cancer, mental health, chronic and degenerative disease, nutrition, diet and lifestyle, cardiovascular diseases and infectious diseases such as malaria, TB and HIV/AIDS.

Cooksey recommended bringing together the research budgets of the MRC and the DH to achieve better coordination of health research and more coherent funding arrangements. He also called for the establishment of the Office for Strategic Coordination of Health Research to act as a central coordinating body for health research.

Further information
A *review of UK health research funding*, HM Treasury, December 2006.

Research organisations
Apart from the main statutory bodies, other organisations play an important part in gathering and analysing evidence and promoting R&D.

UK Cochrane Centre
The UKCC was established in 1992 by the NHS R&D programme 'to facilitate and coordinate' systematic reviews of randomised controlled trials. It is now one of 12 Cochrane Centres around the world which provide the infrastructure for coordinating the Cochrane Collaboration, an international, not-for-profit, independent organisation, dedicated to making up-to-date, accurate information about the effects of healthcare readily available worldwide. The Cochrane Library is a regularly updated collection of evidence-based medicine databases, including the Cochrane database of systematic reviews, which provides high-quality information to professionals and the public.
www.cochrane.co.uk

UK Clinical Research Collaboration
The UK Clinical Research Collaboration brings together the NHS, research funders, industry, regulatory bodies, Royal Colleges, patient groups and academe to promote high-quality clinical research. Its main activities are:
• developing a comprehensive infrastructure to underpin clinical research
• building an expert research workforce to support clinical research

- developing incentives for research in the NHS
- streamlining regulations and governance
- developing a coordinated approach to research funding.
www.ukcrc.org

Health Services Research Network

HSRN aims to connect all universities, commercial and professional organisations, charities and NHS bodies with an interest in research underpinning improvements in how health services are financed, organised, planned and delivered, including health technology assessments and health policy research. It seeks to influence policy-makers and managers to support better use of research, campaigns for secure funding for health services research and for measures to improve the careers of those engaged in it.
www.nhsconfed.org/HSRN

SDO Network

This is a network of NHS organisations supporting research, evaluation and innovation. It aims to provide services customised to the needs of senior, middle and new NHS managers to help their organisations develop leading-edge services. It does this by facilitating their access to and use of the latest health services research. The network provides a safe place for managers to work and reflect with their peers, academics and leaders from the private sector on the best ways of using research knowledge to improve the services they manage. The network is provided by the NHS Confederation.
www.nhsconfed.org/sdonetwork

Spotlight on policy: **The innovation landscape**
Innovation is seen as a vital means by which the NHS can tackle the 'quality and productivity challenge' of improving care and increasing efficiency while coping with financial restraint.

Since 2009 strategic health authorities have had a legal duty to promote innovation 'for the purpose of securing continuous improvement in the commissioning and provision of healthcare'. They must produce an 'annual innovation report' detailing action taken, progress, investment, outcomes and impact. The DH has contributed £220 million to regional innovation funds 'to identify, grow and diffuse tomorrow's best practice', focusing specifically on innovations in healthcare delivery, health improvement and patient empowerment and engagement. The intention is to accelerate innovation and diffuse it more widely. In addition, 'innovation challenge prizes' will be awarded to individuals for innovations directly benefiting patients and the public, to help foster an enterprise and innovation culture in the NHS.

Health Innovation Council
Drawing members from the NHS, academe and industry, the Health Innovation Council's purpose is to provide strategic advice on how to develop innovation in health and social care, and how to tackle its variable uptake, building on 'work already underway in existing structures'. It supports the discovery and development of new products and techniques, encouraging the adoption of cost-effective innovations especially in pharmaceuticals, clinical practice, delivery models of service and management. HIC is intended to complement NICE and the NHS Institute for Innovation and Improvement.

NHS Institute for Innovation and Improvement
A special health authority based at Warwick University, the NHS Institute supports the rapid adoption and diffusion of new ideas by providing practical guidance on local, safe implementation. With an £80 million annual budget, the Institute is particularly interested in service transformation, technology and product innovation, leadership development and learning. At the DH's request it is developing ways of measuring whether the NHS is getting better at promoting innovation and using cost-effective technology. www.institute.nhs.uk

NHS National Innovation Centre
Hosted by the NHS Institute, the NIC aims to speed up development of pre-commercial technologies likely to benefit the NHS. It provides free online tools to help assess ideas and find resources. It can link with national and international organisations to tailor-make plans for rapidly developing intellectual property. The NIC also issues to industry and academe 'calls for solutions' to meet particular NHS needs. www.nic.nhs.uk

Innovation hubs
NIC coordinates nine regional innovation hubs, which support entrepreneurial activity by helping trusts identify and commercialise their innovations, protecting intellectual property and seeking appropriate partners so the NHS can benefit financially from its own inventions.

The hubs are now responsible to the SHAs, which have taken over their funding from the DH and other government departments.
www.innovations.nhs.uk

NHS Technology Adoption Centre
Based in Manchester and launched in 2007, NTAC's mission is to increase the NHS's uptake of new technology, identify technologies that will improve healthcare and promote greater cooperation between organisations developing and using healthcare technologies. It works at a clinical, managerial and procurement level, scanning the medical technology industry for innovations and organising regular calls for innovative products. If NTAC is aware that increased uptake of a technology would benefit the NHS, it carries out a technology adoption review to identify barriers to adoption.
www.technologyadoptioncentre.nhs.uk

Academic health science centres
Five partnerships between research, education and health service bodies were designated as 'academic health science centres' in 2009, chosen by an international peer review panel. They will benefit mainly from recognition and prestige rather than extra funding, enabling them to compete with internationally renowned centres such as Harvard and Johns Hopkins in the USA and Sweden's Karolinska Institute. AHSC status is awarded for five years, when designation will be subject to review and re-application.

Health innovation and education clusters
The 17 HIECs announced at the end of 2009 will be collaborations across primary, community and secondary care, universities and colleges, and industry. They will provide professional education and training and promote innovation in healthcare by speeding up the adoption of research. They will also provide professional education and training.

Further information
National innovation procurement plan, DH, December 2009.
Briefing 5: Making sense of the new innovation landscape, Health Services Research Network/NHS Confederation, April 2009.
Future of leadership paper 3: Leading innovation, NHS Confederation, April 2009.

10 Information technology

A modern IT infrastructure is vital to improving patient safety and enabling choice, helping clinicians to work efficiently and allowing them access to patient information promptly and securely. In his 2002 report on the NHS's long-term future (see page 199), Sir Derek Wanless recommended doubling the IT budget and instituting a national programme to secure a 'major advance' in how the NHS used IT. He warned that without this, 'the health service will find it increasingly difficult to deliver the efficient, high-quality service which the public will demand. This is a major priority which will have a crucial impact on the health service over future years.'

The Labour Government made major investments in NHS IT, devising an ambitious national programme to install systems throughout the service. The programme's scale has been daunting and not without critics who claim – despite some important achievements – that it is too centralised, too expensive and running late. The coalition Government may make significant changes to IT policy and its implementation.

National Programme for IT

Why have a national programme?

The National Programme for IT (NPfIT), launched in 2002, is more extensive than any other IT programme in the world, and represents the largest ever single IT investment in the UK. It is intended to ensure that lost records, inconvenient appointments and delayed test results are a thing of the past. National systems are replacing organisations' separate IT systems that did not communicate with each other. Once installed, the new IT infrastructure will connect more than 110,000 doctors, 390,000 nurses and 120,000 other healthcare professionals, giving patients access to their personal health and care information while transforming the way the NHS works. (NHSScotland has its own national eHealth IM&T strategy, see page 270; NHS Wales has its own approach, Informing Healthcare, see page 287; the health service in Northern Ireland has now embarked on a ten-year programme of investment in IT, see page 300.)

Costing the programme

NPfIT represents around 25 per cent of the NHS's total IT spend. Its overall cost is expected to be £12.65 billion over ten years to 2013/14. Since it started, costs have increased by £666 million due to the purchase of extra functionality. In addition to national IT spending, trusts have increased their investment in – for example – payroll, finance and HR systems in line with the 2002 Wanless Report's recommendation that they should devote 4 per cent of their budgets to IT by 2008. By March 2009, spending had reached £4.47 billion. The cost of delays to parts of the programme is being met by suppliers.

As part of the response to the economic downturn, the 2009 pre-Budget report announced plans for savings on NPfIT. The then Secretary of State explained that the DH was 'working towards achieving a reduction of £600 million in the lifetime cost of the programme', and would 'pare back the programme to the core elements that have been identified as critical by clinicians', including:
• systems that clinicians regard as most important to them, such as electronic prescribing
• linking national systems with those provided by local service providers
• allowing the NHS to design IT systems to fit local needs.

Although this would involve 'cancelling certain additions to the system' and savings on running costs, there was 'no intention whatsoever of cancelling the programme overall'.

Implementing NPfIT

Implementing NPfIT has not involved a 'big bang'. Systems and services have been gradually phased in, according to priorities and when NHS organisations are ready to implement them. However, the National Audit Office reported in 2008:

Delivering NPfIT is proving to be an enormous challenge. All elements of the programme are advancing and some are complete, but the original timescales for the electronic care records service, one of the central elements of the programme, turned out to be unachievable, raised unrealistic expectations and put confidence in the programme at risk.

Nevertheless, it added that 'the original vision remains intact and still appears feasible'. By the end of 2009, many of the programme's systems and most of the infrastructure had been delivered successfully. All acute trusts and over 90 per cent of PCTs had at least one system delivered through NPfIT, and all GPs in England were using systems delivered as part of the programme. But the Care Records Service is unlikely to be fully deployed before 2014/15, four years later than planned. The software has taken much longer to develop than envisaged so some trusts have installed an interim system. Problems with the system for the North, Midlands and East area may still lead to further delay.

Spotlight on policy: Health informatics

Health informatics is: 'knowledge, skills and tools which enable information to be collected, managed, used and shared to support the delivery of healthcare and to promote health'. The DH's 2008 health informatics review found the range and quality of information needed to be enhanced and integrated into all aspects of health and social care. The DH now includes routine informatics assessments of new policies to ensure their information requirements are considered from the outset.

In consulting 1,400 stakeholders, including patients, public and clinicians, the review discovered concerns about:
• ownership of strategy and future objectives
• potential future skills shortages
• getting maximum benefit from systems
• increasing trust in information and its management
• delivering effective solutions and closing gaps in data coverage
• improving access to information
• overcoming fragmented governance and reporting arrangements
• agreeing common standards.

The review found that lack of progress with key aspects of NPfIT, particularly the Care Records Service, had caused major problems for trusts. As a result, trusts have since been allowed to implement interim local IT solutions if they are consistent with NPfIT's overall objectives.

For 2010/11 the NHS is following four main informatics themes:
• connecting all – in particular, connecting citizens with information, patients with clinicians, clinicians with each other and with information
• supporting new models of care – NPfIT components such as Choose and Book can be used to help redesign services
• reducing costs – by removing geography and time constraints, delivering transactions online, increasing convenience and shortening the supply chain
• integrated planning and performance – PCT operating plans should describe how informatics will be used to maximum effect on key national policies as well as regional and local initiatives.

Further information
Informatics planning 2010/11, DH, December 2009.
Health informatics review report, DH, July 2008.
Briefing 170: The 2008 health informatics review, NHS Confederation, August 2008.

The Commons public accounts committee felt the departure from the programme of two of the original four local service providers had heightened risks, and was sceptical that care records systems would be fully implemented by 2014/15. Deployment of the care record system in a London acute trust highlighted significant problems with the software that has raised further doubts about achieving this target.

The DH has said it is committed to opening the IT market to new suppliers and new technological developments to inject more pace into the programme.

Further information
Second report of session 2008–09: the National Programme for IT in the NHS: progress since 2006, House of Commons public accounts committee, January 2009.
The National Programme for IT in the NHS: progress since 2006, National Audit Office, May 2008.

Who does what
The NPfIT Local Ownership Programme (NLOP) was devised in 2006 to enable NHS organisations to define their own IT priorities and align NPfIT with new information governance arrangements. Strategic health authorities and primary care trusts became accountable in 2007 for delivering NPfIT, with support from NHS Connecting for Health (NHS CFH).

To ensure relationships with local service providers continue effectively, NPfIT management boards have been established in three areas – London; the North, Midlands and East; and Southern.

In addition:
• two national application service providers are responsible for purchasing and integrating IT systems common to all users
• local service providers deliver IT systems and services locally for the three areas.

The DH's chief information officer for health is responsible for health informatics for the NHS and social care in England. This includes overall digital health strategy and the development of national and local information systems. A member of the NHS management board and reporting to the NHS chief executive, the CIO provides professional leadership to the key informatics organisations inside and outside the DH, including NHS CFH and NPfIT.

Further information
Supporting transformation: a practical guide to NHS Connecting for Health, NHS CFH, 2008.
Better information, better health, NHS CFH, April 2007.

Key organisation: NHS Connecting for Health
NHS Connecting for Health is a directorate of the Department of Health, set up in 2005. It succeeded the NHS Information Authority, and was formed after the review of arm's-length bodies (see page 22). NHS CFH's main role is supporting local NHS organisations in the planning, development and deployment of systems locally. Its staff are drawn from across the NHS, civil service, academe and the private sector, and encompass management, IT, clinical and medical skills.

NHS CFH is delivering NPfIT in England only. Scotland, Wales and Northern Ireland are developing their own IT programmes, but NHS CFH recognises the importance of compatibility. The UK Information Management & Technology Forum has been set up to allow interaction among policy leads from England, Wales, Scotland and Northern Ireland. In addition, the Information Standards Board has representatives from each of the home countries.
www.connectingforhealth.nhs.uk

IT infrastructure

The NPfIT infrastructure includes:
- the NHS Care Records Service (CRS)
- GP2GP, allowing electronic health records to be transferred between practices
- Choose and Book, the electronic booking service for hospital appointments
- Electronic Prescriptions Service (EPS)
- a national broadband IT network (N3)
- NHSmail, a central email and directory service for the NHS
- NHSweb
- NHS Choices
- HealthSpace
- picture archiving and communications systems (PACS)
- IT supporting GP payments, including the quality management and analysis system (QMAS).

NHS Care Records Service

A single electronic record system to which all care providers have access is essential because patients attend various institutions at different times, encountering a range of care professionals and organisations including social care and the independent sector. The NHS Care Records Service will connect GPs and trusts in a single, secure national system, providing all 50 million NHS patients in England with an individual electronic care record detailing key treatments in the health service or social care.

Every patient will have a two-part care record. The detailed care record – held locally – will be formed from the detailed notes made by every healthcare professional who treats the patient; the summary care record – held nationally – will contain essential information selected from the detailed record, such as allergies or medication. Patients will be able to access their own summary care record using HealthSpace (see page 242). They may choose not to have a record created or not to have it shared, though so far only 0.8 per cent have done either.

Clinical need and patient wishes will decide who has access to records. Access to the computer system will only be allowed after training. Organisations needing to access patient information in the NHS Care Records Service set up registration authorities, which are responsible for verifying the identity of healthcare staff who wish to register to use these services. Once authorised, the authority issues the individual with an NHS CRS smartcard with a passcode, which they must use each time they log on. Users must be directly involved in the care of the patient whose record they wish to access, and access will depend on their role: for example, a receptionist booking an appointment will only have access to basic information to identify a patient and make the booking. Every time someone accesses a patient's record, a note will be made of who, when and what they did. Patients will be able to request this information. A 'care record guarantee', overseen by the National Information Governance Board (see page 243), sets out the principles governing storage and access to records for patients.

A core data storage and messaging system, known as 'the Spine' is central to the CRS. In addition to storing patients' personal characteristics, summarised clinical information and security systems, this will offer a secondary users service providing anonymised data for business reports and statistics for research and planning.

Initially every patient was to have an electronic care record by 2010, but developing detailed care records has proved a far greater challenge than anticipated, according to the NAO. The first phase was completed during 2004, and included the infrastructure to enable booking of outpatient appointments and professionals to view basic patient information. Implementation of the summary care record began in 2007 and so far covers ten areas. By January 2010, there had been 972,095 summary care records uploaded to the spine, and 757,972 smartcard holders were registered and approved for access.

The GP2GP project enables the electronic transfer of patients' healthcare records from one GP surgery to another. It is designed to ensure records are available to the new GP within 24 hours of a patient registering with their practice. By early 2010, a total of 5,214 practices were using GP2GP and had made 921,640 transfers.

Further information
The care record guarantee: our guarantee for NHS care records in England, National Information Governance Board, 2009.
www.nhscarerecords.nhs.uk
National Information Governance Board www.nigb.nhs.uk

Choose and Book
Choose and Book, the electronic booking service, is designed to underpin the policy of enabling patients to choose which hospital to attend at a date and time to suit them. The software allows GPs and other primary care staff to make initial hospital or clinic outpatient appointments before the patient has left the surgery. This enables clinicians to track referrals more easily and conduct email discussion about cases when necessary. It also provides more consistent, accurate and efficient referral information without the delays of paper correspondence. Choose and Book should reduce the chance of patients not turning up for appointments and improve clinical governance by providing an audit trail.

Between its introduction in 2004 and January 2010, over 20.5 million bookings had been made. Choose and Book was being used for more than 50 per cent of NHS referral activity from GP surgery to first outpatient appointment. All hospitals and over 90 per cent of GP practices were using it, sending 35,000 referrals a day.
www.chooseandbook.nhs.uk

Electronic prescription service

The Electronic Transmission of Prescriptions programme will create and implement the electronic prescription service (EPS), then integrate it with the NHS CRS. EPS will operate throughout England.

Prescriptions are transferred electronically to a pharmacist nominated by the patient. If a pharmacy has not been nominated, the patient is given an ePrescription to present at a pharmacy. This has a barcode which enables the pharmacist to obtain details of the prescription from the NHS CRS. The prescribed medication details are added to the patient's electronic record held by the NHS CRS. Electronic transmission will increase patient safety by reducing prescription errors and providing better information at the point of prescribing and dispensing. This creates the opportunity to reduce adverse drug events where the patient responds poorly to medication. Almost 285 million prescription messages had been transmitted electronically by January 2010. Over 7,000 GP practices and 9,000 pharmacies were using EPS. Eventually other locations such as walk-in centres, dental practices and hospitals will be included.

N3: the New National Network

N3 provides the entire NHS with fast broadband networking services, and forms the essential technical infrastructure for NPfIT's other major projects. It replaced the earlier NHSnet, saving £900 million over seven years, and is one of the world's largest virtual private networks. Clinicians can send high-quality images to specialists for remote diagnosis and use N3 for secure clinical messaging. It makes video conferencing and remote working easier, and saves on telephone costs by enabling NHS organisations to converge their voice and data networks. It is intended to be flexible enough for future needs and allow the NHS to take early advantage of improvements in technology. Connections to N3 started in 2004. About 1.4 million NHS employees have access, including all GP practices.
www.n3.nhs.uk

NHSmail

NHSmail is a secure national email and directory service for NHS staff in England and Scotland, developed specifically to meet the British Medical Association's requirements for clinical email between NHS organisations. It provides a national directory of people in the NHS, containing the name, email addresses, telephone numbers, name and address of their organisation, and information about departments, job roles and specialties. Staff are assigned an email address that moves with them if they change job or location within the NHS. By February 2010, 500,000 staff were registered; over 500 million emails have been sent since April 2009. When complete NHSmail will have 1 million users, making it the world's largest private, single-domain email service.

Nhsweb

Websites can be hosted exclusively on N3 for NHS use, and are described as being on NHSweb as opposed to being on the worldwide web. NHSweb also hosts intranets for individual NHS organisations. Users connected to other networks are blocked at the firewall and cannot access NHSweb sites, although they may send emails.

NHS Choices

NHS Choices is the NHS's online service for the public, providing information on 750 health conditions and treatments, healthy living and health and social care services. It provides a single 'front door' for the public to all NHS online services and information through the country's biggest health website. This includes information to help people find services and compare hospitals. NHS Choices receives 7 million visits a month.

Further information
Better access health care quality lives: NHS Choices annual report 2009, NHS Choices, June 2009.
www.nhs.uk

HealthSpace

HealthSpace is a secure website where patients can store personal health information online, such as height, weight and blood pressure. It is free and available for all NHS patients living in England aged 16 and over. Anyone living in an area that has adopted a care record system can view their summary care record through an Advanced HealthSpace account. HealthSpace has plans eventually to introduce patient-to-clinician messaging, self-care support for long-term conditions, primary care appointment bookings, requests for repeat prescriptions and access to NHS Choices information.
www.healthspace.nhs.uk

NHS number

The NHS number is the common currency of NHS information and fundamental to NPfIT. Babies born in England and Wales are allocated an NHS number at birth. It is a unique identifier that provides a common link between a patient's records – electronic and manual – across the NHS. It consists of ten digits: the first nine are the identifier and the tenth is a check digit used to confirm the number's validity. It is the cornerstone of the move towards an electronic health record, and enables disparate information to be collated into a comprehensive record of a person's health.

Key organisation: National Information Governance Board for Health and Social Care

NIGB was set up in 2008 to ensure patient data is stored and used securely. It promotes consistent standards for information governance across health and social care, and tackles the ethical and legal interpretation and application of policies, procedures and guidance. It is responsible for the care record guarantee (see page 239), and administers applications to set aside the duty of confidentiality in certain circumstances. NIGB has also issued guidance on topics such as the children's summary care record, locums' access to NPfIT systems and the security of NHS data.
www.nigb.nhs.uk

Collecting and using data

Collecting data from frontline NHS organisations is necessary to ensure patient safety and provide accountability. But it became apparent that the burden of data collection had grown disproportionately, with much duplication and overlap to satisfy the demands of inspection and regulatory bodies. The DH therefore introduced a policy of collecting only essential data, designed to ensure that:
• collections fit with national policies
• requests for the same information are not repeated
• NHS organisations can complete these in as little time as possible.

During 2004/05 the DH examined data requirements and identified 61 central collections to be eliminated or streamlined. Since then it says data collection has been reduced by 28 per cent for the NHS overall, with about half of all central collections being stopped or cut in size for foundation trusts. In 2007 the Labour Government set a target to reduce the data burden from central departments on frontline staff by 30 per cent by 2010, and had achieved 24 per cent by December 2009.

The Information Centre's Review of Central Returns (ROCR) process aims to minimise central data demands on the NHS from the DH and its arm's-length bodies. It regularly reviews all information requirements and approves requests for information – including one-off surveys – taking account of the NHS effort involved in supplying the data requested. Only collections that have been through this process are added to the list of authorised central returns. If a request does not contain an ROCR number, NHS staff do not need to complete it. Even the need for data to answer parliamentary questions or support public expenditure survey negotiations is not a justification in itself for ROCR support.

The DH has developed UNIFY to act as a single 'warehouse' for information previously recorded on several local systems to meet different reporting requirements. Once data is captured, it now needs to be input only once, via NHSweb. This frees the NHS from multiple requests for additional information.

The Audit Commission has noted that 'the quality of data in the NHS is often not what it needs to be to meet the demands now being placed upon it'. It proposed five steps to improve data quality in the NHS:
• clear leadership from the DH, senior managers, clinicians, regulators and the National Quality Board
• greater clinical engagement
• a stronger interest from boards
• external monitoring and review
• more support for organisations, such as that provided by the Information Centre's data quality programme.

Further information
Figures you can trust: a briefing on data quality in the NHS, Audit Commission, March 2009.
Review of NHS data collections 2005, DH/Information Centre, July 2006.
UNIFY **nww.unify2.dh.nhs.uk/unify**

Key organisation: **Health and Social Care Information Centre**

The Health and Social Care Information Centre is a special health authority that collects data from across health and social care, analyses it and converts it into useful information. Set up in 2005, it aims to improve information quality and data standards, improve access to information and deliver the information that frontline services need, as well as being the source of data for official statistics. It provides data to support commissioning and clinical audit, together with statistics on the NHS workforce, finance and performance, public health and social care. Recent initiatives include:

- Indicators for Quality Improvement (see page 139)
- patient-reported outcomes measures (see page 142)
- National Clinical Audit Support Programme.

www.ic.nhs.uk

11 The NHS in Scotland

The NHS in Scotland has abolished the structure which was a legacy of the internal market of the 1990s, replacing it with an integrated system that stresses collaboration and cooperation between organisations rather than competition. While variations in the NHS's structure and policy emphasis have always existed in different parts of the UK, they have become more prominent since devolution, especially in Scotland.

The structure of NHSScotland

Ultimate responsibility for the NHS in Scotland lies no longer with Westminster but with the Scottish Parliament, and specifically the Scottish Government's cabinet secretary for health and wellbeing. The Scottish Government Health Directorates have strategic responsibility for the service. A range of special health boards provide services nationally, while locally 14 NHS boards both plan and provide services. Community health partnerships manage primary and community health services.

The Scottish Parliament

The Scottish Parliament at Holyrood opened in 1999 with powers devolved from the UK Parliament covering matters that include health, social work, education, housing and local government. Its 129 members (MSPs) can therefore pass primary and secondary legislation affecting Scotland on a range of domestic issues. Issues concerning Scotland that have a UK or international impact are dealt with by the UK Parliament in Westminster. These 'reserved matters' include foreign affairs and defence, but also certain health-related issues:

• professional regulation
• abortion
• human fertilisation
• genetics
• control and safety of medicines.

The UK Parliament can also make laws that will apply to Scotland on any subject, but does not normally legislate on devolved matters without the consent of the Scottish Parliament.

Committees play a central part in the Parliament's work, taking evidence from witnesses, scrutinising legislation and conducting inquiries. The health and sport committee considers health policy and matters such as community care, public health and food safety, as well as sport. It is responsible for considering any proposed legislation that falls within its remit. This includes legislation setting out the Scottish Government's budget proposals for each financial year. The committee also commissions research, conducts inquiries and considers petitions submitted by the public. It has eight members, assigned between the parties on a proportional basis.

In addition, some of the Parliament's seven mandatory committees take an interest in NHSScotland: for example, the finance committee is concerned with public expenditure and how the Scottish Government's budget is spent, while the public audit committee holds NHS boards to account for how they spend taxpayers' money and ensures public funds are spent effectively.

The Scotland Office, led by the Secretary of State for Scotland, represents Scottish interests in the UK Government and Parliament and manages day-to-day devolution issues from the Westminster perspective. There are 59 MPs at Westminster representing Scottish constituencies.
www.scottish.parliament.uk
www.scotlandoffice.gov.uk

The Scottish Government

The devolved Scottish Government's relationship with the Scottish Parliament is similar to the relationship between the UK Government and the UK Parliament at Westminster. Members of the Scottish Government are chosen from the party or parties holding the largest number of seats in the Parliament. The Scottish Government was known as the Scottish Executive from its formation following devolution until it was renamed after the elections in May 2007.

The Scottish Government is led by a First Minister, elected by the Scottish Parliament, who appoints a six-strong cabinet of Scottish ministers. Although the civil service in Scotland remains part of the home civil service, civil servants there are accountable to Scottish ministers, who are themselves accountable to the Scottish Parliament. The Scottish Government administers an annual budget of over £30 billion.
www.scotland.gov.uk

Scottish Government Health Directorates

The Scottish Government Health Directorates are responsible for NHSScotland as well as for developing and implementing health and community care policy. These directorates cover:
• Office of the chief medical officer and public health
• chief nursing officer
• health delivery
• performance management and finance
• health workforce
• healthcare policy and strategy
• primary and community care
• housing and regeneration
• equalities, social inclusion and sport
• eHealth.

They provide the statutory and financial framework for NHSScotland and hold it to account for its performance. The Scottish Government has discretion to intervene if serious problems arise locally.

On its election in May 2007, the Scottish Government created a new, expanded Health and Wellbeing portfolio, adding housing, community regeneration, equality and anti-poverty strategies and sport to the traditional health ministerial responsibilities. This is intended to ensure coordinated cross-cutting policy and action to address the root causes of ill health and inequalities in health status in Scotland.

Health and Wellbeing has three ministers: the cabinet secretary for health and wellbeing, the minister for public health and sport and the minister for housing and communities. The director general health, as well as having overall responsibility for this expanded remit, is the chief executive of NHSScotland, and is accountable to ministers for the efficiency and performance of the service.

Scotland's chief medical officer is the Scottish Government's principal medical adviser, with direct access to ministers. The CMO is also head of the Scottish Medical Civil Service. The post has direct involvement in developing health policy, including prevention, health promotion, health protection and harm reduction. The CMO has lead responsibility for issues such as clinical effectiveness, quality assurance, accreditation and research, and covers the spectrum of health-related issues ranging from public health policy to NHS operations.

Special health boards

Eight special health boards provide services nationally. They account for about £1.3 billion of the total NHSScotland budget of £10.5 billion. They are:

- **National Waiting Times Centre**, comprising the Golden Jubilee National Hospital and the Beardmore Hotel and Conference Centre, both in Clydebank near Glasgow and bought from the private sector in 2002. The hospital carries out only elective procedures in key specialties to reduce waiting times. The NHS-owned four-star Beardmore Hotel has 168 bedrooms and a 170-seat auditorium, and is a national NHS and public sector conference facility.
www.nhsgoldenjubilee.co.uk
www.thebeardmore.com

- **NHS 24**, which provides 24-hour telephone access (0845 242424) to medical advice from clinical professionals and acts as a referral point to local out-of-hours services. It takes 1.5 million calls a year.
www.nhs24.com

- **NHS Education for Scotland**, which designs, commissions and provides education, training and development for NHSScotland's workforce.
www.nes.scot.nhs.uk

- **NHS Health Scotland**, whose work involves tackling inequalities and all aspects of health improvement, from gathering evidence to planning, delivery and evaluation.
www.healthscotland.com

- **NHS Quality Improvement Scotland**, which provides advice and guidance on effective clinical practice – including setting standards – drives and supports improvements in quality and assesses NHS performance, reporting its findings. A Public Services Reform Bill being considered by the Scottish Parliament would create a new body, Healthcare Improvement Scotland, with an expanded role and functions covering all healthcare services, including those provided by the independent sector. It would be established by primary legislation as a corporate body in its own right, rather than as a special health board.
www.nhshealthquality.org

- **Scottish Ambulance Service**, which employs over 3,000 staff who responded to 600,000 emergencies and carried out almost 4,000 air ambulance missions in 2008/09.
www.scottishambulance.com

- **State Hospitals Board for Scotland**, which serves both Scotland and Northern Ireland and cares for 140 male mentally ill patients needing treatment under secure conditions at Carstairs.
www.tsh.scot.nhs.uk

- **National Services Scotland**, which provides specialist legal services, counter-fraud services, health statistics, screening programmes, family health service payments and patient registration. It also monitors clinical standards, as well as overseeing Health Facilities Scotland, the Scottish National Blood Transfusion Service and Health Protection Scotland, which carries out surveillance of communicable diseases, environmental health hazards and public health.
www.nhsnss.org

NHS boards

NHSScotland abolished trusts in 2004 in favour of local single-system working based on 14 (originally 15) NHS boards (11 mainland and three island boards). This was intended to instil shared aims, common values and clear lines of accountability while breaking down traditional barriers between primary and acute care.

NHS boards are mainly responsible for:
- protecting and improving their population's health
- delivering hospital, community and primary care services
- developing a local health plan to address health priorities and needs
- allocating resources according to the board's strategic objectives
- performance management of the local health system.

Boards have a statutory duty to take part in regional and national planning as part of regional planning groups. The three island health boards – Western Isles, Orkney and Shetland – are being strengthened through partnerships with mainland boards designed to allow the larger organisations to use their wider range of resources to support the island boards. For example, Orkney has partnered Grampian, which will provide support in public health, healthcare-associated infections, financial analyst support, human resources and delivery of Orkney's clinical services strategy. Each is receiving an extra £250,000 a year for this.

Scottish NHS board areas

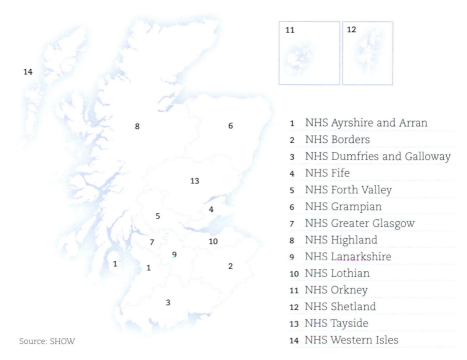

1 NHS Ayrshire and Arran
2 NHS Borders
3 NHS Dumfries and Galloway
4 NHS Fife
5 NHS Forth Valley
6 NHS Grampian
7 NHS Greater Glasgow
8 NHS Highland
9 NHS Lanarkshire
10 NHS Lothian
11 NHS Orkney
12 NHS Shetland
13 NHS Tayside
14 NHS Western Isles

Source: SHOW

All board members are currently appointed by Scottish ministers, although appointments of non-executives are overseen by the Office of the Commissioner for Public Appointments in Scotland. Members divide into three categories:
• non-executive lay members, including the board chair
• non-executive 'stakeholder' members
• executive members.

Boards have between five and nine non-executive lay members. The chair, who is appointed directly by ministers – not elected by board members – is always a non-executive lay person. Each NHS board includes, as full non-executive directors:
• an employee director
• the chair of the area clinical forum
• the chair of the community health partnership advisory forum
• a representative from the university medical school (where applicable)
• an elected council member from each local authority area covered by the board.

Spotlight on policy: Elected NHS boards

After the Scottish Parliament unanimously passed the Health Boards (Membership and Elections) Bill in March 2009, NHS Fife and NHS Dumfries and Galloway will pilot the first ever direct elections to health boards, in 2010.

Directly elected members and elected councillors will then form a majority of members on the two boards, with the elected members replacing some of those previously appointed by ministers. They will receive the same level of remuneration as appointed members, currently around £7,500 per year.

The elections will use the single transferable vote system, and be carried out as all-postal ballots. For the first time in any UK election, 16- and 17-year-olds will have the right to stand and vote. The elections will run for at least two years, and full rollout will only take place with the Scottish Parliament's agreement. The pilots will cost £2.86 million, funded from central Scottish Government budgets.

Fife and Dumfries and Galloway were chosen to ensure the pilots could test the full range of issues likely to be encountered by a health board in both predominantly urban and rural settings. NHS Lothian and NHS Grampian will run two non-statutory pilots that will test ways to improve the existing engagement and involvement mechanisms between the public and the NHS.

The policy intention behind the Health Boards (Membership and Elections) Act is to improve public engagement and increase trust in decision-making processes by strengthening the NHS's local democratic accountability.

Further information
7th Report, 2008 (Session 3): Stage 1 report on the Health Boards (Membership and Elections) (Scotland) Bill, Scottish Parliament health and sport committee, December 2008. *Consultation document: local healthcare bill,* Scottish Government, January 2008.

There is no limit to the number of members per board, and overall size and balance varies. The largest – Greater Glasgow and Clyde – has 32, while the three island boards have 13 to 15 each.

Community health partnerships

CHPs were set up in April 2005 to manage primary and community health services and replace the 79 local healthcare cooperatives. The Scottish Government elected in 2007 has reaffirmed their central role in NHSScotland. They number 40, with every NHS board having at least one. CHPs act as a focus for integrating primary and specialist services locally, forging partnerships with local authorities and the voluntary sector. Eight CHPs – five of them in Glasgow – have developed particularly advanced partnership arrangements with local authority community care services, and have evolved into community health and care partnerships (CHCPs).

Boards are expected to devolve power and responsibility to frontline staff in CHPs. Each CHP has a director or general manager, as well as a chair who is either a health board non-executive director or local authority elected member. CHPs have evolved to replace the old primary care operating divisions within NHS boards, and are now the mechanism for designing, planning and delivering all community-based services. CHP directors and general managers are core members of a board's senior management team.

They must currently address three key policy areas:
• shifting the balance of care to more local settings
• reducing health inequalities
• improving the health of local people.

Within that overall agenda, their specific priorities are:
• better access to primary care
• taking a systematic approach to long-term conditions
• anticipatory care
• supporting people at home
• preventing avoidable hospital admissions
• more local diagnosis and treatment
• enabling discharge and rehabilitation
• improving specific health outcomes.

Further information
Association of CHPs www.achp.scot.nhs.uk

Scottish Health Council

The Scottish Health Council exists to ensure the views of patients and the public are properly taken into account by NHS boards. It assesses how boards are involving patients in decisions about health services, develops examples of best practice in public involvement and helps patients give feedback to boards about their experiences of services. Although part of NHS Quality Improvement Scotland (see page 251), the council has its own identity and responsibilities, with a national office in Glasgow and local offices in each board area, where most of its staff are based. Members of the community are appointed to serve on a local advisory council for each NHS board area.

www.scottishhealthcouncil.org

Scottish Medicines Consortium (SMC)

The Scottish Medicines Consortium, an independent group within NHS QIS, advises NHSScotland on the clinical and cost-effectiveness of all newly licensed medicines, new formulations of existing medicines and all new conditions the medicines will treat. It has 35 members, including healthcare professionals from NHS boards, pharmaceutical industry representatives and lay members. The SMC also has a database of 180 experts to advise on its decisions. The introduction of the SMC as a single advisory body has led to Scotland leading the UK in early, post-launch assessment of new medicines. It ensures that NHSScotland receives regular and standardised advice to enable it to introduce effective medicines as rapidly as possible. The SMC's decisions do not have statutory force, however, and it cannot insist that NHS boards prescribe a particular drug.

www.scottishmedicines.org

Healthcare Environment Inspectorate (HEI)

Set up in 2009, HEI is designed to ensure public confidence in all aspects of the care environment in Scottish hospitals. In particular, it has a mandate to ensure the correct procedures are followed to prevent the spread of healthcare-associated infections. Every acute hospital will receive at least one announced and one unannounced inspection within the three-year inspection cycle, with extra visits as required. HEI operates independently of the Scottish Government and NHS boards. It is based within NHS QIS.

Vital statistics: life expectancy 2006–08 (years)

	Men	Women
England	77.7	81.9
Scotland	75.0	79.9
Wales	76.9	81.2
Northern Ireland	76.3	81.2

Source: Office for National Statistics

Managed clinical networks

Managed clinical networks for a wide range of conditions became well established in Scotland before the rest of the UK. They are defined as:
> linked groups of health professionals and organisations from primary, secondary and tertiary care, working in a coordinated manner, unconstrained by existing professional and health board boundaries, to ensure equitable provision of high-quality clinically effective services throughout Scotland.

They are seen as an important way of integrating systems of care and developing clinical leadership. Managed care networks are a development of the concept, designed to cross boundaries between the NHS and social work departments. The Scottish Government has pledged to encourage expansion of managed clinical networks as part of its health strategy, providing 'national leadership and resources' to set up networks for respiratory and neurological conditions. It envisages some networks recruiting staff and leading changes to specialist children's services, neurosurgery and laboratories.

Strategy and policy

Bringing the NHS under the control of MSPs has resulted in new directions for the Scottish health service often quite distinct from policies pursued by the NHS in England. For example, NHSScotland has explicitly rejected market-based reforms introduced south of the border, and the Scottish Parliament voted in favour of providing free personal care for elderly people, for which charges are levied in England. But like the English NHS, NHSScotland has revised its position on 'topping up' to ensure patients paying for additional treatment or medication are not excluded from NHS care.

Recent milestones in Scottish health policy

Designed to care – 1997 white paper that announced primary care trusts and local healthcare co-ops were to be set up from 1999. PCTs were responsible for all primary and community health services, while LHCCs involved GPs in developing service provision.

Health Act 1999 – ended the purchaser–provider split in Scotland, cutting trusts from 46 to 28 and abolishing GP fundholding.

Our national health – the Scottish NHS plan, published in December 2000, establishing unified NHS boards from 2001, under which trusts became integrated into a single local system, though remaining separate legal entities.

Community Care and Health (Scotland) Act 2002 – enabled the NHS and local authorities to pool budgets for community care and created Joint Futures management bodies for community care services. Provides legislative backing for implementing free nursing and personal care.

Partnership for care – white paper, published in February 2003, that abolished trusts from 2004 and replaced LHCCs with community health partnerships.

Fair to all, personal to each – the next steps for NHSScotland – in December 2004, this set new targets for 'radical improvements' to the patient's journey through the system, particularly 18-week waiting-time targets.

Building a health service fit for the future: a national framework for service change in the NHS in Scotland **(the Kerr Report)** – published in May 2005 after a 14-month inquiry, this recommended improvements in long-term care, action on health inequalities, support for self-care, implementation of a new IT system, separation of planned care from emergencies and more community-based diagnostics, with specialist and complex care to be concentrated on fewer sites.

Delivering for health – published in October 2005, this was the Executive's response to the Kerr Report and set new priorities for NHSScotland based on it.

Better health, better care: action plan – the SNP minority government's plans for the NHS, published in December 2007 (see page 260).

Equally well – published in June 2008, this unveiled plans to tackle health inequalities by providing intensive support for young mothers, strengthening school nursing, improving play opportunities, creating jobs for people on health-related benefits, expanding checks on people with anxiety and depression and regularly assessing the health of people with learning disabilities.

This divergence has become more marked now that opposing political parties control the administrations in Holyrood and Westminster. On forming the minority government in 2007, the Scottish National Party adopted five core strategic objectives around which it focuses government and public services. One of these is 'Healthier: help people to sustain and improve their health, especially in disadvantaged communities, ensuring better, local and faster access to health care'. Population health improvement and the reversal of health inequalities are strong policy themes across government. As well as being the first part of the UK to ban smoking in public places, Scotland recently passed legislation to ban all retail displays of tobacco products by 2013. A minimum unit price for alcohol has also been proposed.

Although the SNP supported the 2005 Kerr report – which underpinned the previous Labour-led administration's health policy – and continues to use its core principles to inform most of its health strategy, since coming to power in 2007 it has also struck out in new directions. For example, it has:

- set up independent expert panels reporting to ministers to scrutinise major service reconfiguration decisions, 'with a general presumption against centralisation'
- reduced prescription charges as part of phased abolition by 2011
- abolished hospital car-parking charges
- legislated for direct elections to NHS boards
- legislated to exclude 'commercial companies with shareholders' holding primary medical services contracts
- banned new private contracts for hospital cleaning and catering services
- expanded GP surgery opening hours
- strengthened waiting-time targets, introducing an 18-week 'referral-to-treatment' standard
- introduced a major focus on healthcare-acquired infections, establishing a new reporting regime and pilots for national screening for MRSA

- announced a national uniform and dress code for staff from autumn 2009
- published a new health strategy, *Better health, better care*, and associated action plans.

Better health, better care – the Scottish health strategy

The Scottish Government's strategy for the health service lays great emphasis on seeing the public and staff as 'partners or co-owners' in 'a more mutual NHS', and promises not to change the funding model. It adds: 'In stressing public ownership through a more mutual approach, we distance NHSScotland still further from market orientated models.' Instead, 'cooperation and collaboration' are to be NHSScotland's guiding principles.

Among its plans are:
- a Patient's Rights Bill
- a charter of mutual rights, providing a clear statement of rights and responsibilities from the perspectives of Government, staff and public
- to develop a 'participation standard' for boards to encourage patient and public involvement
- an annual 'ownership report' embodying the concept of mutuality, sent to every home
- extending GP practice opening hours
- piloting walk-in services through community pharmacies in shopping centres and at commuter points.

Proposals in the Patient's Rights Bill, to be introduced into the Scottish Parliament during 2010, include:
- a 12-week waiting-time guarantee from agreement to treatment to starting treatment for day cases and inpatients
- patients' rights officers for every health board
- reinforcement of existing rights to make a complaint and strengthening support to patients through the complaints process
- better clarity about responsibilities for patients – for example, attending agreed appointments and offering feedback on health services.

Managing performance

Local delivery plans agreed between the Scottish Government and each NHS board are based on the HEAT key targets, which reflect ministers' priorities for the service. The HEAT objectives are :
- Health improvement – improving life expectancy
- Efficiency and governance – continually improving NHS efficiency and effectiveness

Spotlight on policy: Quality strategy and patient experience programme
The Scottish Government is placing increasing emphasis on measuring and improving the quality of care based on patients' own experiences, alongside more traditional targets such as waiting times and efficiency. Its quality strategy, launched in early 2010, aims to improve standards in areas of care identified by patients as being particularly important:
• caring and compassionate treatment
• clear communication and explanation
• effective collaboration with the clinician
• clean and safe care environment
• continuity of care
• clinical excellence.

The work of the national patient safety programme and the healthcare-associated infection taskforce will be incorporated into the strategy, and during 2010 boards will be asked to identify steps to improve quality. The strategy is complemented by a national patient experience programme, Better Together, which collects and disseminates information gathered from surveying groups of patients about their care experience.

• Access to services – recognising patients' need for quicker and easier use of NHS services
• Treatment appropriate to individuals – ensuring patients receive high-quality services that meet their needs.

Each year, HEAT consists of targets due for delivery in that year, well-established targets due for delivery in the following years, and new targets agreed with NHSScotland as emerging priority areas for improvement and development.

In 2008/09, NHSScotland achieved or exceeded most of its HEAT targets, especially for improving access. For 2010/11, 24 HEAT targets have been set, including:
• at least 60 per cent of three- and four-years olds, including the most deprived communities, are to routinely get fluoride teeth varnishing by 2014
• an annual 3 per cent reduction in CO_2 emissions over the next five years
• a further 15 per cent reduction in MRSA cases by 2011, on top of a 30 per cent reduction by March 2010

Free personal care

Uniquely in the UK, personal care services for people over 65 have been available free in Scotland since 2002 (only nursing care is free in the rest of the UK, although the Northern Ireland health minister has said he is committed to introducing free personal care – which could cost £40 million – when resources allow). Eligibility depends on a needs assessment by the local authority, but is intended to be irrespective of income, capital assets, marital status or any care contribution by an unpaid carer. Personal care is defined as including help with personal hygiene, continence management, eating, simple treatments and personal assistance tasks.

Free personal care appears to have strong public support in Scotland, with 75 per cent saying the state should pay for those who need it. By 2008/09, there were 44,660 people receiving free personal care at home at a cost of £257 million, a 100 per cent increase on 2003/04.

In 2006, the Scottish Parliament health committee's care inquiry report found teething problems in implementing the policy but overall judged it to have been a success. In 2008, Audit Scotland said the policy had been launched without proper information about its costs or outcome measures, and it needed to be better planned, managed and funded: central funding was falling short of councils' costs by up to £63 million. Three-quarters of local authorities had introduced eligibility criteria.

Lord Sutherland's review commissioned by the Scottish Government recommended increased funding of £40 million and a more open and transparent system. He also criticised the UK Government for continuing to withhold attendance allowances previously paid to care home residents and currently valued at £30 million a year. All 12 of his recommendations were accepted by the Scottish Government, which provided the additional funding and pledged to work with local authorities to ensure 'greater consistency in how people access personal and nursing care services, including standard eligibility criteria and waiting times'.

As public finances deteriorated in Scotland as elsewhere in the UK during 2009, Audit Scotland warned that policies such as free personal care may be difficult to sustain. But as the policy retains strong cross-party political support in the Scottish Parliament it is likely to continue to be provided for in Scottish budgets for the foreseeable future.

Further information
Scotland's public finances: preparing for the future, Audit Scotland, November 2009.
Free personal and nursing care, Scotland, 2007–08, Scottish Government, November 2009.
Independent review of free personal and nursing care in Scotland, Scottish Government,
April 2008.
A review of free personal and nursing care, Audit Scotland, February 2008.

- 90 per cent of people who need treatment for a drug problem to receive it within three weeks
- faster access to specialist child and adolescent mental health services.

Each health board's performance is assessed through an annual review chaired by the cabinet secretary or health minister and held in public.

Further information
NHSScotland chief executive's annual report 2008/09, Scottish Government, December 2009.

Financing NHSScotland

Sources of funding

General taxation and national insurance contributions form the main source of funding for NHSScotland, as they do for the NHS in the rest of the UK. Charges and receipts from land sales or other assets add comparatively small sums to the total. However, the Scottish Parliament is able to raise additional taxes, although it has yet to do so.

The Scottish Government intends to phase out prescription charges by April 2011, at an estimated cost of £57 million in 2011/12. It abolished charges for eye tests in 2006, estimated to cost £91 million in 2010/11. In 2009 it abolished car-parking charges at 14 hospitals, at a cost of £1.4 million. In the three hospitals where PFI contracts made abolition too expensive, health boards were told to limit or reduce charges. These measures are seen as reaffirming the principle that the NHS is 'free at the point of use'. Scotland's Auditor General has warned that demand for such services will increase, 'placing pressure on their long-term affordability'. But since the Scottish Government began to reduce charges for prescriptions and pre-payment certificates, the proportion of the NHSScotland budget spent on prescriptions has continued to fall annually, despite a significant increase in the take-up of pre-payment certificates.

Resource allocation

UK Government spending reviews, which take place every two years and cover a three-year cycle, determine the amount of public expenditure available for Scotland. Increases to the Scottish budget are made according to the population-based Barnett formula, introduced in 1978 and modified slightly since devolution.

The Scottish Government then decides how this sum should be allocated among its departments, subject to the Scottish Parliament's approval. The Health and Wellbeing budget covers the NHS, housing and regeneration, well-being, sport and grants to local authorities.

Part of the budget is top-sliced to fund national projects and Scottish Government spending on national programmes such as nurse education and training. Then resources are allocated to NHS boards under two categories:
- cash-limited unified budget – spent on hospital and community health services, including GP prescribing, and forming about 70 per cent of boards' discretionary allocation
- non-cash limited demand-led expenditure – spent on family health services provided by primary care contractors.

Allocations to boards, formerly made using the Arbuthnott weighted capitation formula devised in 2000, have been made since 2009/10 using a new formula. Devised by the NHSScotland resource allocation committee, the NRAC formula:
- is built up from 6,500 small areas – 'datazones' – more sensitive to differences within communities, which will assist health board planning
- keeps better pace with changing board populations by using population projections
- is more sensitive to the costs of treating the very young and very old
- uses three measures to reflect additional healthcare needs and adjusts for underuse of services in deprived populations
- assesses the unavoidable costs of hospitals in remote and rural areas, taking account of the islands' special situation
- involves a new model of excess costs of community services using information from Scottish nursing, midwifery and allied health professionals.

The Scottish Government has pledged that moving to NRAC targets will not cut funding to boards receiving a greater share under the Arbuthnott formula, and boards currently funded below the NRAC formula will receive an additional uplift. But there is no timescale for when boards will reach their NRAC target shares.

Further information
Delivering fair shares for health in Scotland: the report of the NHSScotland resource allocation committee, NHSScotland, September 2007.
NHSScotland resource allocation committee **www.nrac.scot.nhs.uk**

NHSScotland spending
Scotland continues to spend more per head on health than the other UK countries (see page 9). NHSScotland's funding increased by 38 per cent in real terms between 2001/02 and 2008/09, but now faces much tighter settlements – 2.4 per cent in 2010/11.

In 2008/09 NHSScotland spent £10.6 billion – about a third of Scotland's £31.3 billion of public spending. It achieved a £4 million underspend against budget – its fourth consecutive underspend – and £297 million in efficiency savings against a target of £215 million. In 2009/10 its budget was £11.1 billion and in 2010/11 it is £11.3 billion, which includes:
- a 2.7 per cent increase to £8.5 billion for health boards
- protection from the £129 million impact of the UK Labour Government's decision to reduce the English NHS's capital budget by £1.3 billion (see page 194)
- £55 million in revenue and capital funding to deal with swine flu.

Audit Scotland has warned that the public sector financial situation will add to the cost pressures facing NHSScotland, and that although all organisations met their financial targets in 2008/09, some had to resort to significant efficiency savings to break even.

Further information
Overview of the NHS in Scotland's performance 2008/09, Audit Scotland, December 2009.

The first NHS-run café in Scotland opened at Glasgow Royal Infirmary in early 2009. Subject to evaluation, other NHS Aroma cafés will open elsewhere – all wholly owned by the NHS. All profits will be reinvested in the NHS and outlets will be staffed by NHS employees. Fifty per cent of products will contain lower fat, sugar and salt.

Staffing and human resources

Staff numbers
A total of 168,976 people were employed in NHSScotland in September 2009 on a headcount basis, a 2.1 per cent increase on 2008. This includes:
- 12,608 doctors and dentists
- 68,681 nurses and midwives
- 9,580 allied health professionals (whole-time equivalent)
- 26,049 administrative staff (WTE)
- 14,761 support staff (WTE).

NHSScotland workforce by staff grouping (September 2009)

1 Medical (HCHS): 6.9%
2 General medical practitioners: 2.9%
3 Dental (HCHS)
4 General dental services
5 Medical and dental support: 1.6%
6 Nursing and midwifery: 40.4%
7 Allied health professions: 6.9%
8 Other therapeutic services: 2.3%
9 Personal and social care
10 Healthcare science: 3.7%
11 Emergency services: 2.3%
12 Administrative services: 18.2%
13 Support services: 12.1%
14 Unallocated/not known

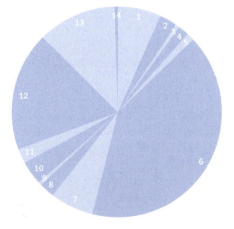

Source: ISD Scotland

Vital statistics: NHS staff: a cross-border comparison (2005)

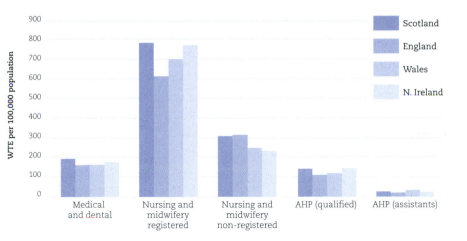

Source: Scottish Executive Health Department

Workforce planning

About 70 per cent of NHSScotland's budget is allocated to the workforce. It published its first national workforce plan in 2006, detailing extra places for trainee GPs and hospital doctors and pledging to maintain numbers for pre-registration nursing and midwifery training. The Scottish Government updated this at the end of 2007 to fit in with its new health strategy, *Better health, better care*.

The rate of growth of NHSScotland's workforce has been lower than the other UK countries', but its staff-to-population ratio is higher. Its workforce is also older than that of other UK countries.

Further information

Better health, better care: planning for tomorrow's workforce today, Scottish Government, December 2007.
National workforce plan 2006, Scottish Executive Health Department, December 2006.

Staff Governance Standard

Our national health, the then Scottish Executive's health plan published in 2000, committed the NHS to becoming Scotland's best employer. The core standards for human resources practice in NHSScotland are set out in the Staff Governance Standard, which all NHS organisations must adhere to. This entitles all staff to be:

• well informed
• appropriately trained
• involved in decisions that affect them
• treated fairly and consistently
• provided with an improved and safe working environment.

The standard is supplemented by a series of best practice guidelines published by the Partnership Information Network Board (PIN). Topics include dignity at work, equal opportunities, family-friendly policies, personal development and dealing with employee concerns. NHS employers are expected to implement these fully. PIN's 13 guidelines are undergoing a review due for completion in 2010.

The 2009 policy document, *A force for improvement*, sets five ambitions for staff in response to *Better health, better care*:

• all staff will be ambassadors for health improvement, safety and quality
• NHSScotland will develop and implement multi-disciplinary and multi-agency models of care
• NHSScotland will be an 'employer of choice'
• all staff will promote the benefits of preventive action and self-care
• staff will work with the education sector to maximise flexible access to education and training.

The NHSScotland staff opinion survey is carried out every two years. The 2008 survey, in which 37 per cent of employees took part, found 73 per cent felt their job made good use of their skills and abilities, 80 per cent were clear about what they were expected to achieve, 76 per cent felt positive about support from colleagues and 77 per cent intended still to be working for the same NHS board in 12 months' time.

Further information

A force for improvement: the workforce response to Better health, better care, Scottish Government, January 2009.

Spotlight on policy: NHS uniform

A new national uniform and dress code are being introduced for NHSScotland staff, 'to promote a professional corporate image and minimise the risk of infection'. Clinical staff will wear tunics in one of four shades of blue with navy trousers. Support staff such as porters and domestic and catering employees will wear tunics in one of two shades of green, with navy trousers. Staff who do not currently wear a uniform will not be required to do so; all others will be required to wear the new uniform by 2012. Staff should not wear uniform out of work.

The dress code applies to all staff, whether or not they are required to wear uniforms. They should:
• wear short-sleeved shirts or blouses
• not wear ties or white coats when providing patient care
• not carry pens or scissors in outside breast pockets
• tie back hair off the collar
• keep nails short and clean.

The Scottish Government is working with partners to develop a suitable uniform for administrative and clerical staff.

Further information
We're changing into something better – NHSScotland new national uniform, Scottish Government, July 2009.
NHSScotland national uniform – Scottish Government consultation on the uniform specification: analysis of consultation responses, Scottish Government Social Research, October 2008.

Partnership forums

Each NHSScotland organisation has a local partnership forum to foster communication between staff, trade unions and managers. Each NHS board area has an area partnership forum. All NHS employers must develop a partnership agreement with staff and their representatives, which must contain – as a minimum – commitments to communication and consultation, access to information and board meetings and organisational change policies. Local partnership forums are mirrored nationally by the Scottish Partnership Forum, comprising senior NHS board managers, trade union national officers and health department representatives. The Scottish Workforce and Staff Governance Committee (SWAG) addresses specific workforce issues that require Scotland-wide solutions.

Every NHS board has an employee director as a full non-executive member. This is usually the elected staff representative from the local area partnership forum.

Further information
Staff governance standard third edition for NHSScotland employees, Scottish Executive, May 2007.

Information technology in NHSScotland

eHealth strategy 2008–11
A revised eHealth strategy was launched in 2008, to support the *Better health, better care* programme. It replaces a strategy from 2004, taking an 'incremental and pragmatic approach' and 'building on what exists and filling gaps where necessary'.

Its main features include:
- procurement of a patient management system for inpatient and outpatient scheduling and waiting-time management, online test ordering and results reporting plus scope for further modules such as A&E, theatres, electronic prescribing and maternity
- a replacement for GPASS (General Practice Administration System Scotland)
- a 'clinical portal' to act as a single online entry point for clinicians to access data about individual patients.

The key groups overseeing the eHealth programme are:
- eHealth strategy board – the governance body providing overall strategic guidance and investment approval
- eHealth programme board – responsible for overall management and implementation
- clinical change leadership group – to ensure clinical input, presenting and consulting with clinical groups
- eHealth leads group – to link NHS boards and the programme at a management level.

At the time of the strategy's launch:
- two health boards were implementing modern patient record systems that support clinical as well as administrative functions
- GPs were using the secure electronic messaging system for 17,000 outpatient referrals a month

- the emergency care summary contained information for over 5.1 million patients and was used 25,000 times a week with patient consent
- there was widespread use of the community health index number (CHI) on key clinical documents sent between GPs and acute hospitals and held on community-held case records
- NHSScotland's PACS services were live in 21 sites, storing over 2 million images
- the ePharmacy programme was sending 1 million prescriptions a month from GP to community pharmacist then onwards for payment.

By mid-2009, the electronic Acute Medication Service (eAMS) was enabled in 99 per cent of Scottish GP practices and pharmacies and 90 per cent of prescriptions were being submitted electronically.

There are 96 national projects and programmes and over 160 local projects implemented by health boards within the national strategy. Funding for eHealth in the Scottish Government's budget for 2010/11 increased by 38.6 per cent from £97.2 million to £134.7 million.

Further information
eHealth strategy 2008–2011, Scottish Government/NHSScotland, June 2008.
www.ehealth.scot.nhs.uk

Scotland's Health on the Web (SHOW)
This website is the official gateway to online information about NHSScotland.
www.show.scot.nhs.uk

12 The NHS in Wales

An awareness that Wales faces major health challenges has shaped its approach to providing care. It has high rates of cancer and heart disease and the highest proportion of elderly people of any of the four UK countries. Poverty levels are high in places, while services have to cater for a complex mix of rural, urban and valley areas.

The structure of NHS Wales

The Welsh Assembly took over ultimate responsibility for the NHS in Wales from Westminster in 1999. Two departments within the Welsh Assembly Government have strategic responsibility for health, one focusing on the NHS and social services, the other on public health matters. After the election of a coalition government in May 2007, plans for significant structural change in the NHS in Wales were drawn up. NHS Wales, like NHSScotland before it, has now abolished the internal market and all but three specialist NHS trusts.

National Assembly for Wales

The National Assembly for Wales opened in 1999 and has 60 elected members (AMs). The UK Parliament devolved to it power to pass secondary legislation to enable it to develop and implement policies, make rules and regulations, set standards and issue guidance in areas that include health and social services, housing, local government, education and economic development. The Assembly's powers were extended by the Government of Wales Act 2006 so that it can now make its own legislation – known as Assembly measures – on devolved matters. Before making measures the Assembly needs to obtain 'legislative competence' on a case-by-case basis from the UK Parliament. This was designed to speed up the time it takes to make laws for Wales, as the Assembly can scrutinise and approve Welsh laws itself, rather than competing for space in the UK Parliamentary programme.

The Assembly provides democratic control of the management and performance of NHS Wales. It draws up strategic policies, sets priorities and allocates funds, but it is not currently able to raise extra taxes.

The Assembly's four scrutiny committees examine the expenditure, administration and policy of the Assembly Government and associated public bodies. Membership reflects the balance of political groups within the Assembly. The nine-member health, wellbeing and local government committee covers health and NHS Wales, local government and public service delivery. Among the Assembly's other committees, the public accounts committee scrutinises the expenditure of NHS Wales by examining reports on its accounts prepared by the Auditor General for Wales. The Wales Audit Office, created in 2005, combines the offices of the Audit Commission and the National Audit Office in Wales.

The Wales Office, led by the Secretary of State for Wales, represents Welsh interests in the UK Government and Parliament. There are 40 MPs at Westminster representing Welsh constituencies.

Further information
National Assembly for Wales **www.assemblywales.org**
Wales Office **www.walesoffice.gov.uk**
Wales Audit Office **www.wao.gov.uk**

Welsh Assembly Government
The Welsh Assembly Government is the Assembly's executive body, led by the First Minister and a nine-strong cabinet that includes a minister for health and social services. The Government of Wales Act 2006 allows up to 12 ministers and deputy ministers, meaning the maximum size of the Welsh Assembly Government is 14, including the First Minister and Counsel General, who is the Government's chief legal adviser.

The First Minister is elected by AMs, and is therefore usually the leader of the largest party. Assembly elections are held every four years, the last being in May 2007 and resulting in a coalition of Labour and Plaid Cymru. Of the Assembly's 60 members, 40 are elected in constituencies using the first-past-the-post system; the other 20 are elected to represent the five regions of Wales using the list system.

Further information
Welsh Assembly Government **http://new.wales.gov.uk**

Department for Health and Social Services
The Department for Health and Social Services (DHSS) is led by the minister for health and social services and is responsible for:
• advising the Welsh Assembly Government on health and social care policies and strategies
• contributing to health and social care legislation
• funding the NHS and other health and social care bodies
• managing and supporting the delivery of health and social care services
• monitoring and promoting improvements in service delivery.

Other responsibilities include research and development, finance, human resources, information management and technology, capital and estates. The department's director general of health and social services is also chief executive of NHS Wales and the accounting officer for the health service. The department's constituent parts are:

- community, primary care and health service policy directorate
- quality, standards and safety improvement directorate
- resources directorate
- children's health and social services directorate
- older people and long-term care policy directorate
- corporate management
- service delivery and performance
- strategy unit
- health and social services human resources
- Children and Family Court Advisory and Support Service in Wales.

The department's current priorities are:

- implementing local health, social care and well-being strategies to deliver integrated health and social care services
- improving health and quality of life
- reducing inequalities in personal health and access to services
- reducing waiting times
- implementing the quality plan for Wales to ensure safe, sustainable and accessible services
- implementing national standards of care for cancer, cardiac, children's, older people's, renal and diabetes services
- implementing policies which better reflect older people's needs
- implementing policies which safeguard children's needs.

The department has regional offices in South East Wales, Mid and West Wales and North Wales.

Department for Public Health and Health Professions
The DPHHP is also led by the minister for health and social services, but its director is the chief medical officer for Wales. Formed in 2007 from the Office of the Chief Medical Officer and the Office of the Chief Nursing Officer, its objectives are:

- to protect the health of the people in Wales and prepare for health emergencies
- to improve health and reduce health inequalities
- to provide professional leadership for health and social care.

To help achieve these, the department is:
• developing a public health strategic framework
• creating new public health structures.

The existence of the DPHHP as a separate entity within the Welsh Assembly Government reflects the high priority attached to improving public health in Wales.

Wales: Local health boards

Welsh Ambulance Service
NHS Trust

Betsi Cadwaladr
University LHB

Powys LHB

Hywel Dda LHB

Abertawe
Bro Morgannwg
University LHB

Cwm
Taf
LHB

Aneurin
Bevan LHB

Cardiff & Vale
University LHB

Velindre
NHS Trust

Source: Welsh Assembly Government

NHS CONFEDERATION

Restructuring NHS Wales

NHS Wales was reorganised in October 2009, creating single local health organisations responsible for delivering all healthcare services within a geographical area, rather than the previous system of trusts and local health boards, which was dismissed as 'complex and over-bureaucratic'. Abolition of the internal market fulfilled a commitment in the policy document *One Wales* (see page 281), drawn up after the 2007 Assembly election. The Welsh Assembly Government hoped this would result in 'a more coordinated approach to healthcare delivery'. Commissioning has been replaced by a new planning system to 'integrate different elements of planning – service, workforce, estate and finance' – and benefit from 'strong clinical engagement throughout'.

Seven newly constituted health boards have replaced the 22 local health boards set up as commissioning bodies in 2004. The new boards have been instructed to focus on:
• changing behaviour, not structures
• collaboration not confrontation
• planning not commissioning
• whole systems not hospitals
• clinical engagement
• partnership working
• wellness not illness.

Each has a decision-making corporate board, a stakeholder reference group and a professional forum; non-executives include representatives of universities, local government, third sector, trade unions and five independent members.

Seven trusts (already reduced from 14 to nine during 2008) were abolished and their staff, property and functions brought under health board control; NHS Wales has more than 130 hospitals and 15,000 beds. The Welsh Ambulance Services NHS Trust and Velindre NHS Trust, which manages specialist oncology services, remained. A third trust, the Public Health Wales NHS Trust (see opposite) was newly formed. Other features include:

National Advisory Board – chaired by the minister and comprising the deputy minister; NHS chief executive; chief medical officer; director of social services; three representatives of local government, third sector and trade unions, and two independent members. Responsible for offering the minister independent advice, it meets in public and publishes its papers.

National Delivery Group – chaired by NHS Wales' chief executive and comprising the DHSS senior directors and up to three independent members; it is responsible for boards' day-to-day operational performance.

Public Health Wales NHS Trust – bringing together in a single organisation a range of public health services and functions previously preformed by the National Public Health Service for Wales, Wales Centre for Health, Welsh Cancer Intelligence and Surveillance Unit and Screening Services Wales.

From 2010, Wales' 19 community health councils will be replaced by six new ones, each relating to a health board area, with the exception of Powys, which will keep its two CHCs. The CHCs are statutory lay organisations with rights to information about, access to, and consultation with all NHS organisations on behalf of the public. The Welsh Assembly Government strengthened their powers in 2004. In addition, Powys Teaching Health Board and Powys County Council have voted to merge into a single body responsible for local services from 2012.

The DHSS has set up the Bevan Commission to act as a think tank and sounding board, advising on emerging health issues and on how effectively the new NHS structure is working. It aims to ensure NHS Wales 'can draw on the best practice from across the world while remaining true to the principles of the NHS as established by Aneurin Bevan', and will exist for up to two years.

Further information
NHS in Wales: why we are changing the structure, Welsh Assembly Government, October 2009.
Unification of public health services in Wales: consultation paper, Welsh Assembly Government, January 2009.
Welsh NHS Confederation **www.welshconfed.org**

Vital statistics: NHS Wales activity
Every year NHS Wales:
• undertakes 700,000 first outpatient appointments
• treats 600,000 inpatients and day cases
• sees 1,059,000 people in A&E
• prescribes 53.9 million items
• carries out 655,000 eye tests.
Source: Welsh Assembly Government

Recent milestones in Welsh health policy

Putting patients first – published in 1998, this abolished GP fundholding and set up local health groups as part of the existing five health authorities.

Better health: better Wales – also published in 1998, this explicitly linked poverty and ill health.

Improving health in Wales – a plan for the NHS with its partners – the Welsh NHS plan published in January 2001, this proposed new structures: establishing the Health and Social Care Department, three regional offices and several other all-Wales bodies, as well as replacing the five health authorities and local health groups with 22 local health boards.

Review of health and social care in Wales: the Wanless Report – Derek Wanless examined how resources could be translated into reform and improved performance in health and social care. In July 2003 he recommended:
- a radical redesign for health and social care services
- an evidence-based approach to best practice and improving system performance
- developing capacity outside acute hospitals
- more public and patient involvement
- stronger performance-management systems.

Designed for life: creating world-class health and social care for Wales in the 21st century – updating *Improving health in Wales*, this is the Welsh Assembly Government's vision for the NHS up to 2015, influenced by the Wanless Report and published in May 2005.

Delivering the new NHS for Wales: consultation paper II – published in December 2008, this set out a new structure for an NHS Wales without the internal market (see page 278).

Rural health planning – improving service delivery across Wales – published for consultation in May 2009, the rural health plan attempted to tackle longstanding problems facing Wales' sparsely populated communities, where people have to travel even for routine services (see page 282).

Our healthy future – a strategy for improving public health by 2020, published in May 2009 (see page 282).

Organisations spanning England and Wales

Organisations whose remit covers both England and Wales include:
• National Institute for Health and Clinical Excellence
• National Patient Safety Agency
• Health Protection Agency
• NHS Direct
• Medicines and Healthcare Products Regulatory Agency.

Strategy and policy

Although the NHS in Wales has had slightly different policy and structural arrangements from England for most of its existence, these have diverged more markedly since devolution in an attempt to find distinctively Welsh solutions for specifically Welsh problems. Wales has some of the UK's highest rates of cancer, heart disease and deprivation, while part of its population suffers the worst health status in Europe.

Following the 2007 Welsh Assembly election, Labour and Plaid Cymru as the ruling coalition drew up a policy document, *One Wales*. Its chapter on the NHS stated: 'We firmly reject the privatisation of NHS services or the organisation of such services on market models. We will guarantee public ownership, public funding and public control of this vital public service.'

It pledged that the Welsh Assembly Government's four-year programme would include:
• a review of reconfiguration
• elimination of the use of private hospitals by NHS Wales
• ruling out use of the private finance initiative in NHS Wales
• an end to competitive tendering for NHS cleaning contracts
• investment in 'multi-purpose wellbeing centres'
• a charter on patients' rights
• separate mental health legislation for Wales
• development of a rural health plan.

A moratorium on proposals for changing community hospitals was agreed, and a pledge made that changes to district general hospitals would only take place once new community services were in place. Some plans approved before the election were subsequently given the go-ahead while others remained under review.

Further information
One Wales – a progressive agenda for the government of Wales: an agreement between the Labour and Plaid Cymru groups in the National Assembly, Welsh Assembly Government, June 2007.

Rural health plan

Community hospitals form a centrepiece of the rural health plan for Wales, published in 2009. The plan seeks to 'add new purpose' to community hospitals and 'exploit their potential' to provide key services closer to rural communities. In addition, it proposes:

- a new 'rural practitioner' role – multi-skilled professionals who will cover services across NHS healthcare and social care
- a network of pharmacies in rural areas to improve access
- more use of telehealth and telecare so that patients do not have to travel long distances for routine treatment and checks
- a rural health innovation fund.

NHS Wales' 2010/11 budget contains £1 million set aside for implementing the rural health plan.

Further information
Rural health plan: improving integrated service delivery across Wales, Welsh Assembly Government, December 2009.

Strategic framework for public health

The Welsh Assembly Government has also published a strategic framework for public health. *Our healthy future* contains four aspirations for 2020:

- across society, people will take care and responsibility for their own and others' health and well-being
- organisations and individuals will work together to improve and protect health
- the gap between communities with poor and those with good health will be reduced
- healthy public policy will support and enable people to lead healthy lives.

The document identifies seven key areas through which to achieve these aims:

- socio-economic, cultural and environmental conditions
- children and young people
- healthy eating, food and fitness
- health-related behaviours and risk

- limiting long-term health conditions
- mental health and well-being
- strengthening local public health delivery.

Further information
Our healthy future, Welsh Assembly Government, May 2009.

Key organisation: Health Inspectorate Wales
HIW was established in 2004 to ensure the safety and quality of health services by reviewing and inspecting standards in Welsh NHS bodies against a range of policies, guidance and regulations. Since 2006 it has also been the regulator for independent healthcare in Wales. It comprises a team of 45 based at Caerphilly and a pool of over 200 external reviewers. HIW has rights to enter and inspect premises, as well as powers to require documents and information.
www.hiw.org.uk

Key targets and priorities

The annual operating framework, first issued in 2007/08, aims to help organisations improve services by setting out what the Welsh Assembly Government expects of them. It contains policy requirements, national targets and efficiency and productivity measures that must be achieved and maintained during the year ahead.

The Welsh Assembly Government and NHS Wales are developing a five-year service, workforce and financial strategic framework to provide 'the overarching direction for delivery of health and social care services over the medium term'. It will be 'grounded in NHS values and have a uniquely Welsh solution to improving health services within the public sector'. It will not pursue market-driven solutions, use of the private sector or PFI. The framework's terms of reference specifically exclude compulsory redundancies.

NHS Wales' 2010/11 operating framework is seen as 'the first step in bridging the gap between the old and new NHS in Wales, and represents the first year of delivery of the five-year framework'. Areas for focus include:
- 'upstream' prevention and well-being, accelerating work on public health
- improving patient care in the community

- reducing waste, harm and variation, partly by embedding the Healthcare Standards for Wales
- improving efficiency and productivity, with emphasis on short-stay surgery, prescribing rates, cancelled operations, sickness and absence rates, better medicines management, delayed transfers from critical care, average length of stay and theatre utilisation
- operating within available financial resources
- an effective and flexible workforce
- improving patient care and safety through the use of ICT
- improving the quality of core services and delivering the national standards.

Further information

NHS Wales: annual operating framework 2010/2011, Welsh Assembly Government, December 2009.

Spotlight on policy: Free prescriptions
The Welsh Assembly Government was the first in the UK to abolish all prescription charges – from April 2007, having reduced them progressively since 2001. Scotland and Northern Ireland are following suit; in England charges are currently £7.20. Only those with a GP and a pharmacist in Wales can take advantage of the scheme. It is estimated the policy benefits 1.5 million people who would not be exempt from charges, and costs about £30 million a year. Amendments to the legislation in 2009 mean that Welsh patients charged for prescriptions after treatment in England can now reclaim the cost. This is expected to benefit about 200 people a year.

Financing NHS Wales

Sources of funding
General taxation and national insurance contributions form the main source of funding for NHS Wales, as they do for the NHS in the rest of the UK. Charges and receipts from land sales or other assets add comparatively small sums to the total. The Welsh Assembly, unlike the Scottish Parliament, is unable to raise additional taxes.

Resource allocation
UK Government spending reviews, which take place every two years and cover a three-year cycle, determine the amount of public expenditure

available for Wales. Increases to the Welsh block grant are made according to the population-based Barnett formula, introduced in 1978 and modified slightly since devolution.

The Welsh Assembly Government then decides how this sum should be allocated among its departments, subject to the Assembly's approval. The health budget comprises seven expenditure groups:
• health boards
• education and training – mainly for doctors and nurses
• family health services – GP pay and prescribing costs, plus dental and ophthalmic costs
• health improvement – public health initiatives, including immunisation
• health promotion – in schools, workplaces, local communities and the NHS
• food standards – funding the Welsh Executive of the Food Standards Agency
• welfare foods – free milk to children and expectant mothers on income support.

Allocations to health boards are made using the Townsend formula devised in 2001. Its principal aim is to curb growth in health inequalities by better targeting NHS resources into areas of greatest need.

In 2010/11, health and social services account for £5.798 billion of the Welsh Assembly Government's £15 billion budget, representing a 2.6 per cent increase of £54 million.

Staffing and human resources

Staff numbers
About 90,000 people work in NHS Wales on a whole-time equivalent basis. Of these, 71,000 people are directly employed, while there are also 1,900 GPs, 1,100 general dental practitioners, 4,000 practice support staff and 600 opticians.

Staff include:
• 5,500 hospital doctors and dentists
• 28,000 nurses, midwives and health visitors
• 10,600 scientific, therapeutic and technical staff
• 9,000 healthcare assistants and other support staff
• 16,000 administration and estates staff
• 1,300 ambulance staff.

NHSCONFEDERATION

Workforce planning

Designed for life noted that NHS Wales needed a new process for workforce planning and commissioning education – a strengthened, integrated and more streamlined model of whole-system workforce redesign. *Designed to work* aims to help bring about the staffing changes needed to achieve the goals of *Designed for life*, particularly cultural change and engaging clinical leaders.

Further information
Designed to work: a workforce strategy to deliver Designed for life, Welsh Assembly Government, July 2006.
Making the connections: connecting the workforce: the workforce challenge for health, Welsh Assembly Government, July 2005.

Key organisation: National Leadership and Innovation Agency for Healthcare NLIAH was set up in 2005 to help build leadership capacity and capability underpinned by technology, innovation, leading-edge thinking and best practice. It helps the Welsh Assembly Government and NHS Wales to identify areas for improvement, then develops tools and techniques to put into practice and maintain these improvements. NLIAH operates across workforce development, leadership and organisational development, partnership development, service improvement and QuIP (quality improvement plan) delivery support.
www.nliah.wales.nhs.uk

Welsh Partnership Forum

The Welsh Partnership Forum consists of representatives of the 14 recognised healthcare trade unions for NHS Wales, senior managers from NHS Wales and representatives from the Welsh Assembly Government.

Its main purpose is developing, supporting and implementing workforce policies on national, regional and local levels. The Forum provides strategic leadership on partnership working between employers and employee representatives. It is involved in planning, education, recruitment, retention, development and support of NHS Wales staff.

Further information
Working in partnership: an organisational change policy for NHS Wales, Welsh Partnership Forum, March 2009.

Information technology in NHS Wales

NHS Wales' IT strategy, Informing Healthcare, was launched in 2003. Its approach is to work through a series of planned and agreed service improvement projects. Its main features include:

Single patient record

Every patient will have a single electronic health record, with the eventual aim of fully integrated health and social care records. The approach is to replace paper-based systems and use new technologies to link existing computer systems so that data can be held in many locations without one central store or data warehouse.

Individual health record

The first stage towards the single record, the IHR connects GP practices with emergency and out-of-hours care providers. It gives health professionals providing unscheduled care access to essential information from the patient's GP-held health record.

Welsh Clinical Portal

The portal is a secure web-based 'healthspace' which supports routine care tasks and unites key information, such as pathology, radiology, cancer and GP data, from the various computer systems in NHS Wales. The portal uses technology similar to internet shopping sites.

Welsh Clinical Communications Gateway

The Gateway manages electronic referrals and other clinical communications between GP surgeries and hospitals. It was pioneered in Scotland as the Scottish Care Information Systems or SCI Gateway, where it is used by over 90 per cent of GPs. The Gateway can manage messages 'from any to any' healthcare setting – including other GPs or professions allied to medicine, from consultant to consultant or from organisation to organisation.

My Health Online

My Health Online allows patients to book appointments with their GP, order repeat prescriptions online, send notifications such as change of address and keep a health diary. Features on self-care may also be developed to include alerts, access to the patient's own medical record and links to personalised health content.

Welsh Demographic Service

WDS gives access to NHS numbers, up-to-date demographic details and the patient's registered GP practice. It is used for managing patients' paper records between practices, calling patients for screening and paying contractors.

Further information

Informing Healthcare achievements 2009: using information and technology for better patient care, Informing Healthcare/NHS Wales, 2009.
National infrastructure strategy for NHS Wales, Informing Healthcare/NHS Wales, July 2008.
Informing Healthcare: transforming healthcare using information and IT, Welsh Assembly Government/NHS Wales, July 2003.
Informing Healthcare **www.wales.nhs.uk/ihc**

Health of Wales Information Service (HOWIS)

This website is the official gateway to online information about NHS Wales. **www.wales.nhs.uk**

13 The NHS in Northern Ireland

Direct rule from Westminster between 2002 and 2007 restricted the healthcare reform process in Northern Ireland, but major restructuring took effect in 2007 and in April 2009. For more than 30 years, health and social services have been bound more closely together in Northern Ireland than in the rest of the UK, and they form the Province's largest employer. After more than three decades of the 'Troubles', Northern Ireland now faces having to tackle in earnest its major health challenges. For example, it has some of the worst mental health problems in the UK and a particularly high suicide rate.

The structure of the NHS in Northern Ireland

Since October 1973, the NHS in Northern Ireland has been integrated with social services and is known as the Health and Social Care system (HSC). Accountability is to the Northern Ireland Assembly at Stormont via the minister who heads the Department of Health, Social Services and Public Safety. Five health and social care trusts and an ambulance trust provide services commissioned by a single regional health and social care board. www.hscni.net

Northern Ireland Assembly

The Northern Ireland Assembly was established as a result of the Belfast (or 'Good Friday') Agreement of 1998. It was elected later that year, operated in shadow form without government powers until full devolution in December 1999, but was then suspended in October 2002. Recalled in May 2006, under the St Andrews agreement it sat as a 'transitional assembly' to prepare for elections in March 2007 and restoration of full devolution in May 2007.

The Assembly has full legislative and executive authority for 'transferred matters', which include areas such as health, social care, education and agriculture. In addition, it is now preparing to take responsibility for 'reserved matters', such as policing and criminal law. 'Excepted matters' remain the UK Parliament's responsibility, and include defence, foreign policy and taxation.

The Assembly has 108 members (MLAs), six from each of Northern Ireland's 18 Westminster constituencies. Currently they represent eight political parties. A First Minister and a Deputy First Minister are elected to lead the ten-strong Executive Committee of Ministers. They have to stand for election jointly, and to be elected must have cross-community support. The parties elected to the Assembly choose ministerial portfolios and select ministers in proportion to their party strength. The Executive Committee brings forward proposals for new legislation in the form of Executive Bills for the Assembly to consider. It also sets out a programme for government each year, with an agreed budget for approval by the Assembly.

Eleven cross-party departmental committees have power to examine, debate and recommend changes to the Northern Ireland departments' policies and decisions. This includes, for example, how money is shared and spent. The health, social services and public safety committee advises and assists the minister of health, social services and public safety to formulate policy and undertakes scrutiny, policy development and consultation. It has 11 members.

Among the Assembly's six standing committees, the 11-strong public accounts committee's remit is to consider accounts covering the NHS in Northern Ireland. The committee has the power 'to send for persons, papers and records'.

The Northern Ireland Office, led by the Secretary of State for Northern Ireland, represents Northern Ireland's interests in the UK Government and Parliament. There are 18 MPs at Westminster representing Northern Ireland constituencies.
www.niassembly.gov.uk
www.nio.gov.uk

Northern Ireland Executive
The Executive forms the government of Northern Ireland and comprises ten departments plus the Office of the First Minister and Deputy First Minister. Each department is headed by a minister who sits on the Assembly's Executive Committee. While devolution was suspended, the departments were run by the Northern Ireland Office.
www.northernireland.gov.uk

Department of Health, Social Services and Public Safety (DHSSPS)
The DHSSPS's mission is to improve the health and social well-being of people in Northern Ireland – by ensuring the provision of appropriate health and social care services in hospitals, GPs' surgeries and the community, through nursing, social work and other professional services. It also leads a major programme of cross-government action to improve health and well-being and reduce health inequalities. The DHSSPS is the largest of Northern Ireland's ten departments, accounting for two-fifths of the Northern Ireland budget.

The DHSSPS is responsible for:
- health and social care – including policy and legislation for hospitals, family practitioner services, community health and personal social services
- public health – policy and legislation to promote and protect the health and well-being of Northern Ireland's population
- public safety – policy and legislation for food safety, emergency planning, fire and rescue services.

Its main functions are:
- determining and reviewing policy
- setting standards, priorities and targets
- overseeing the safety and quality of services
- HSC workforce planning, education and training
- HSC capital investment
- financial planning and control
- regional performance management
- overseeing the governance of Northern Ireland's 17 HSC organisations.

The permanent secretary is also chief executive of the HSC system, as well as principal accounting officer for all the DHSSPS's responsibilities. In addition, five professional groups are each led by a chief professional officer:
- medical and allied services
- social services inspectorate
- nursing and midwifery advisory group
- dental services
- pharmaceutical advice and services.

Further information
Corporate business plan 2009–2011, DHSSPS, October 2009.
www.dhsspsni.gov.uk

Restructuring health and social care in Northern Ireland
Health and social care in Northern Ireland were reorganised in April 2009. The process began in 2005 while Northern Ireland was under direct rule from Westminster, when a new structure was proposed that would have reduced the Province's 47 health and social care organisations to 18. After devolution was restored in May 2007, further implementation was suspended while the proposals were reviewed and revised. Other reform models elsewhere in the UK and in the Republic of Ireland were taken into account in drawing up the new streamlined structure.

Structure of HSC in Northern Ireland

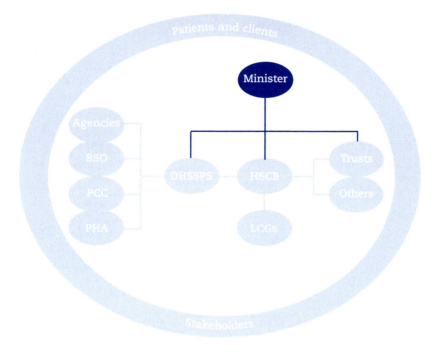

BSO: Business Services Organisation
PCC: Patient Client Council
PHA: Public Health Agency
HSCB: Health and Social Care Board
LCGs: Local commissioning groups
Others: GPs, independent and private sector, voluntary and community
Source: DHSSPS

Key organisation: Regulation and Quality Improvement Authority
RQIA is the independent body responsible for monitoring and inspecting
the availability and quality of health and social care services in Northern
Ireland. Established in 2003, it registers and inspects services based on a
set of minimum care standards. As well as services provided by health and
social services boards, trusts and agencies, its inspectors visit nursing and
residential care homes and children's homes.
www.rqia.org.uk

Five health and social care trusts (reduced in 2007 from 18), an ambulance trust and several smaller bodies continue. Changes now comprise:

- the Health and Social Care Board, which replaces four health and social services boards, to focus on commissioning, resource management and performance management
- five local commissioning groups – as statutory committees of the regional board – involve primary care professionals in planning and resourcing services, covering the same area as the five trusts, with membership including four GPs, a pharmacist, a dentist, four elected representatives, two social care professionals, a nurse, a public health professional, an allied health professional and two voluntary sector representatives
- the Public Health Agency incorporates the work of the Health Promotion Agency but with wider responsibility for health protection, screening and health improvement to address health inequalities and public health issues
- the Business Services Organisation provides support functions for the entire system, including administrative support, financial services, human resources, personnel and corporate services, training, estates, information technology and information management, procurement of goods and services, legal services, internal audit and fraud prevention
- the Patient and Client Council replaces the four health and social services councils, with five local offices operating in the same geographical areas as the trusts, and comprises 16 non-executive directors and a non-executive chair.

The reforms reduced the number of senior managers from 137 to 40, and are intended to save £53 million a year. However, redundancy costs stood at £16 million by 2008.

Further information
Proposals for health and social care reform: consultation report, DHSSPS, September 2008.

Key organisation: Regulation and Quality Improvement Authority
RQIA is the independent body responsible for monitoring and inspecting the availability and quality of health and social care services in Northern Ireland. Established in 2003, it registers and inspects services based on a set of minimum care standards. As well as services provided by health and social services boards, trusts and agencies, its inspectors visit nursing and residential care homes and children's homes.
www.rqia.org.uk

Strategy and policy

Given Northern Ireland's unique geographical and political circumstances within the UK, it is to be expected that the NHS there has distinct characteristics – most notably that health and social care are integrated. While spending per head on health and social care is higher in Northern Ireland than in England, outputs and outcomes have lagged behind. Although this may be partly due to inefficiency, and therefore perhaps susceptible to reform, other reasons may include acknowledged greater needs, better quality of provision, the need to maintain hospitals in rural locations and the higher costs of delivering services in deprived areas.

Key targets and priorities

The Northern Ireland Executive published at the beginning of 2008 its programme for government, in which promoting tolerance, inclusion, health and well-being is a priority. It acknowledged:

> The overall health status of our population needs urgent attention. We continue to have higher than average mortality from coronary heart disease, cancer and stroke, while obesity levels, particularly among our children, are rising at an alarming rate. Waiting times for treatment are still too long and the outcomes from treatment should be better. In mental health and learning disability, we are over-reliant on long-stay hospitals and the range of primary and community services is limited.

Key goals include:
- by 2009 ensuring no one waits longer than nine weeks for a first outpatient appointment or diagnostic test, and 17 weeks for treatment – a cumulative reduction of 12 weeks from the present standard
- ensuring by 2013 that anyone with a mental health problem or learning disability is promptly and suitably treated in the community and no one remains unnecessarily in hospital
- reducing mortality from bowel cancer by 15 per cent and acting to reduce cervical cancer by 70 per cent by 2013
- ensuring by 2013 that everyone who suffers a stroke is assessed for thrombolysis within 90 minutes, and reducing stroke mortality rates by 15 per cent
- by 2013 helping people with chronic illnesses to live more active lives and reducing unplanned hospital admissions for such patients by 50 per cent
- by 2011 reducing suicides by 15 per cent
- increasing to 125,000 the number of children and young people participating in sport and physical recreation by 2011

NHS CONFEDERATION

Recent milestones in Northern Ireland health policy

Investing for health
Published in 2002, this noted that health and well-being are largely determined by the social, economic, physical and cultural environment. This DHSSPS strategy document sought to shift emphasis from treating ill health to preventing it. It contained a framework for action to improve health and well-being and reduce health inequalities based on partnership.

Developing better services: modernising hospitals and reforming structures
Under the programme that resulted from this consultation document published in June 2002, Northern Ireland's 15 acute hospitals were to be replaced by a network of nine acute hospitals supported by seven local hospitals, with additional local hospitals in other locations as appropriate.

A healthier future: a twenty-year vision for health and wellbeing in Northern Ireland 2005–2025
Published in December 2004, this identifies key policy directions, actions and outcomes that will contribute to achieving the vision. It is built around five cross-cutting themes: investing for health and well-being; involving people; teams which deliver; responsive and integrated services and improving quality. A key element is reforming HPSS planning to become more integrated. Actions identified are intended to support implementation of Investing for health. Tackling chronic diseases and socio-economic disadvantage is the strategy's main focus.

Independent review of health and social care services in Northern Ireland: the Appleby Report
In the manner of the Wanless reports in England and Wales this report, published in August 2005, set out to examine the likely future resource needs of Northern Ireland's health and social services. It concluded that 'a significant increase in resources is required in the coming years, but with slower growth thereafter', but also that 'a significant underlying reason for current problems with the Northern Ireland health and social care sector relate to the use of resources rather than the amount of resources available'.

Proposals for health and social care reform: consultation report
Finalised blueprint for structural reform, published in September 2008.

- at least a third of people with disabilities participating in sport and physical recreation by 2013
- reducing child poverty by 50 per cent by 2010.

In 2009 the Northern Ireland Audit Office noted that several organisations faced significant spending pressures, and that despite improvements in waiting times, further progress was necessary. By the end of 2009, 19 per cent of patients waited more than nine weeks for a first outpatient appointment.

Further information
Programme for government 2008–11, Northern Ireland Executive, January 2008.
Priorities for action 2009–10, DHSSPS, March 2009.
General report on the health and social care sector in Northern Ireland – 2008, NIAO, June 2009.

Financing HSC in Northern Ireland

Sources of funding
General taxation and national insurance contributions form the main source of funding for HSC in Northern Ireland, as they do for the NHS in the rest of the UK. Charges and receipts from land sales or other assets add comparatively small sums to the total. Like Wales and (from 2011) Scotland, Northern Ireland has abolished prescription charges, at a cost of £13 million a year. The Northern Ireland Assembly, unlike the Scottish Parliament, is unable to raise additional taxes.

Vital statistics: Inpatient admissions 2005/06 (per 1,000 population)

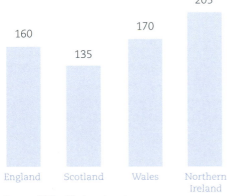

England	Scotland	Wales	Northern Ireland
160	135	170	205

Sources: UK health departments

Resource allocation

The Northern Ireland Executive sets targets for each of its departments in its programme for government.

Once the chancellor has announced the Northern Ireland settlement, each department submits a position report with its financial requirements to the Department of Finance and Personnel (DFP) and Office of the First Minister and Deputy First Minister. The DFP drafts a budget, which the Assembly considers alongside the draft programme for government. The Executive then revises the budget before deciding final allocations, which the Assembly debates and votes on.

The minister for health, social services and public safety then decides in detail how to allocate the department's resources for the coming year. The bulk is allocated to the Health and Social Care Board to commission services from the trusts.

Allocations are made according to a weighted capitation formula which includes factors for demography, social deprivation and rurality. The allocation covers social services as well as health. The formula has been developed incrementally since the mid-1990s by the capitation formula review group. Some distinctive additional needs indicators are used in Northern Ireland, notably receipt of family credit and for maternity services, no previous births and multiple births.

The DHSSPS budget is divided among:
• hospital and community health services
• personal social services
• family health services.

The DHSSPS has the largest budget of any Northern Ireland department. DHSSPS revenue spending on health and personal social services in 2010/11 is £4.29 billion and capital spending £196.7 million. The DHSSPS is expected to make savings of 2.1 per cent in 2010/11 compared to an average of 2.6 per cent in other Northern Ireland departments, 'reflecting the priority afforded to health and social care services'. However, it is expected to have made £700 million savings in the three years to 2011.

With demand for hospital services in Northern Ireland having risen by 20 per cent since 2007, HSC faced a £31 million deficit by the end of 2009/10.

Further information

Review of 2010–11 spending plans for NI departments, Northern Ireland Executive, January 2010.
Budget 2008–11, Northern Ireland Executive, January 2008.
Strategic resources framework 2008/09, DHSSPS, February 2009.
www.pfgbudgetni.gov.uk

Staffing and human resources

Staff numbers

HSC is Northern Ireland's largest employer, accounting for just over 10 per cent of the Province's workforce. In 2009 it employed 78,000 people either full-time or part-time. These included:

- 3,851 medical and dental staff
- 16,336 qualified nurses and midwives
- 7,133 professional and technical staff
- 13,140 social care staff
- 1,033 ambulance staff
- 12,655 administrative and clerical staff

In addition, about 1,000 GPs work in Northern Ireland. In terms of headcount, staff increased by 24 per cent between 2000 and 2009.

Workforce planning and pay

The DHSSPS's human resource directorate provides advice and guidance to HSC employers on pay and terms and conditions of employment for health and social care staff. The directorate comprises:

- education and training unit
- HSC superannuation branch
- pay and employment unit
- workforce planning unit.

Legislation requires the DHSSPS to ensure that pay rates in the HSC correspond as closely as possible to rates in the rest of the UK. This is known as the 'parity principle', and has existed in one form or another since 1949. Senior executives are the only staff group without a direct link to the comparable group in the rest of the UK, but this may change as a result of a current review by the Senior Salaries Review Body.

The workforce planning unit undertakes comprehensive workforce planning reviews regionally across the main professions and supporting groups so that the DHSSPS can judge the number of training places to commission. The workforce planning cycle comprises a major review of each group every three years, supported by annual update reviews.

Information technology in HSC

The DHSSPS intends to invest £300 million over the next ten years – £55 million by 2011 – for new and upgraded ICT systems across primary, secondary and community care. It will be aimed at improving record-keeping and sharing information between professional groups, while a medicines management system will be a foundation for electronic prescribing. A picture archiving and communications system will improve diagnostic imaging. Systems will be upgraded to ensure a better flow of information between primary and secondary care.

In 2009, the DHSSPS agreed a contract with a major IT supplier that allows HSC organisations to procure ICT equipment and services. It includes projects such as a modernised patient administration system, and is estimated to be worth £10 million–70 million over four years: actual value will depend on how many projects are procured.

Other aspects of the strategy include:

Electronic care record – containing structured data, text and images from various sources.

Person-centred community information system (PCIS) – an integrated community health and social care record for all patients and clients receiving services in the community.

Picture archiving and communications systems (PACS) – a national digital imaging service.

Electronic prescribing in hospitals – to improve patient safety and cost control.

Health and care number (HCN) project – allocation of a unique identifier to all HSC service users for all GP and patient administration systems.

Further information

Information and communications technology strategy, DHSSPS, March 2005.

HSC in Northern Ireland website

This website is the official gateway to health and social care services. www.hscni.net

14 The NHS in Europe

The European Union now represents 27 countries and over 490 million people. It is governed by a series of treaties negotiated at intergovernmental conferences and ratified by each member state. Its work is carried out by different institutions – from the Council of Ministers to the European Commission, European Parliament and European Court of Justice.

It is estimated that at least half the laws enacted in the UK stem from EU legislation. The EU's work on health has developed substantially over the last 15 years. In the past, health policy was seen as very much the responsibility of member states, and little work took place at EU level, but especially since 2000 the EU has aimed for a more coordinated approach. Developments in the single European market and rulings in the European Court have also had an important impact on healthcare systems. The NHS needs to keep abreast of developments in Europe and seek to influence them when appropriate.

Key organisation: **NHS European Office**
The NHS European Office was established in 2007 because of the increasing impact of EU policy and legislation on the NHS. Based in Brussels and London, and part of the NHS Confederation, it is funded by the strategic health authorities. Its main activities are:
• monitoring EU policy and legislative developments important to the NHS
• informing NHS organisations of EU developments, including funding opportunities
• influencing EU proposals in the NHS's interest
• raising the NHS's profile and promoting its expertise and good practice in Europe.

Further information
NHS European Office: policy priorities 2010, NHS European Office, January 2010.
www.nhsconfed.org/europe

The European Union

Member states

1 Austria
2 Belgium
3 Bulgaria
4 Cyprus
5 Czech Republic
6 Denmark
7 Estonia
8 Finland
9 France
10 Germany
11 Greece
12 Hungary
13 Ireland
14 Italy
15 Latvia
16 Lithuania
17 Luxembourg
18 Malta
19 Netherlands
20 Poland
21 Portugal
22 Romania
23 Slovakia
24 Slovenia
25 Spain
26 Sweden
27 United Kingdom

Candidate countries

28 Croatia
29 Macedonia
30 Turkey

Source: Foreign Commonwealth Office

European Commission

The Commission is the EU's executive arm, responsible for formulating policies, initiating legislation and the day-to-day running of the EU. It comprises a president and 26 commissioners, each leading a directorate and supported by 38,000 civil servants – administrative officials, policy experts, translators, interpreters and secretarial staff. Since 2000 it has had a directorate for health and consumer protection.
http://ec.europa.eu

Council of the European Union

Sometimes called the Council of Ministers, this defines the EU's overall political direction and priorities. It has a president elected by Council members – EU member countries – who serves for two and a half years. The Council meets in various formations to discuss different policy areas. Meetings are attended by the relevant minister from each country's national government, and decisions are usually taken by either qualified majority – voting weighted to take account of population size – or unanimity. Health ministers usually meet once every six months as part of the Employment, Social Policy, Health and Consumer Affairs Council.
www.consilium.europa.eu

European Parliament

This is the directly elected parliamentary body of the EU. With the Council of Ministers, it forms the legislative branch of the EU institutions. It has over 700 members, who are elected proportionally from the member states every five years. MEPs sit in political groups, and not as national delegations. Elections last took place in 2009, when the UK chose 72 MEPs. Most EU legislation is passed according to 'co-decision', under which the Parliament and Council amend and approve it jointly. Where co-decision does not apply, the Parliament has the right to be consulted on legislation. It also holds other EU institutions to account – for example, by asking parliamentary questions – and can reject or censure the Commission and the EU budget.
www.europarl.europa.eu

European Courts
The EU's judicial branch comprises the European Court of Justice and the
Court of First Instance. Together they interpret and apply EU law and
treaties, ensuring consistency throughout Europe. The Court of First
Instance mainly deals with cases taken by individuals and companies, and
the ECJ deals with cases taken by member states, other EU institutions
and those referred to it by the courts of member states. Judgments from
the European Courts are legally binding and must be implemented
throughout the EU, even if they establish rights in areas previously
without EU legislation.
http://curia.europa.eu

EU health policy

While the organisation, financing and management of healthcare remain
the national responsibility of member countries, the EU undertakes
health-related activities – in particular, fostering cooperation on protecting
and promoting public health and enabling the free movement of people.

EU policy and legislation have a substantial impact on the NHS as a
provider and commissioner of healthcare, as a major employer and as a
business. Developments in internal market rules, employment law,
competition legislation and environment and energy policy and legislation
must all be considered in parallel with EU health policy to determine
potential implications for the NHS.

For example, European Court rulings clarifying how EU internal market
rules apply to health services have a wide-reaching impact on the NHS.
The European health insurance card (EHIC), created under EU
arrangements for cooperation on social security, allows citizens to access
urgent healthcare when travelling in the EU. And the working-time
directive, designed to protect workers' health and safety, has had a
significant impact on healthcare organisations throughout the EU.

EU health strategy

Although the scope for legislation in health policy is limited, the EU can
adopt initiatives to promote and improve health, and this provides the
basis for its official health strategy launched in 2000 and revised in 2007.
The strategy sets the direction of EU activities in health by establishing
some core principles: taking a value-driven approach, recognising the links

between health and economic prosperity, integrating health in all policies and strengthening the EU's voice in global health. It also sets the main strategic objectives for action: fostering good health in an ageing Europe, protecting citizens from health threats and creating dynamic health systems and new technologies.

The EU approach emphasises coordination and cooperation, especially on disease prevention. Examples of traditional EU-wide public health work include joint action to address major diseases such as cancer and HIV/AIDS, coordinating efforts to combat communicable diseases, and major campaigns against drug abuse.

The strategy recognises that huge differences in health exist between and within member states. It affirms the importance of tackling health inequalities and working across different sectors. It also recognises the importance of patient empowerment and of focusing on health determinants.

Further information

Together for health: a strategic approach for the EU 2008–2013, European Commission, October 2007.

Key work priorities for 2010

NHS organisations are represented in EU institutions by the NHS European Office. The Office's work has a broad policy focus since EU developments across a wide range of areas potentially have implications for the NHS. For 2010 the Office's main policy priorities include the following.

Patient mobility

Negotiations are ongoing on EU proposals aiming to clarify patients' rights to receive healthcare in other European countries and the responsibility of health systems to facilitate and fund this. The proposals may have significant implications for the NHS in terms of financial and capacity planning. The Office is working closely with EU decision-makers to ensure that the NHS retains the right to determine entitlements at the local level and that health inequalities will not be exacerbated as a result of these proposals. Pending an agreement on these proposals, the Office will also focus on raising NHS trusts' awareness of the current patient mobility rules based on European Court decisions.

Quality and safety of healthcare

The Office will engage with EU proposals on organ donation and transplantation, which aim to ensure high quality and safety standards in transplant processes and increase the availability of organs for donation. Working with NHS Blood and Transplant and others, it will seek to ensure developments complement UK arrangements.

Employment

The Office will assess implementation of the working-time directive, which could lead to new EU proposals. Other priorities include the revision of rules on minimum health and safety requirements for workers exposed to electromagnetic fields, which has major implications for use of MRI scanners, and the revised law on maternity leave.

Competition and public procurement

New EU law on public procurement will make it easier to challenge contract award decisions and in certain circumstances have contracts overturned where rules have been breached. The Office will provide guidance on this and how other competition and public procurement rules apply to NHS activity, as well as on potential risks from current practices and policy developments.

Commercial transactions

The European Commission is proposing to revise rules on late payments in commercial transactions, introducing tough penalties for public authorities that do not pay bills on time. The proposed 5 per cent fixed-rate late-payment fee, in addition to statutory interest and recovery fees, is seen as arbitrary and disproportionate. The Office will seek to amend these proposals to ensure public authorities are treated fairly. It will also monitor plans to review rules allowing exemptions from VAT for activity performed in the public interest, such as providing healthcare.

Environment

Proposals to restrict use of hazardous substances in electrical and electronic equipment may affect the availability of certain medical devices. The Office will press for changes to EU proposals on industrial emissions that – despite targeting industrial plants rather than healthcare facilities – could have unintended consequences for around 70 NHS hospitals.

Pharmaceuticals and medical devices

The Office will try to influence the revision of the clinical trials directive, exploring NHS experiences of clinical trials and ensuring the EU addresses shortcomings and unintended consequences in existing legislation. It will continue to examine proposals on providing information on medicinal products to patients and measures to improve the safety and monitoring of medicines. It will also continue monitoring developments on medical devices.

Research and innovation

The NHS European Office will support the NHS's research and innovation agenda by informing it of relevant EU developments and providing access to successful innovative practices across Europe. The Office will also advise on EU funding opportunities.

Acronym buster

ABPI	Association of the British Pharmaceutical Industry
AC	Audit Commission
ACAD	ambulatory care and diagnostic unit
ACCEA	Advisory Committee on Clinical Excellence Awards
ACDP	Advisory Committee on Dangerous Pathogens
ACEVO	Association of Chief Executives of Voluntary Organisations
ACGT	Advisory Committee on Generic Testing
ACRA	Advisory Committee on Resource Allocation
A&E	accident and emergency
AHP	allied health professional
AHSC	academic health science centre
AIR	(strategic health authority) annual innovation report
ALB	arm's-length body
ALE	auditors' local evaluation
AM	Assembly Member (Wales)
AME	annually managed expenditure
APMS	alternative provider medical services
ASCT	Asylum Seeker Coordination Team (Department of Health)
AWP	any willing provider (commissioning)
BAMM	British Association of Medical Managers
BMA	British Medical Association
BME	black and minority ethnic
BNF	British National Formulary
BRC	biomedical research centre
BROMI	Better Regulation of Medicines Initiative
BRU	biomedical research unit
CAA	comprehensive area assessment
CAMHS	child and adolescent mental health services
CAS	Central Alert System
CAT	computerised axial tomography (scan)
CHCP	community health and care partnership (Scotland)
CDO	chief dental officer
CDU	clinical decision unit
CEAC	Clinical and Excellence Awards Committee (Northern Ireland)
CEMACH	Confidential Enquiry into Maternal and Child Health
CEP	Centre for Evidence-based Purchasing
CFH	(NHS) Connecting for Health
CHC	community health council
CHD	coronary heart disease

CHI	community health index (Scotland)
CHIQ	Centre for Health Information Quality
CHMS	community health and miscellaneous services
CHP	community health partnership (Scotland)
CHRE	Council for Healthcare Regulatory Excellence
CIC	community interest company
CIMP	clinical information management programme
CIO	chief information officer
CIP	cost improvement programme
CLAHRC	collaboration for leadership in applied health research and care
CLG	(Department of) Communities and Local Government
CMB	corporate management board (Department of Health)
CME	continuing medical education
CMHT	community mental health team
CMIC	corporate management and improvement committee (Department of Health)
CMO	chief medical officer
CNO	chief nursing officer
CNST	Clinical Negligence Scheme for Trusts
CO	Cabinet Office
COMARE	Committee on Medical Aspects of Radiation in the Environment
COMEAP	Committee on the Medical Effects of Air Pollutants
COSLA	Convention of Scottish Local Authorities
CPA	care programme approach
CPD	continuing professional development
CPR	Child Protection Register
CQUIN	commissioning for quality and innovation
CRD	Centre for Research and Dissemination
CRS	(NHS) Care Records Service
CRHP	Council for the Regulation of Healthcare Professionals
CSA	Common Services Agency
CSCI	Commission for Social Care Inspection
CSM	Committee on the Safety of Medicines
CSO	chief scientific officer
CSR	comprehensive spending review
CSU	commercial support unit
CTO	compulsory treatment order
DAT	drug action team
DCSF	Department for Children, Schools and Families

DDRB	doctors and dentists (pay) review body
DEFRA	Department for Environment, Food and Rural Affairs
DEL	departmental expenditure limit
DES	directed enhanced services
DFP	Department of Finance and Personnel (Northern Ireland)
DFT	distance from target
DGH	district general hospital
DH or DoH	Department of Health
DHSS	Department for Health and Social Services (Wales)
DHSSPS	Department of Health, Social Services and Public Safety (Northern Ireland)
DMB	departmental management board (Department of Health)
DMS	Defence Medical Services
DNR	do not resuscitate
DPH	director of public health
DPHHP	Department for Public Health and Health Professions (Wales)
DPR	Data Protection Registrar
DRE	delivering race equality
DSO	departmental strategic objective
DSSA	delivering same-sex accommodation
DSU	day surgery unit
DTC	diagnosis and treatment centre
DWP	Department for Work and Pensions
EAU	emergency assessment unit
EBH	evidence-based healthcare
EBM	evidence-based medicine
EBS	emergency bed service
ECCT	extended community care team (NHSScotland)
ECHR	European Convention on Human Rights
ECJ	European Court of Justice
ECN	extended choice network
E&D	equality and diversity
EFL	external financing limit
e-GIF	(electronic) Government Interoperability Framework
EHPF	European Health Policy Forum
EHIC	European health insurance card
EHR	electronic health record
EHRG	equality and human rights group (Department of Health)
ENT	ear, nose and throat
EO	employers' organisation
EPP	Expert Patient Programme

EPR	electronic patient record
EPS	electronic prescription service
ERDIP	Electronic Record Development and Implementation Programme
ESR	electronic staff record
ETP	electronic transmission of prescriptions
ETS	emissions trading scheme (EU)
EWTD	European working-time directive
FCE	finished consultant episode
FCN	free choice network
FESC	Framework for procuring External Support for Commissioners
FHS	family health services
FMP	financial management programme
FOI	freedom of information
FPNC	free personal and nursing care (NHSScotland)
FSA	Food Standards Agency
FT	foundation trust
GDC	General Dental Council
GDS	general dental services
GMC	General Medical Council
GMS	general medical services
GO	Government Office (of the English Regions)
GOS	general ophthalmic services
GPC	(BMA) General Practitioners Committee
GPhC	General Pharmaceutical Council
GPSI or GPwSI	general practitioner with a special interest
GSCC	General Social Care Council
GTAC	Gene Therapy Advisory Committee
GTN	(UK) Genetic Testing Network
GWC	General Whitley Council
HA	health authority
HAZ	health action zone
HB	health board
HCAI	healthcare-associated infection
HCHS	hospital and community health services
HCSU	Health Care Standards Unit
HCW	Health Commission Wales
HDA	Health Development Agency
HDL	Health Department letter
HEAT	health efficiency access treatment (targets – Scotland)

HEFCE	Higher Education Funding Council for England
HEI	Healthcare Environment Inspectorate (Scotland)
HES	hospital episode statistics
HFEA	Human Fertilisation and Embryology Authority
HIA	health impact assessment
HIC	Health Innovation Council
HIEC	health innovation and education cluster
HIMP	health improvement and modernisation plan
HIW	Health Inspectorate Wales
HLC	healthy living centre
HLE	healthy life expectancy
HMO	health maintenance organisation (USA)
HOWIS	Health of Wales Information Service
HPA	Health Protection Agency
HPC	Health Professions Council
HPMA	Healthcare People Management Association
HQIP	Healthcare Quality Improvement Partnership
HRG	healthcare resource group
HSC	(House of Commons) health select committee
HSCI	health service cost index
HSCT	health and social care trust (Northern Ireland)
HSCT	High Secure Commissioning Team
HSE	Health and Safety Executive
HSE	Health Survey for England
HSRN	Health Services Research Network
HTA	health technology assessment
IAPT	Improving Access to Psychological Therapies (programme)
IC	information commissioner
ICAS	Independent Complaints Advocacy Service
ICD	international classification of diseases
ICO	integrated care organisation
ICP	integrated care pathway
ICR	(NHS) injury costs recovery (scheme)
ICT	information and communication technology
ICU	intensive care unit
IMAS	interim management and support
IMCA	independent mental capacity advocate
IM&T	information management and technology
IP	inpatient
IPR	individual performance review
IQI	indicators for quality improvement

IRP	Independent Reconfiguration Panel
ISB	(NHS) Information Standards Board
ISD	Information and Statistics Division (Scotland)
ISTC	independent sector treatment centre
IWL	Improving Working Lives
JIP	joint investment plan
JSNA	joint strategic needs assessment
KSF	(NHS) Knowledge and Skills Framework
LAA	local area agreement
LAL	local authority letter
LDP	local delivery plan
LES	local enhanced services
LGA	Local Government Association
LHB	local health board (Wales)
LHP	local health plan
LINks	local involvement networks
LIS	local implementation strategy
LIT	local implementation team
LPSA	local public service agreement
LSP	local strategic partnership
LTA	long-term agreement
MAU	medical assessment unit
MCN	managed clinical network
MCO	managed care organisation
MEE	Medical Education England
MFF	market forces factor
MHAC	Mental Health Act Commission
MHRA	Medicines and Healthcare Products Regulatory Agency
MHRT	mental health review tribunal
MLA	Member of the Legislative Assembly (Northern Ireland)
MMC	Modernising Medical Careers
MMR	measles, mumps, rubella (vaccination)
MPIG	minimum practice income guarantee
MQI	measuring for quality improvement
MRC	Medical Research Council
MRI	magnetic resonance imaging
MRSA	methicillin-resistant *Staphylococcus aureus*
MSP	Member of the Scottish Parliament
MTS	(NHS) management training scheme
N3	new national network
NAO	National Audit Office

NAW	National Assembly for Wales
NBA	National Blood Authority
NBAP	national booked admissions programme
NBI	national beds inquiry
NCAAG	National Clinical Audit Advisory Group
NCAF	National Clinical Audit Forum
NCAPOP	National Clinical Audit and Patients' Outcomes Programme
NCAS	National Clinical Assessment Service
NCASP	National Clinical Audit Support Programme
NCE	national confidential enquiry
NCEPOD	National Confidential Enquiry into Patient Outcome and Death
NCG	National Commissioning Group
NCSS	National CAMHS Support Service
NCVO	National Council for Voluntary Organisations
NDPB	non-departmental public body
NEAT	new and emerging applications of technology
NED	non-executive director
NES	national enhanced services
NES	NHS Education for Scotland
nGMS	new general medical services (contract)
NHSI	NHS Institute for Innovation and Improvement
NHSL	NHS Logistics
NHSLA	NHS Litigation Authority
NHS LIFT	NHS Local Improvement Finance Trust
NHS QIS	NHS Quality Improvement Scotland
NHST	NHS trust
NIA	Northern Ireland Assembly
NIAO	Northern Ireland Audit Office
NIC	national insurance contribution
NIC	(NHS) National Innovation Centre
NICE	National Institute for (Health and) Clinical Excellence
NIGB	National Information Governance Board
NIHR	National Institute for Health Research
NIMHE	National Institute for Mental Health in England
NIO	Northern Ireland Office
NLH	National Library for Health
NLIAH	National Leadership and Innovation Agency for Healthcare (Wales)
NLOP	National Programme for IT local ownership programme
NMC	Nursing and Midwifery Council
NMHDU	National Mental Health Development Unit

NOF	New Opportunities Fund
NOG	National Oversight Group (for high-security hospitals)
NPDG	National PALS Development Group
NPfIT	National Programme for IT (in the NHS)
NPG	national priorities guidance
NPHS	National Public Health Service (Wales)
NPSA	National Patient Safety Agency
NQB	National Quality Board
NRAC	NHSScotland resource allocation committee
NRCI	national reference cost index
NRES	National Research Ethics Service
NRLS	National Reporting and Learning Service
NRPB	National Radiological Protection Board
NRT	nicotine replacement therapy
NSCG	National Specialist Commissioning Group
NSF	national service framework
NSR	Next Stage Review
NSRC	national schedule of reference costs
NSS	National Services Scotland
NTA	National Treatment Agency (for Substance Misuse)
NTAC	NHS Technology Adoption Centre
NTO	national training organisation
NWP	(NHS) national workforce projects
OCPA	Office of the Commissioner for Public Appointments
ODP	operating department practitioner
OFMDFM	Office of the First Minister & Deputy First Minister (Northern Ireland)
OGC	Office of Government Commerce
OHE	Office of Health Economics
OHPA	Office of the Health Professions Adjudicator
OLS	Office for Life Sciences
ONS	Office for National Statistics
OP	outpatient
OSC	(local authority) overview and scrutiny committee
OSCHR	Office for Strategic Coordination of Health Research
OSHA	Office of the Strategic Health Authorities
OT	occupational therapist/therapy
OTC	over-the-counter
OTS	Office of the Third Sector
PAC	(House of Commons) public accounts committee
PACS	picture archiving and communications system

PAF	performance assessment framework
PALS	patient advice and liaison service
PASA	(NHS) Purchasing and Supply Agency
PBC	practice-based commissioning
PbR	payment by results
PCIP	primary care investment plan
PCO	primary care organisation
PCT	primary care trust
PCTPS	primary care trust-provided services
PDP	personal development plan
PEC	professional executive committee (of PCT)
PFI	private finance initiative
PHeL	Public Health electronic Library
PHO	public health observatory
PICD	procurement, investment and commercial division (DH)
PLIC	patient-level information and costing
PMETB	Postgraduate Medical Education and Training Board
PMS	personal medical services
POPP	Partnerships for Older People Project
PPA	Prescription Pricing Authority
PPC	(prescription) pre-payment certificate
PPE	patient and public engagement
PPF	priorities and planning framework
PPI	patient and public involvement
PPIF	patient and public involvement forum
PPO	preferred provider organisation
PPP	public–private partnership
PPRS	Pharmaceutical Price Regulation Scheme
PRB	pay review body
PROM	patient-reported outcome measure
PRP	policy research programme
PSA	public service agreement
PSS	personal social services
QA	quality assurance
QALY	quality-adjusted life year
QIPP	quality innovation productivity prevention
QMAS	quality management and analysis system
QOF	quality and outcomes framework
QQUIP	quest for quality and improved performance
RAB	resource accounting and budgeting
RCD	research capacity development

RCN	Royal College of Nursing
RCP	Royal College of Physicians
RCPE	Royal College of Physicians of Edinburgh
RCPSG	Royal College of Physicians and Surgeons of Glasgow
RCS	Royal College of Surgeons
RCSE	Royal College of Surgeons of Edinburgh
RCT	randomised controlled trial
RGH	rural general hospital (NHSScotland)
ROCR	Review of Central Returns
RTA	road traffic accident
RTT	referral to treatment
SACDA	Scottish Advisory Committee on Distinction Awards
SARS	severe acute respiratory syndrome
SAS	Scottish Ambulance Service
SAS	staff and associated specialist (doctors)
SASM	Scottish Audit of Surgical Mortality
SBS	(NHS) Shared Business Services
SCG	specialised commissioning group
SCI	Scottish care information
SCS	senior civil servants
SCVO	Scottish Council for Voluntary Organisations
SDO	service delivery and organisation
SDU	(NHS) Sustainable Development Unit
SEIF	Social Enterprise Investment Fund
SES	Single Equality Scheme (Department of Health)
SEU	Social Exclusion Unit
SFA	statement of fees and allowances
SGHD	Scottish Government health directorates
SHA	strategic health authority (and special health authority)
SHO	senior house officer
SHOW	Scottish Health on the Web
SHRINE	Strategic Human Resources Information Network
SIGN	Scottish Intercollegiate Guidelines Network
SLA	service level agreement
SMAC	Standing Medical Advisory Committee
SMC	Scottish Medicines Consortium
SMDU	strategic market development unit (Department of Health)
SMR	standardised mortality ratio
SNMAC	Standing Nursing and Midwifery Advisory Committee
SNOMED	systematised nomenclature of medicine
SPF	Social Partnership Forum

SPI	Scientific Pandemic Influenza Advisory Committee
SPMS	specialist provider of medical services
SRB	single regeneration budget
SSA	standard spending assessment
SSC	shared service centre
ST&T	scientific, therapeutic and technical (staff)
TUPE	Transfer of Undertakings (Protection of Employment) Regulations 1981
UKCC	UK Cochrane Centre
UKCRC	UK Clinical Research Collaboration
UKCRN	UK Clinical Research Network
VCS	voluntary and community sector
VFM	value for money
WAG	Welsh Assembly Government
WAO	Wales Audit Office
WCH	Wales Centre for Health
WHO	World Health Organisation
WIsH	Welsh Innovations in Healthcare
WORD	Wales Office of Research and Development for Health and Social Care
WPF	Welsh Partnership Forum
WRT	workforce review team
WTD	working-time directive

Index

NHS CONFEDERATION

Acknowledgements

The NHS Confederation is grateful to all those involved in the production of this edition of the NHS handbook (formerly known before 2008 as the pocket guide). Particular thanks are due to:

- our sponsor, PSCAL
- those who have supported the guide through advertising (listed below)
- those organisations that have kindly allowed us to reproduce diagrams and other materials
- Caroline Ball and John Cox for their expert editing and proofreading
- Grade Design, for designing and typesetting this year's handbook and for also designing the front cover.

We are also grateful to our members and other customers who have provided valuable feedback on previous editions of the pocket guide, to enable us to make year-on-year improvements.

List of advertisers
PSCAL (back cover)

The author
Peter Davies is a freelance writer and editor. He has written extensively on health policy and management issues, for which he won a major award from the Medical Journalists Association. He was editor of Health Service Journal from 1993 to 2002, and has contributed a regular column to Guardian Unlimited. He is married with two children and lives in London.